AUSTRALIAN ARTS GUIDE

Roslyn Kean

Art Guide Publications
A & C Black
35 Bedford Row
London WC1R 4JH

Art Guide Series Editor: Heather Waddell

AUSTRALIAN ARTS GUIDE
Third edition 1989 ISBN 0 7136 3047 7. Editor Roslyn Kean
Second edition 1984
First edition 1981

British Library Cataloguing in Publication Data
Australian arts guide—3rd ed.
1. Australia—Practical information—For visual artists
1. Kean, Roslyn
919.4'0463'0247
ISBN 0-7136-3047-7

Published by
Art Guide Publications
A & C Black
35 Bedford Row
London WC1R 4JH
Printed in Great Britain by
William Clowes Ltd
Beccles and London

ARIEL
42 Oxford St.,
Paddington 2021.
Telephone (02) 332 4581
Open 7 days
10 a.m. to 12 midnight.

CONTENTS

Photographs

(all photographs by Roslyn Kean unless credited otherwise.)
Cover photo: Hare Wallaby Dreaming (see detailed explanation).
Ramingining artists community Aboriginal memorial Australian Biennale 1988.
Figure and Bird Graham Fransella (Macquarie Galleries Sydney).
Guy Warren's Rainforest (Macquarie Galleries, Sydney).
Graeme Murphy as Jean Cocteau in Poppy, Sydney Dance Company (Branco Gaica).
Graeme Murphy's After Venice, Sydney Dance Company (Branco Gaica).
Books on display at Ariel Bookshop, Sydney.
Still from Shame (Barron films).
Detail from an Aboriginal bark painting (Hogarth Gallery Sydney).
Scotland Island, Northern Sydney area, New South Wales.
The Craft Centre the Rocks, Sydney.
Art Gallery of New South Wales, Sydney.
New England regional art museum, Armidale New South Wales with local school group.
Norman Lindsay's house, Springwood, Blue Mountains.
Power House Museum, Ultimo, Sydney.
Rainforest paintings by Guy Warren.
Eileen Chanin of the Macquarie Galleries, Sydney.
Painting on canvas by an Aboriginal artist (Hogarth Gallery, Sydney).
Roslyn Oxley Gallery, Sydney.
Glass Artists' Gallery, Glebe, Sydney.
Aboriginal bark painting.
Art students in a printmaking department.
Oxford Art Supplies, Darlinghurst, Sydney.
Ariel Bookshop, Darlinghurst, Sydney.
Lamella art bookshop, Sydney.
Macquarie Street Parade 200 year celebration, Sydney.
Sydney Opera House from the harbour (Heather Waddell).
Sydney Harbour Bridge.
Botanical Gardens, Sydney.
Paddington Market, Paddington, Sydney with young busker.
Sydney Dance Company, Graeme Murphy's Shining (Branco Gaica).
Doyles seafood restaurant, Watsons Bay, Sydney.
The Akuna Bay restaurant, Sydney.
Victorian Arts Centre, Melbourne.
Stuart Purves, director Australian Galleries.
Realities Gallery, Toorak, Melbourne.
Christine Abrahams Gallery, Richmond, Melbourne.
Stuart Gertsman galleries, Richmond, Melbourne.
Realities Gallery sculpture garden, Toorak, Melbourne.
Powell Street Gallery, South Yarra, Melbourne.
Port Jackson Press, Fitzroy, Melbourne.
Victorian Print Workshop, Fitzroy, Melbourne.
The Arts Bookshop, Melbourne.
Italian coffee shops, Carlton, Melbourne.
Cleland Park, Adelaide Hills (Heather Waddell).
Adelaide Festival Centre, Adelaide.
Coledale and Laurence, Colin Lanceley (Bonython-Meadmore Gallery).

Eerie Mountain, Lawrence Davis (Bonython-Meadmore Gallery).
Printmakers at work.
Gum tree.
Australian art books.
Bushman's pub
Terraced houses, Adelaide, South Australia (Heather Waddell).
Bushman's pub.
Queensland Art Gallery
Mother and child, Joe Furlonger, (Ray Hughes Gallery)
The University campus, Perth, West Australia (Heather Waddell).
Windsurfing on a Perth beach (Heather Waddell).
Art Gallery of Western Australia, Perth Cultural Centre.
Art Gallery of Western Australia courtyard with sculpture (Heather Waddell).
Sculpture in the Cultural Centre courtyard, Perth (Heather Waddell).
Detail from an Aboriginal bark painting.
Sailing on the Swanriver, Perth (Heather Waddell).
Perth city looking across the Swan river from South Perth (Heather Waddell).
Saigon Vietnamese restaurant, Northbridge area, Perth (Heather Waddell).
Colonial houses.
Light and shade (Heather Waddell).
Opening of the new houses of Parliament, Canberra, ACT.
Australian National Gallery, Canberra.
Aboriginal rights protest at the opening of the new houses of Parliament, Canberra 1988.
Australian National Gallery sculpture garden with sculpture by Bert Flugaman.
University Drill Hall Gallery (National Gallery annexe) Canberra.
Art school student performance, Canberra Institute of the arts.
Henry Moore sculpture in the National Gallery sculpture garden.
Studio One printmaking workshop, Canberra.
Basil Hall at Studio One printmaking workshop.
Tidbinbilla Nature Reserve, ACT.
The Olgas, Central Australia.
Detail from an Aboriginal bark painting.
Canowindra County show, New South Wales.
After Venice, Bill Pengelly and Garth Welsh, Sydney Dance Company (Branco Gaica).
Sydney Harbour Bridge from Circular Quay (Heather Waddell).
Walcha, New South Wales, grazing country.
Sailing, Sydney Harbour.
The Tall ships at the Bicentennial celebrations (1788–1988), Darling Harbour, Sydney.
Roslyn Kean—the author (Heather Waddell).

Hare Wallaby Dreaming

This painting comes from Central Northern Australia, was originally photographed at the Hogarth Gallery in Sydney and is now in the West Australian Art Gallery collection.

The cover story

Artist: Joe James Japanoryl
Name of the Painting:
Kuruwarri Kujurnu Lajamanurlarlu 1987
Wampana Jukurrpa
(Wallaby Dreaming)

This is about the Hare Wallaby dreaming. It starts at Kujukur-landu. It belongs to Japangardi and Japanagka. He travelled west to Yatunjamalu. An old man hare wallaby watched him go by. He went west through Kunajardunyungu. He stopped at Malititi Warnu where there was a Coolibah tree. He took off again until he reached Putalya and there he hit the ground with his tail. This is where a man, of Jungal skin group, called Wirliya jarlu came from the hare wallaby dreaming. It was here that Purla which is a type of tick bit the hare wallaby and stopped him from going any further.

So then the wallaby went back under the ground to Kuyukurlandu, then he set off in another direction to Kunajar-rayi (mt Nicker). At Kunajarrayi he turned into a Japaljorri/Jungarayi dreaming.

INTRODUCTION

The fact that 'Art' flourishes in Australia may surprise many people, as it is often still thought of as 'the last frontier' or simply as 'down under'. It seems a fantastic continent to an outside world that is still largely ignorant of its existence, despite its enormous size of three million square miles, of which one-third is desert.

Australia has a special spirit and anyone visiting the country cannot help feeling its haunting, unpredictable oddity. It has rare and highly attractive qualities: the climate, the bush and the people, the 'Aussies'. They are openhanded, humorous, adventurous, fanatically independent and contemptuous of fuss. There is a greatness about the Australian people especially for heroic gestures.

Early Australian artists were concerned with the pictorial discovery of the continent which, as it had never been painted before, could be vividly portrayed free from the inhibiting example of great European painters. Australian artists from all fields have strived for a deep understanding of both the spirit and the physical appearance of the country. Painting in particular has played a decisive role in creating an Australian consciousness and what it feels like to be an Australian.

The population is small compared to the geographical size of the continent and is well divided amongst the capital cities, with no one major overriding artistic or culture centre, although Sydney and Melbourne are the largest cities. History and geography, as mentioned, have become the major influences in the direction of the Australian arts and in 1988 our European heritage was celebrated with major national and international Bicentennial events (1788–1988). These events projected a major focus on the Australia of today, making the world more aware of the increasing importance of Australia's role as we head towards the 21st century. Australia lives very much in the present. This tension is often evident in the works of Australian artists. The unique arts of the Australian Aborigine have managed to survive the recent encroachment of European civilisation and with a new resurgence of interest in Aboriginal culture, Aborigines are being encouraged to produce more and more artifacts in the way that they have done since their first arrival in Australia 40,000 years ago.

The last two decades have shown a significant development in all the arts and with increased government assistance, there has been greater communication between Australian and overseas artists through visits, lecture tours, exhibitions, concerts, overseas publications, performances and through the increasing number of art schools. There has also been increased exposure of work by Australian artists overseas with vital criticism and competition essential to Australia's future development. Events such as the Sydney

Biennale and the Adelaide Arts Festival also add to the exchange between Australian and overseas communications in the arts.

This guide attempts to bring together a comprehensive listing of Australia's arts organisations, museums and galleries with both the resident Australian and the long term visitor in mind. A selection of workshops, government institutions, art schools, art suppliers, bookshops and framers have been made where possible for each capital city. Art publications are increasing annually, showing the wide scope of interests enjoyed throughout Australia.

Other information includes theatres, concert halls, parks, travel, restaurants, embassies and information centres. An Australian guide would not be complete without mention of its outdoor life, as this plays a significant part in the lives of most Australian people. This is by no means a definitive guide to Australian arts organisations as there will always be an increasing and changing number of organisations and galleries throughout the country and some have been overlooked due to the vastness of the country. Any further information would be greatly appreciated for inclusion in the next edition.

My thanks to the various people and organisations who have helped supply me with information and a special thanks to the Arts Councils in each state, and to my friends for their help and support.

ROSLYN KEAN

AUSTRALIAN ARTS INTO THE 90s

This is a period of great flowering in Australian art, in achievement, confidence and audiences. Artists are exhibiting in greater numbers than ever before, specialist dealer galleries and artists' co-operatives continue to open and auction houses are booming, despite the 1987 stockmarket crash. Major museums sponsor exhibitions of originality and interest, especially in the field of historical Australian art; art publishing is lively and debate within the art community livelier still. Appropriately for the Bicentennial year of European conquest, appreciation of the importance of Aboriginal art and culture is growing and the great eclectic vigour of the independent Australian artistic cultures is at last being recognised.

Sydney or the bush?

Where are Australian artists and their works found? Overwhelmingly in the capital cities. Research in the early 1980s showed that about 40% of Australian visual artists lived and worked in Sydney. Why? Perhaps through the location in Sydney of the Australia Council, the federal funding agency, because of the renewed growth in the early' 80s of a thriving commercial sector and especially through the Art Gallery of New South Wales' dominance of contemporary exhibitions. It alternates the **Biennale of Sydney**, last staged in May–June 1988, with a series of Australian survey exhibitions, entitled **Perspecta**.

Rivalry between the cities, especially the tradition of Sydney versus Melbourne, continues. In 1988, in a move to open up new audiences to contemporary art, the Sydney Biennale was re-named the **Australian Biennale** and shown in Melbourne for the first time. The 1988 Biennale continued the Sydney Biennale's history as a thematic, polemic exhibition, but curator Nick Waterlow's Biecentennial attempt to redress two centuries of cultural dependency met with mixed success. Australian audiences are remarkably sensitive to issues of cultural influence, as the process of cultural, social and economic emergence from formal and informal imperial ties continues. Thus the installation of two hundred Aboriginal burial poles, from the Ramingining Artists Community in Arnhemland in the Northern Territory, now in the collection of the Australian National Gallery, received critical acclaim, but the comparison of Australian Julie Brown-Rrap with Balthus and Bonnard (two of her sources) was widely criticised as too simplistic.

Ramingining artists community Aboriginal memorial Australian Biennale 1988

A national perspective

Despite Sydney's hotly-debated but incontrovertible dominance, the visual arts are thriving in all states in Australia. Each capital boasts increased numbers of commercial galleries and each (with the exception of Darwin) hosts a federally-funded contemporary art space. But the activities of the regional galleries network and decorative arts outlets in even the most remote areas are also of great interest. It's worth asking about the local art gallery in areas as distant from each other as the Araluen Centre Gallery, at Alice Springs, or the Queen Victoria Museum and Art Gallery in Launceston in northern Tasmania.

There have been many notable developments recently, as national interest and involvement in the arts grows. In **Brisbane** the **Museum of Contemporary Art** opened in 1987, the first privately-funded and managed art museum in the country. Perth, reeling from the October Crash of 1987, still raised enough entrepreneurial spirit and funds to open PICA, the **Perth Institute of Contemporary Art** in late 1988. With an interesting charter encompassing inter-action between diverse art forms, a commitment to discussion, residencies and publishing, PICA promises to be one of the most exciting initiatives in contemporary Australian art for some years.

In **Canberra**, the national capital, **New Parliament House** is the setting for a great collection of art works of all media, from the great wallhanging made by members of the Embroiderer's Guild from all states, to the largest oil painting in Australia, Mandy Martin's landscape **Red Ochre Cove**. And in **Sydney**, the newly-opened **Powerhouse**, part of the Museum of Applied Arts and Sciences, holds one of the largest collections of Australian and international decorative arts in the country. Look for contemporary jewellery by Helge Larsen and Darani Lewers or Lyn Tune, works by glass artist Warren Langley or textile artist Mona Hessing. The historical ceramics, featuring indigenous flora and fauna from the nationalist 1890s are fascinating, and take in STYLE, a permanent display of around one thousand pieces of international decorative arts from the 18th century to the present.

Aboriginal arts

During 1988, the Bicentennial year of European conquest of Australia, Aboriginal arts achieved greater prominence and recognition. The Australian National Gallery mounted **Aboriginal art: the continuing tradition**, a comprehensive survey exhibition between June and September, 1989 and several important exhibitions focused on relationships between Aboriginal and European artists in Australia, like the Print Council of Australia's touring show, **Aboriginal views in print and poster**. Recent years have seen Aboriginal artists adapting western printmaking techniques in order to reach wider audiences. **Sally Morgan** and **Jimmy Pike**, both from Western Australia, and **Alice Hinton-Bateup**, from the Garage Graphix group in Western Sydney, are among artists showing very strong work.

Important recent works by Aboriginal artists include the collection of Western Desert paintings at the South Australian Museum and the mosaic forecourt at New Parliament House, Canberra, designed by the distinguished painter **Michael Nelson Tjakamarra**. Aboriginal artists have formed co-operative groups in the cities, such as Boomalli, in Sydney's inner-urban Chippendale, and in the bush, where well-established groups like the Utopia, Ernabella and Tiwi fabric printers continue to operate successfully. Look for their work at Coo-Eee Australian Emporium or the Aboriginal Artists' Gallery in Sydney, or at the Aboriginal Art galleries in Alice Springs, Darwin and Perth.

Talkfests

The diversity of contemporary arts by Aboriginal people was a dominant theme at Artists' Week, staged in March 1988, at the biennial **Adelaide Arts Festival**. This visual arts conference is the most important in the Australian calendar, a litmus test of current opinion and a must for serious followers of contemporary art. Visitors to Australia often remark on the well-informed and passionate discussions included in arts festivals and accompanying important exhibitions. The term "forum" in the arts pages of newspapers and journals will alert visitors to public airings of the robustly divided positions characterising Australian arts discourse.

16

Young artists and the return to painting:

The 80s controversy about the resurgence of interest in painting continues, as in other countries, with avid attention from both critics and the market, though perhaps with the sobering edge of several years experience of the phenomenon. The spotlight in Australia has been on younger artists and some commentators have expressed anxiety lest the expanding market and museum collections run the risk of forcing immature talents inthe hot-house of (con)temporary taste.

James Mollison, Director of the Australian National Gallery, fuelled this issue with his exhibition **A New Generation, 1983–1988**, held at the Australian National Gallery, Canberra, in mid-1988. Young artists from Melbourne, such as David Larwill and Jan Nelson and Sydney painters Carole Roberts and Gary Carsley were seen in the company of approximately 300 artists under the age of 45.

Whatever the outcome of this debate, and Australian artists practice in a bewildering variety of media and modes, younger artists are now receiving institutional and market support unparalleled in Australian history. The Australian National Gallery undoubtedly holds the country's finest collection of contemporary Australian arts across all fields.

Growth in the decorative arts

In May 1988 the World Crafts Council's Annual Conference was held at the newly-opened Powerhouse Museum in Sydney and in November the first comprehensive museum survey of the history of the decorative arts in Australia was staged at the Australian National Gallery. New outlets have sprung up in the past few years, such as the Contemporary Jewellery Gallery in Sydney, and the magnificent **Meat Market Craft Centre** in **Melbourne**, with its interesting mixture of artists' workshops and exhibition spaces. (The Meat Market was a tourist award-winner in 1987) Moreover, mainstream dealer galleries, such as Melbourne's **Devise** exhibit works by artists in ceramic, jewellery or glass, though textile arts remain poorly served.

These events dramatise the growing confidence and sophistication of the decorative arts in this country and their wider, more discriminating audiences. However, the achievement of successful indigenous design on a broad scale still seems remote, due to the small domestic market and massive imports from other countries.

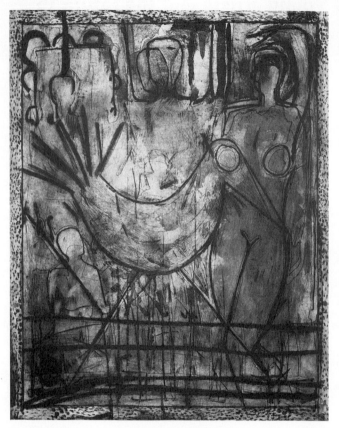

Figure and Bird Graham Fransella (Macquarie Galleries Sydney)

Future prospects?

The arts in Australia are flourishing as never before. This is due to the cultural growth of the country and the new enthusiasm of audiences for the arts, spurred on by the upsurge in nationalist sentiment in the last twenty years and (very importantly) fuelled by judicious support from government from federal to local levels. Corporate sponsorship is increasing too, with the annual A$50,000 Moët and Chandon initiative in contemporary painting the most spectacular of a recent rash of prizes and fellowships. The first **Australian Arts Fair**, organised upon the lines of European art fairs, was held in Melbourne in mid-1988, a sure sign that the commercial sector is heating up. In short, the arts are blooming.

Yet Australian artists continue to suffer a low (though rising) level of public recognition and support compared with other professional groups. Often artists with established reputations are forced to rely on the classic jobs of the avant-garde: waitressing and working behind the bar. Employment as studio assistants is still relatively rare, though increasing, and younger artists have been hard hit by a contraction of employment in art schools, even the strong group of younger women artists. Look for Lindy Lee and Alison Clouston in Sydney, Louise Hearman in Melbourne and Anna Platten and Bronwyn Platten in Adelaide, to name only a few.

This note of caution serves to point out that all is not perfect in this remarkably buoyant arts scene. Yet the overall picture is very bright. This is a growing arts community and it welcomes visitors to the ranks of its practitioners and audiences. The wealth of information in this guide will alert the reader to the brevity of my introduction. Art in Australia is energetic, extraordinarily eclectic and very rewarding. Exploring it is a pleasure I recommend.

Julie Ewington
Canberra School of Art
June, 1988

THE SYDNEY BIENNALE

Heather Waddell interviewed **Nick Waterlow**, director of the **Sydney Biennale** (called the **Australian Biennale** in 1988 Australia's Bicentennial year). Originally under the patronage of Franco Belgiorno-Nettis, Chairman of Transfield Pty Ltd, the 1988 Biennale was held in Sydney and also for the first time in Melbourne. The next Biennale will be in 1990 at the National Gallery of Victoria.

Heather Waddell: What are the key events at this year's Biennale?

Nick Waterlow: This year the Biennale is far more ambitious than ever before and the public will be able to see work by famous 20th century Masters such as Francis Bacon, Max Beckmann, Leger, de Kooning, Picasso, Rothko and Warhol alongside Australian Masters of the 20th century such as Arthur Boyd, Fred Williams, Sidney Nolan, Margaret Preston, Joy Hester, Tony Tuckson, Ian Fairweather and Ralph Balson. The rest of the Biennale will be presenting work by artists from about twenty countries.

HW: Who are the key artists from overseas?

NW: Starting with the UK Brian Eno, Caroline Wilkinson and Gary Stevens the performance artists and the art critic Lynne Cooke. From the USA Ed and Nancy Keinholz (Nancy Reddin), from France Gérard Garouste, Giuseppe Penone from Italy and Gerhard Merz from Germany. Gruppe Irwin a group of painters from Slovenia are also coming over and Japanese Butoh artists.

HW: What about the Australian artists?

NW: This year it is particularly interesting as we are showing the major Australian precursors such as Fred Williams, Arthur Boyd and Sidney Nolan interwoven into an exhibition called 1940–88 alongside work by contemporary Australian artists. The latter include Imants Tillers, Mike Parr, Rosalie Gascoigne, Peter Booth and many others. There is also going to be an Aboriginal Memorial at Pier 2/3 during the Biennale with 200 poles to represent the 200 years of the country's 200th birthday in 1988. The poles will be displayed like a forest and each pole would normally represent a person's spirit and contain their bones and the display will therefore be representing the spirits of deceased Aborigines.

HW: What is special about the Biennale this year?

NW: Normally the Biennale concentrates on the most remarkable art from the rest of the world but this year it is a reversal of contexts which is appropriate for 1988. The main exhibition of art from 1940–88 will give the public a chance to look at key Australian contemporary artists alongside some of the important precursors. Antipodean imagery really

Guy Warren's "Rainforest" (Macquarie Galleries, Sydney)

started in 1940. The contemporary work will remain afterwards in public collections in Australia.

HW: Over the years since the first Biennale in 1973 what have been the most outstanding events and which has been the most memorable Biennale?

NW: In 1973 the Biennale took place in Sydney Opera House and from 1976 onwards at the Art Gallery of New South Wales and that year a Japanese artist called Fujiko Nakaya caused a sensation in the Domain, Hyde Park, with a fog sculpture which is now in the collection at the Australian National Gallery in Canberra. 1979 was a radical Biennale in the field of conceptual and post object work concentrating on European work rather than America. In 1982 Vision in Disbelief explored new painting and in 1984 Social Metaphor saw art in a social context and in 1986 Values of Post Modernism gave the public a chance to see work from a wider range of countries including for example India, Japan and Papua New Guinea.

HW: Who funds the Biennale?

NW: It was originally Franco Belgiorno-Nettis, Chairman of Transfield Pty Ltd but this year it is partly the Australian Council, partly the State government of New South Wales, The Australian Bicentennial Authority and to a lesser degree private companies such as American Express and Qantas. The total budget is only a million dollars whereas the Paris Biennale is some 9 million dollars, also Documenta is about the same.

HW: Why did you decide to come to Sydney to work in the Visual Arts?

NW: I came out here first in 1965 as an art critic and lecturer and met an Australian girlfriend who later became my wife. We returned to England in 1967 and in 1977 we returned to Sydney and have been here ever since.

HW: What do you find most refreshing about the visual arts in Australia and which artists do you feel are the most exciting and most interesting at present?

NW: You can work with different artists around the world something you used to be able to do in the UK but I think that the Channel is a barrier now, creating an island mentality in the UK. Here you have an Oceanic culture which is quite different and an Aboriginal culture which is very refreshing. The most exciting contemporary artists at the moment are Bill Henson, Michael Johnson, Peter Booth, Imants Tillers, Vivienne Shark le Witt, Hilarie Mais, Mike Parr, Richard Dunn, Julie Brown-Rrap, Colin Lanceley, Brian Blanchflower over in Perth West Australia, Rosalie Gascoigne, John Firth-Smith, John Wolseley, Gary Sansom, Bill Robinson to give you an idea.

HW: How do you see the visual arts developing in Australia in the future?

NW: It will become far more inward looking, the opposite to post modernism. There will be a greater awareness of Australian ideas, Australian themes but in a broader sense. Photograph based work is becoming increasingly important. Did you see the Bill Henson exhibition at Rex Irwin? Jackie Redgate who is working a present in Berlin is also an interesting artist.

HW: Yes, at present there seem to be photographic exhibitions on everywhere, both contemporary and historical. I was in Canberra to see the three photographic shows at the Australian National Gallery and the large works by Bill Henson were interesting at Rex Irwin's also John Nixon's photos at the Photography Gallery in Paddington.

HW: Do you know about any of the Australian exhibitions in London this year? Jeff Makin had a show at Bernard Jacobson's gallery before I came over to Australia and Fred Williams at the Serpentine with the Pilbara series.

NW: The Hayward Gallery is showing work by the "Angry Penguins", the 1940s artists and Jonathan Watkins organised a contemporary art show at the Commonwealth Institute.

HW: What are your plans for the future after the Biennale?

NW: I've been commissioned to write a book for **Penguin** about the **Development of Post Modernism in Australian art from 1919**. I'll also be curating shows with individual artists here and elsewhere. I'm really interested in the communications between artists across the world.

AUSTRALIAN BALLET

The Vast project

In 1988, Bicentennial year, four of Australia's major regional dance companies were involved in an enormous dance project called **Vast**, performing a work created by Graeme Murphy. The four companies were **The West Australian Ballet Company**, **The Queensland Ballet Company**, **Australian Dance Theatre** and **Sydney Dance Company**. The result was a major national Bicentennial event.

The idea of **Vast** was to convey an impression of Australia through music, dance, and design. Barry Conyngham was commisioned to write the score, Andrew Carter the stage design and Graeme Murphy the choreography. The touring schedule took in Melbourne, Adelaide, Perth, Brisbane and Sydney.

The first act begins beneath the sea moving through reefs to a crescendo of surf followed by complete calm. The second act continues along the beach towards a dripping tropical rainforest and to hillier terrain with the sounds of animal and bird life and out to a wide open landscape. The third act is the heart of the project, the centre of Australia, with memorable music and the final act is set in the city vibrating with life. Humorous and quirky pieces appear in the city scenes.

This project was a unique experience and a major step in Australian dance history which had really begun in 1936 when the Ballets Russes visited Australia and two members stayed behind. One of these Edouard Borovansky built up a small ballet company with local dancers and invited overseas artists. After his death the company was continued by Dame Peggy van Praagh and the Australian Ballet emerged.

Graeme Murphy as Jean Cocteau in Poppy, Sydney Dance Company (Branco Gaica)

The Australian Ballet

The Australian Ballet is Australia's major classical company with some 56 dancers. Maina Gielgud is the current artistic director and the company was formed in 1962 using the British Royal Ballet as one of its role models. Dame Peggy Van Praagh was the founding director of the Australian Ballet in 1962 with co-operation from the Australian government. Sir Robert Helpman, the famous dancer was the company co-director from 1964 to 1974 helping build up the company name nationally and internationally along with Dame Peggy Van Praagh.

In 1988 a major tour to Russia, London and Athens included "Gallery" choreographed by Graeme Murphy, composed by Graeme Koehne and designed by Kristian Fredrikson, and "Beyond Twelve" also by Murphy. Cranko's, "Romeo and Juliet", Glen Tetley's "Orphans", Jiri Kylian's "Forgotten Land", Timothy Gordon's "Sonata for Seven", Serge Lifar's "Suite en Blanc", Maurice Bejart's "Gaité Parisienne", Maina Gielgud's "Sleeping Beauty" and "The Sentimental Bloke" choreographed by Robert Ray, who teaches at the company's ballet school in Melbourne.

Sydney Dance Company

The Sydney Dance Company is the jewel in the crown of Australian ballet with Graeme Murphy as its artistic director. Based at The Wharf, Walsh Bay since 1986 the company not only performs nationally and internationally but gives public dance classes in the new studios at The Wharf. Here you can learn classical, jazz, afro jazz, modern dance, mime and tap dancing from excellent freelance dance teachers. The Sydney Theatre Company is also based here at The Wharf.

Graeme Murphy is a rare phenomenon with a gifted creative mind and ability to adapt his ideas from Australian inspired ballets as in the Vast project to the world famous "Fire and Ice" television skating and dance spectacular for Torvill and Dean and even an opera, Brian Howard's "Metamorphosis", for the **Australian Opera**.

In 1987 I saw "Poppy" based on the life of Jean Cocteau at Sydney Opera House and it was certainly a memorable experience with Graeme Murphy dancing as Cocteau, Janet Vernon as his mother, Alfred Williams as Diaghilev, Ross Philip as Dargelas, Bill Pengelly as Radiguet and Victoria Taylor as the Angel of Death. The evocative atmosphere of Paris in the early 1900s is created with the visit of Serge Diaghilev and his Russian ballet company, which was to inspire and change many artistic lives, including that of Pablo Picaso who designed the sets and costumes for Parade and also married one of the company dancers, his first wife Olga Koklova.

Sydney Dance Company in the late 1980s is experiencing a creativity, dynamism and life comparable to that of the Ballet Rambert in London in the late 1970s. Many of the Ballet Rambert dancers at that time left London and created the famous (South) but now known as **Australian Dance Theatre** in Adelaide and to this day there are many links with British ballet companies. London would welcome a visit from the company with open arms.
Heather Waddell

Sydney Dance Company
The Wharf
Pier 4/5
Hickson Road
Walsh Bay
NSW 2000
Tel. (02) 221 4811

The Queensland Ballet
129 Margaret Street
Brisbane
Queensland 400
Tel. (07) 229 3355

Australian Dance Theatre
120 Gouger Street
Adelaide
SA 5000
Tel. (08) 212 2084

The Australian Ballet
11 Mount Alexander Road
Flemington
Victoria 3031
Tel. (03) 376 1400

The West Australian Ballet Company
825 Hay Street
Perth
WA 6000
Tel. (09) 481 0707

Graeme Murphy's "After Venice", Sydney Dance Company (Branco Gaica)

WHO'S WHO IN AUSTRALIAN LITERATURE

by **Leonie Henschke**

Australia's best-known novelist is undoubtedly PATRICK WHITE (b. in 1912) who was awarded the Nobel Prize for literature in 1973. He is remembered for numerous novels, including **The Tree of Man** (1955), **Voss** (1957), **A Fringe of Leaves** (1973), **The Twyborn Affair** (1976), plays and short stories, and his autobiography, **Flaws in the Glass**, 1981. He has made an immense contribution to contemporary Australian writing and his non-naturalistic approach to his subject matter has presented new perspectives for other writers to follow.

Artistic activity in Australia in the early years after British settlement in 1788 followed European traditions. Most of the early works were diaries and journals of life in a penal colony.

The first Australian novel is recognised as HENRY SAVERY's Quintus Servinton (1830–31), a rather melodramatic account of early colonial life as a convict. Another convincing picture of life from the convict's point of view was JAMES TUCKER's **Ralph Rashleigh**, written in the 1840s.

The 1850s saw the emergence of three important novelists:- HENRY KINGSLEY, MARCUS CLARKE and "ROLF BOLDREWOOD" (Thomas Alexander Browne). Kinglsey, younger brother of the English novelist, Charles Kingsley, visited Australia between 1853 and 1858. He published several books idealising upper-class pioneering during this pastoral period. His most notable work was **The Recollections of Geoffrey Hamlyn** (1859).

Marcus Clarke, unlike Kingsley, settled permanently in Australia, becoming a significant figure in the literary and journalistic life of Melbourne. His **For The Term of His Natural Life**, published as a serial in 1870–72, again drew its inspiration from early convict history.

Rolf Boldrewood is also identified strongly with **one** novel, **Robbery Under Arms** (1882–83), which invests the adventures of a gang of bushrangers, during the goldrush period, with some romantic glamour.

The novels of this period were relying heavily on youthful, adventurous plots and a rather simplified psychology expressed in typically English structures. However, with the moves to Federation of the separate states in 1901, a new nationalism was born and expressed in writing. The **bush ballad** was the first truly Australian literary form to emerge. Many folk songs from the British Isles had been imported into the new colony but they soon took on a distinctly anti-authoritarian quality. Some of the ballads were even identified as treason songs and their performance banned.

The increasingly influential Sydney newspaper, the **Bulletin**, fostered scores of outback versifiers. The most celebrated were HENRY LAWSON and A. B. ("BANJO") PATERSON. Paterson's collection, **The Man From Snowy River and Other Verses** (1895) was one of the first authentic Australian best-sellers. Paterson also wrote Australia's famous national song, "Waltzing Matilda".

Along with verse, the short story flourished and here Henry Lawson was to be the most acclaimed. Pieces like "The Union Buries its Dead", "The Drover's Wife", "Telling Mrs Baker" and "The Loaded Dog" have become touchstones of Australian achievement in the form. His collections, **While the Billy Boils** (1896) and **Joe Wilson and His Mates** (1901), are indispensable volumes for understanding the development and quality of Australian writing. Lawson's gift is essentially for the snapshot of life, in which all the elements of composition, perspective and exposure are perfectly calculated.

The turn of the century produced only one full-length work of fiction—**Such is Life** (1903) by JOSEPH FURPHY under the pseudonym, "TOM COLLINS". Furphy instilled in his book the best and most characteristic attitudes of his generation—the ardent patriotism, the equally ardent socialism, the belief in mateship and the superiority of bush life to that of the coastal cities.

In the first decade of the 20th century, "STEELE RUDD" (Arthur Hoey Davis) produced his toughly humorous stories of the battlers in the bush, **On Our Selection** (the Dad and Dave stories), C. J. DENNIS developed his vein of popular comic verse (**The Sentimental Bloke** (1915), **The Glugs of Gosh** (1917), and MARY GILMORE published her first volume of poetry, **Marri'd and Other Versus** (1910), inaugurating a long and important career.

NORMAN LINDSAY'S first novel was **A Curate in Bohemia** (1913). Throughout a long life devoted to painting and literature Lindsay made it his business to outrage the middle classes. His novels, many of which were initially banned, include **Redheap** (1930) and **Saturdee** (1933).

At this time Australian writers were recognising the growing importance of urban industrialism in Australian experience. EDWARD DYSON turned his attention to the urban proletariat in **Fact'ry 'ands** (1906) and **Benno and Some of the Push** (1911). The classic urban novel of the period, however, is LOUIS STONE's **Jonah** (1911), a strongly imagined and executed piece of fictional realism.

"HENRY HANDEL RICHARDSON" (Ethel Richardson) also emerged as a major writer. She wrote a number of novels—**Maurice Guest** (1908), **The Getting of Wisdom** (1910) and **The Young Cosima** (1939)—but her greatest achievement was the trilogy, **The Fortunes of Richard Mahony**. The trilogy, consisting of **Australia Felix** (1917), **The Way Home** (1925) and **Ultima Thule** (1929), has great weight and substance. The books combine a profuse documentation of the social and cultural history of Victoria in the

19th century, with a penetrating study of the disentegration of a single soul.

The long-term effects of **World War I** appeared in episodes and characters of many novels in the years after 1918; KATHERINE SUSANNAH RICHARD'S **Intimate Strangers** (1937), for example, and VANCE PALMER's **Daybreak** (1932).

Other important Palmer works include **The Passage** (1930), **The Swayne Family** (1934) and the trilogy **Golconda** (1948), **Seedtime** (1957), and **The Big Fellow** (1959).

Pritchard's stress was more on the regional and occupational aspects of her character's lives in **Black Opal** (1921), **Working Bullocks** (1926), and **Haxby's Circus** (1930).

The novel of radical protests was further exemplified in JOHN HARCOURT's **Upsurge** (1934) and JEAN DEVANNY's **Sugar Heaven** (1936).

Other important novelists of the period were M. BARNARD ELDERSHAW, (the collaborative work of Marjorie Barnard and Flora Eldershaw), ELEANOR DARK, LEONARD MANN, JOHN K. EWERS and FRANK DALBY DAVISON.

Many books were also published concentrating on the physical environment, for example, MILES FRANKLIN, **All that Swagger** (1936) and **Childhood at Brindabella** (not published till 1963 after her death). Franklin is best remembered, however, for **My Brilliant Career** (1901), which she wrote when only sixteen; seventy-five years later it was made into an award-winning film. The prestigious Miles Franklin Award for Australian fiction, which bears her name, was funded from her estate.

The most striking use of outback material was that of BRIAN PENTON in **The Landtakers** (1934) and its sequel, **Inheritors** (1936).

CHRISTINA STEAD's first novel, **Seven Poor Men of Sydney** (1934), fused a symbolic technique with a keen social consciousness. Later works (many written in Europe) won her an international reputation. Among the most memorable are **The Man Who Loved Children** (1940) and **For Love Alone** (1945).

In a similar vein were the sophisticated and urbane novels of MARTIN BOYD, for example, **Lucinda Brayford** (1946), **The Cardboard Crowd** (1952), **A Difficult Young Man** (1955), **Outbreak of Love** (1957) and **When Blackbirds Sing** (1962).

New novelists were appearing in this period who broadened the boundaries of fictional achievement. EVE LANGLEY in **The Pea Pickers** (1942) made out of potentially sentimental material a uniquely fantastic tale; and XAVIER HERBET harnessed his own enormous energy to the external conventions of the historical safa in **Capricornia** (1938). Herbert did not match the success of his first book until the appearance of his massive novel, **Poor Fellow, My Country** in 1975. Both works derive their strength from Herbert's passionate love of the Australian wilderness and his scorn for those who despoil it.

Books on display at Ariel Bookshop, Sydney

At the same time novelists of established reputations seemed to find new sources of creative inspiration. **ELEANOR DARK, with The Timeless Land** (1941), began a trilogy which recreated the earliest years of life in the New South Wales Colony. KYLIE TENNANT contrived her blend of social protest and optimistic good humour in **The Battlers** (1941), **Ride on Stranger** (1943) and **Time Enough Later** (1943). RUTH PARK wrote **Harp in the South** and **Poor Man's Orange** (1949). LEONARD MANN's **The Go-Getter** (1942) is perhaps the best socialist-realist novel generated by Australia's Depression years.

A flood of short stories were published, most notably by FRANK DALBY DAVISON, DAL STIVENS, PETER COWAN, JOHN MORRISON and O. E. SCHLUNKE.

The 50s and early 60s were a time of great cultural change in Australia with massive European immigration. Australian writing began to move away from a conformist Anglo-Saxon structure to an integration of various nationalities. JUDAH WATEN (born of Russian Jewish parents) gave the first and still the best account of a European family's settlement in Australia in **Alien Years** (1952). MORRIS LURIE, also of Jew-

31

ish parents, continued to chronicle the newcomer in his work in the 70s and 80s.

One outstanding collection of "ethnic writing" published in 1988 is **Reflections** (ed. T. Spilias and S. Messinis)—a bilingual anthology of writing by the most significant Greek/Australian writers. Another example is **The Strength of Tradition** (1983), edited by R. F. Holt, a collection of stories of the immigrant presence in Australia.

Widely read writers of the period included JON CLEARY, D'ARCY NILAND **(The Shiralee** (1955), TOM RONAN **(Vision Splendid)** (1954), OLAF RUHEN **Naked Under Capricorn** (1958), DYMPHNA CUSACK **Come in Spinner** (with Florence James) and RUSSELL BRADDON **The Naked Island** (1952).

The Devil's Advocate published in 1959 brought international popularity to the now prolific and highly acclaimed MORRIS WEST.

JOHN O'GRADY (as "NINO CULOTTA") again looked at the immigrant in Australia in the hilariously funny **They're A Weird Mob** (1957).

CYRIL PEARL documented local and overseas social history with zest and a piquant wit and ARTHUR W. UPFIELD established the mystery and detective story in an Australian setting with his part-Aboriginal detective "Bony". This genre has been followed with even greater success in the 80s by Sydney writer, PETER CORRIS, who has established the laconic private eye, Cliff Hardy.

The towering literary figure of the 50s right up into the 80s has, of course, been PATRICK WHITE.

Two other novelists often associated with his manner of writing are CHRISTOPHER KOCH and RANDOLPH STOW. After a fine first novel, **The Boys in the Island** (1958), Koch published **Across the Sea Wall** (1965) and much later, **The Year of Living Dangerously** (1978). The last of these reflected through its Indonesian setting the growing interest of Australians in their neighbours in the near North and Pacific. Stow, a poet as well as a novelist has been more prolific. His most famous work is **To the Islands** (1958) written when he was only twenty-two, before White's **Voss**, with which it is often compared. His more recent books include **The Girl Green as Elderflower** (1979) and **Suburbs of Hell** (1984).

ELIZABETH HARROWER's novels were also studies of personal themes and HAL PORTER received new recognition, although he had been writing for at least a quarter of a century. Some of his best writing is in his autobiographies, **The Watcher on the Cast-Iron Balcony** (1963) and **The Paper Chase** (1966).

Both these books are representative of a class of writing which enjoyed considerable success in the 60s—literary autobiography. One of the best of the kind, ALAN MARSHALL's **I Can Jump Puddles** was published in 1955, and it has had a number of sequels. Among others were FRANK HARDY's **The Disturbing Element** (1963), poet DOUGLAS STEWART's **The Seven Rivers** (1966), and DONALD

HORNE's **The Education of Young Donald** (his classic socio-logical study of Australia, **The Lucky Country**, was written in 1964).

GEORGE JOHNSTON's life story is also closely woven with the events in his acclaimed novels, **My Brother Jack** (1964), **Clean Straw for Nothing** (1969) and **A Cartload of Clay** (1971).

A. B. FACEY's classic, **A Fortunate Life** (1981), has become one of the best-loved autobiographical tales in Aus-tralian literature. An unsophisticated country man, he had an extraordinary story to tell. He treats it with the cool detach-ment of a born writer although he had no education and had to teach himself to read and write.

Other fiction of the 60s, 70s and 80s has been more diver-sified, away from formal conventions and, in some writers, towards the investigation of highly personal lifestyles and states of feeling. There has been a more assured relationship with international trends, while maintaining a greater maturity and independence from founding Anglo-Saxon traditions. There has been a greater awareness of Australia's antiquity; it's Aboriginal heritage.

THOMAS KENEALLY's first novel, **The Place at Whitton** (1964), amalgamated an almost Gothic plot with the life of the Roman Catholic Church in modern Australia. Many of his subsequent books pursue religious concerns, though the manner has been subject to certain modulations. **Three Cheers for the Paraclete** (1968) has a distinct flavour of Graham Greene and **The Survivor** (1969) incorporates aca-demic satire and quasi-Freudian psychology. After **The Chant of Jimmy Blacksmith** (1972), a superb compressed study of some of the central moral problems generated by Australian history, Keneally found his next theme in the life of Joan of Arc in **Blood Red, Sister Rose** (1974), Jewish perse-cution in **Schindler's Ark** in 1982, and early drama in **Playmaker** (1988.

PETER MATHERS (b. 1931) and DAVID IRELAND (b. 1927) have produced in their novels deeply anarchic accounts of Australian experience. Peter Mathers is best known for **The Trap** (1966), **The Wort Papers** (1972) and **A Change for the Better** published in 1984. He has been quoted:- "As writers, we must practise and preach subversion. Pattern and order can be pleasant. But still...If we feel that disorder is necessary, it's to be disorder".   David Ireland's common concern is with the eternal issues between God and man. His novels include **The Unknown Industrial Prisoner** (after an 11 year stint at a Shell oil refinery) in 1971, **The Glass Canoe** (1976) and **A Woman of the Future** (1969).

PETER CAREY and MICHAEL WILDING have demonstrated a comparable taste for disquiescing fantasy in their short stories in the 70s. Peter Carey has extended his range to become one of Australia's premier authors. His novels included **Bliss** in 1981 (made into a feature film in 1985), **Illywacker** (1985) and **Oscar and Lucinda** (1988), also to be made into a film. The latter won the prestigious Booker prize in 1988 in London.

FRANK MOORHOUSE's affinities, on the other hand, seem closer to some of his contemporary Americans. His discontinuous narratives, **The Americans, Baby** (1972) and **The Electrical Experience** (1974) mix documentary and fictional techniques. His latest work **Forty-Seventeen** was published in 1988 and he has also been writing for film and television (e.g. the script for **Between Wars**).

Some writers like ROBERT DREWE **The Bodysurfers** (1983), **Fortune** (1986), or KENNETH COOK **Wake in Fright** (1961), searched for new perspectives, or peculiarly Australian experience. Other such as DAVID MALOUF and MURRAY BAIL **Homesickness** (1980), and **Holden's Performance** (1988), explored anew the relevance of European history and culture to Australian life.

David Malouf, also well known as a poet, produced his first novel **Johnno** in 1975. His other books include **An Imaginary Life** (1978), **Fly Away Peter** (1982), **Harland's Half-Acre** (1984) and **12 Edmonstone Street** (1985).

GERALD MURNANE (b. 1939) is recognised for his highly individual novels **Tamarisk Row** (1974), **The Plains** (1982), and **Landscape with Landscape** (1985).

DAVID FOSTER (b. 1944) is another highly idiosyncratic writer. A science graduate, he turned to literature in 1973, producing books of fiction, poetry and radio plays. His novels include the award-winning **The Pure Land** (1984) and **Moonlite** (1981), **Christian Rosy Cross**, a work about mediaeval and Renaissance gnosticism and alchemy, and **Dog Rock** (1985), a murder mystery spoof set in a small country town.

In the 70s and 80s feminist ideology also had an impact on Australian literary output—both by women **and** men.

HELEN GARNER and BLANCHE D'ALPUGET are important mediators of these feminist ideas.

Helen Garner published her first novel **Monkey Grip** in 1977 to widespread acclaim. It was made into a highly successful film in 1982. Her other works include **Honour and Other People's Children** (1980) and a novelisation of the film **Moving Out** in 1982.

Blanche D'Alpuget, probably best-known for her revealing biography of Australia's Prime Minister, Bob Hawke, is also the author of fiction, most notably **Monkeys in the Dark** (1980) and **Turtle Beach** (1981).

The end of the 70s also saw increasing recognition of JESSICA ANDERSON and SHIRLEY HAZZARD.

Anderson's **Tirra Tirra by the River** (1978) and **The Impersonators** (1980) took out literary prizes as did Hazzard's **Transit of Venus** (1980).

THEA ASTLEY, born in 1925, and established as a writer in the 50s and 60s with **Girl with A Monkey** (1958), **A Descant for Gossips** (1960), and **The Slow Natives** (1965), has received more widespread recognition in the 80s with paperback reprints of her previously undervalued stories. She continues to publish prolifically. Recent books include **Hunting the Wild Pineapple** (1980), **An Item from the Late News** (1982), **Beachmasters** (1985) and **It's Raining in**

Mango (1987). Other older writers have found the climate encouraging including ELIZABETH JOLLEY, BARBARA JEFFERIS, NENE GARE, GLEN TOMASETTI and GWEN KELLY. Also the works of OLGA MASTERS (who died in 1987) have received new attention.

The stories, plays and poems of Elizabeth Jolley have been published in numerous literary journals and anthologies. Her fiction includes the novels, **Palamino** (1980), **The Newspaper of Claremont Street** (1981), **Miss Peabody's Inheritance** (1983), **Mr Scobies Riddle** (1982), **Milk and Honey** (1984), and **The Sugar Mother** (1988).

Younger writers becoming established include KATE GRENVILLE, CHRISTINE TOWNSEND, GABRIELLE LORD, JEAN BEDFORD, ELIZABETH RILEY, VICKY VIIDIKAS, BEVERLEY FARMER and GLENDA ADAMS.

Glenda Adams had an award-winning year in 1988 with her **Dancing on Coral** taking out two major literary prizes and Kate Grenville has received acclaim for her **Joan Makes History** (1988)—an entertaining history of Australia with an important social and political message.

Aboriginal Australia also won due recognition in the Bicentennial year, 1988. Numerous recollections and anthologies were published. **Black Words, White Page** (1988) was the first full-length, serious study of Black Australia's literature.

COLIN JOHNSTON's **Wild Cat Calling** (1965) was the first published novel by an Aborigine and still stands today as a work of distinction as is SALLY MORGAN's evocative **My Place** (1987). KEVIN GILBERT is widely published in prose and in 1988 published his first play **The Cherry Pickers**. Other Aborigines receiving literary attention are the poets FAITH BANDLER and OODGEROO NOONUCCAL (formerly KATH WALKER).

Drama has also blossomed in the 70s and 80s, in part because of more Government support. By 1970 each capital city had a permanent professional drama company and many experimental groups were also active. The growth of professional activity gave both established and emerging playwrights unprecedented opportunities; the plays of DAVID WILLIAMSON, DOROTHY HEWITT, JACK HIBBERD, MICHAEL BODDY, ALEX BUZO and BARRY OAKLEY have been highly acclaimed.

THE AUSTRALIAN FILM INDUSTRY

by **Leonie Henschke**

Australia's rebirth as a major film-producing nation began in the late 1960s and early 70s. Commonwealth and State Governments began to provide finance and facilities for film-making which brought a new confidence to the industry.

Major films of this period were Peter Weir's **Picnic at Hanging Rock** in 1972 (which went on to become the symbol of the Australian film industry's coming of age) and **The Last Wave** (1977), Michael Thornhill's **Between Wars** (1974), Donald Crombie's **Caddie** (1976), Fred Schepisi's **The Devil's Playground** (1976) and **The Chant of Jimmy Blacksmith** (1978), Phil Noyce's **Newsfront** (1978) and John Duigan's **Mouth to Mouth** (1978).

My Brilliant Career (1979), directed by Gillian Armstrong, was runner-up at the Cannes Film Festival in 1979 and the following year Judy Davis won the British Best Actress award for her performance in the film.

In a completely different mood—bizarre and unrelentingly violent—George Miller's **Mad Max** (starring Mel Gibson in his first film role) was released the same year. Undoubtedly the most vital film produced to that date it flagrantly set up scenes of blood and destruction to bring in the cinema audiences in droves.

Bruce Beresford's **Breaker Morant** (1980) won the Cannes Best Supporting Actor Award for Jack Thompson's performance and it was the most successful foreign film of 1981 in the US, rating in the top third of box office hits for that year.

My Brilliant Career, **Breaker Morant** and **Gallipoli** (1981), starring Mel Gibson and Mark Lee, are historical/nostalgic pieces so typical of Australian film-making in the 70s and early 80s. Australian films from this genre have been described as having "a delicacy, commitment, freshness and independence of spirit". Other 1981–82 films showed a definite move to comedies, musicals and contemporary Australian themes— particularly the latter with John Duigan's **Winter of Our Dreams** and Ken Cameron's **Monkey Grip**, based on the best-selling novel by Helen Garner. Other films in this category included Phil Noyce's **Heatwave** (starring Judy Davis), Donald Crombie's **The Killing of Angel Street**, and Bruce Beresford's slick teenage move, **Puberty Blues** (starring Nell Schofield).

The humourous side of life featured prominently:- among these were **Norman Loves Rose**, a Jewish comedy set in Sydney; David Steven's **The Clinic; Captain Invincible**, a comic book hero spoof; and John Lamond's **A Slice of Life**.

The Pirate Movie joined **Starstruck** in the musical comedy categroy.

The industry also ventured into Asia with the Japanese-Australian joint production, **Southern Cross**, Peter Weir's **The Year of Living Dangerously**, set in Indonesia, and John Duigan's **Far East** (starring Bryan Brown and Helen Morse), set in Singapore.

Squizzy Taylor and **Kitty and the Bagman**—both gangster films—were two of the few films produced in the nostalgic mood, along with the film of Mrs Aeneas Gunn's Australian classic, **We of the Never-Never.**

Mad Max II (1981), known in the US as **The Road Warrior**, continued the same violent theme as its predecessor and was even more successful.

An old-fashioned tale about a mountain lad and a mob of mountain brumbies (wild horses) was turned into one of Australia's most photographically beautiful movies, **The Man from Snowy River** (directed by George Miller) in 1982.

Careful, He Might Hear You, 1983, (from a book by Sumner Locke Eliot) was one of the most successful Australian films dealing with women. A child's view of an adult conflict over his own custody, it is set in a Sydney of the 1920s and 30s.

Another 1983 production was **Phar Lap**, the story of Australia's greatest racehorse.

Youthful issues preoccupied director, Ken Cameron (of **Monkey Grip**), in **Fast Talking** (1984)— disaffected youth in the suburbs of a modern Sydney.

Again on issues—**One Night Stand** (1984)—was John Duigan's contribution to the cinema of nuclea foreboding, ingenuous in mood and ironically poignant.

Co-production and distribution deals with other countries have been economically necessary to the Australian film industry to recoup the enormous budgets of modern feature films. Another strategy for international acceptance has been the importation of fashionable and internationally known actors to accompany the local casts. **The Wild Duck** (1984), from Henri Ibsen's play, became a United Nations of accents (Liv Ullman, Jeremy Irons and Australia's John Meillon) transferred to an underterminate setting. Another later film, **Evil Angels**, brought in Meryl Streep as the lead in the dramatic retelling of the Lindy Chamberlain story.

The year 1985 saw the release of **Bliss**, from the award-winning Peter Carey novel.

The year 1986 was a memorable one in terms of box office success. **Crocodile Dundee**, starring Paul Hogan (ex Sydney Harbour Bridge rigger turned television funny man), made move history as the top grossing film worldwide ($US 300 million). With all the ingredients of adventure, rugged hero and beautiful American heroine **and** two locations—Australia and the US—it had international appeal. The sequel, **Crocodile Dundee II**, released in 1988 has also made its mark, opening simultaneously at 2,500 screens across the US.

Malcolm (from Nadia Tass and David Parker) was a highly

Still from Shame (Barron films)

idiosyncratic release of 1986 and took out numerous film awards internationally. From the same producers came **Rikky and Pete**, one of the hits of 1988.

The Year My Voice Broke and **Shame** (from Barron Films) were movies to note of 1987.

Yet another sequel, **The Man from Snowy River II**, was released in 1988. Another historical piece was **The Lighthorseman**, a true story about the last great cavalry charge in history.

Australian actress, Wendy Hughes, has featured prominently on both sides of the camera. Co-starring with Colin Friels, she gave one of her finest performances in **Warm Nights on a Slow Moving Train** (1988)—a mysterious tale of seduction, intrigue and murder. She featured in and was associate producer, with husband Patric Juillet, of **Boundaries of the Heart** (1988) and is working again with Juillet on **Luigi's Ladies** for 1989.

A number of thrillers appeared on the screens in 1988— **Dangerous Game**, **The Dreaming**, **The Everlasting Secret Family** (starring Gallipoli's Mark Lee), **Incident at Raven's Gate**, **Grievous Bodily Harm** (starring Colin Friels), and the **Hungry Heart**.

Other features in production for 1989 include The Concubine from a best-selling novel by Australian author, Morris West; **Sweetie**, produced by John Maynard, described as an ironic look at modern relationships—the confused, the sulking and the banal; and two more Juillet films **Indian Ocean** and **A Quiet Weekend**.

Many of the top Australian producers have also turned their attention to serials (e.g. **Home and Away** and **Neighbours**), mini-series (e.g. **Return to Eden**, **Tanamera** and **Eden's Lost**), and telemovies, which have been released internationally. Another mini-series, **Darlings of the Gods**, produced in Australia by Thames Television and Australian producers, explores the lives of actors Laurence Olivier, Vivian Leigh and Peter Finch during their visit to Australia in 1948.

ALTERNATIVE ART PERFORMANCE SPACES

Throughout Australia this area has increased enormously in the last five years. The following is a list of spaces across the country in the main cities that will be of interest to Australian and overseas artists. They have been grouped together to save artists time when applying for exhibitions.

Melbourne

Artists Space, 150 Park Street, North Fitzroy, Melbourne. Tel. (03) 489 2749.
Open Wednesday–Saturday 1–5. Run on a rental basis by artists.

Gertrude Street Artists Spaces Inc., 200 Gertrude Street, Fitzroy, Victoria 3065. Tel. (03) 419 3406.
Open Tuesday–Fridat 10–5.30, Saturday 1–5. Artists studios and gallery for group and individual shows and installations.

Gryphon Gallery, Melbourne College of Advanced Education, Carlton Campus, Cnr Grattan and Swanston Streets, Carlton, Victoria 3053. Tel. (03) 341 8587.
Open Tuesday–Saturday 10–4, Wednesday until 7.30. Helps to show unknown artists.

Australian Centre for Contemporary Art, Dallas Brooks Drive, The Domain, Melbourne, Victoria 3004. Tel. (03) 654 6422.
Open Tuesday–Friday 10.30–5, Saturday & Sunday 2–5. Started in 1984, ACCA presents contemporary art, publishes catalogues and arranges lectures.

Ewing and George Paton Galleries, 2nd Floor, Union House, University of Melbourne, Parkville, Victoria 3052.
Open Monday, Tuesday, Thursday 10–6, Wednesday 12–8, Friday 1–6. Presents local, national and international new art. Lectures, seminars and talks by artists also.

Linden, 26 Ackland Street, St Kilda. Tel. (03) 536 1427.
Open Wednesday–Friday 1–6, Saturday & Sunday 11–6.

Roar 2, 115a Brunswick Street, Fitzroy, Victoria 3065. Tel. (03) 419 9975.
Open Tuesday–Sunday 11–6. Exhibitions on a rental basis to young and new artists. Run by a collective of artists.

Sydney

The Tin Sheds Art Workshop, Sydney University, City Road, Darlinghurst, NSW.

Kelly St Kolektiv, Kelly Street, Ultimo, NSW 2007. Tel. (02) 281 1398.

First Draft, 2/27 Abercrombie Street, Chippendale, NSW 2008. Tel. (02) 698 4439.

Hobart

Chameleon Inc., Hobart
A Tasmanian Contemporary Art Space. Artist-in-residence, lectures, 2 large galleries and a darkroom.

Cockatoo Workshop, Launceston
Gallery space, artist-run.

Adelaide

Experimental Art Foundation, 68 North Terrace, Adelaide. Tel. 211 7505.
Director: Michael Snelling. Open Monday–Friday 11–6, Saturday & Sunday 2–5. Artist-in-residence programme, lectures, facilities for video , audio, printing and graphic art. Dark Horsey bookshop and Australian Network for art and technology.

Contemporary Art Centre, 14 Porter Street, Parkside, Adelaide. Tel. 272 2682.
Director: Margo Osborne. Open Monday–Friday 11–5, Saturday & Sunday 1–5. Publishes Broadsheet journal. Applications six months in advance. 33⅓% commission on sales.

Vizarts Festival Theatre Foyers, Adelaide Festival Centre Trust, King William Road, Adelaide. Tel. 216 8758.
Open 1–6 daily. Manager: Karin Ostermann. Plaza gallery has 54 metre wallspace. Access to facilities for printing, graphic design and technicians. 50% Aboriginal and multi cultural artists shows. Many artists first shows. Pays $100–$300 artists fees. 33⅓% commission on sales.

North Adelaide School of Art Gallery, 42 Stanley Street, North Adelaide. Tel. 267 4811.
Manager: Trevor Goulding. Open Monday–Friday 9–4.30. Gallery of 200 square metres. To show students local, national and international art 25% commission. Exhibition fee and transport costs covered.

Artzone Gallery, 80 Hindley Street, Adelaide, South Australia. Tel. 212 4678.

Open Wednesday–Sunday 12–6. Artist-run gallery space above Imprints booksellers. Flat rate fee of $100 per week for rent and costs. No commission charged.

College Gallery, South Australian School of Art, Holbrooks Road, Underdale, South Australia. Tel. 354 6479.
Open Tuesday–Saturday 11–4. Gallery and sculpture court-yard. Lectures and gallery for recent work from local, national and international visiting artists. 10% commission.

Club Foote, 26 Blyth Street, Adelaide. Tel. 212 7998.
Director: Rodin Genoff. Open 9–6 daily. Public access gallery for individuals and groups. Nightclub venue. Sound, lighting and projector. Ideal for performance. 20% commission.

The Union Gallery, Level 6, Union House, University of Ade-laide, North Terrace, Adelaide. Tel. 228 5834. Director: Jenny Jones. Open Monday–Friday 10–5. Multi purpose space. 33⅓% commission on sales.

Perth

Praxis, to become (PICA), currently at Old Bag Factory Build-ing, 33 Pakenham Street, Fremantle, WA 6160. Tel. (09) 335 9770.
Publishes Praxis M art magazine. Now about to become part of PICA (Perth Institute of Contemporary Art) to be based next to the Art Gallery of Western Australia in Perth. See Praxis under Perth, West Australia for details.

The Beach Gallery, next to the Art Gallery of Western Aus-tralia in Perth.
Sponsored by Curtin University and Robert Holmes à Court. Alternative art space and gallery.

Brisbane

Institute of Modern Art, 106 Edward Street, Brisbane, Queensland 4000. Tel. (07) 229 5985.
Director: Sue Cramer.
The following Brisbane galleries now also show alternative and new art. **Milburn and Arte, Roz MaCallan Gallery** and **Bellas Gallery. Queensland Art Gallery** also shows experi-mental art and installations. **Museum of Contemporary Art (MOCA)** has a performance and installation studio and a **mini MOCA** streetside gallery as well as 3 main galleries.

Art and Australia had a special Bicentennial issue, its 101st, which covered articles on contemporary and alternative art spaces throughout Australia with articles by art writers and artists across the country. It is recommended that artists read this issue for further information.

Art and Australia, 653 Pacific Highway, Killara, NSW 2071. Tel. (02) 498 4933.

NATIONAL ARTS ORGANISATIONS

Aboriginal Artist Agency Ltd, 23 McLaren Street, North Sydney, NSW 2620. Tel. (02) 923 2366.
Aim: To promote the use of indiginous arts nationally and internationally and to protect the cultural property of Australian Aboriginal and Torres Strait Islander people.

Art Association of Australia, c/o Fine Arts Dept, University of Queensland, St Lucia, Qld 4067.
To help study and reserarch in art. Promoting annual conferences in the arts.

ACGA—Australian Commerical Galleries Association, 20 Powell Street, South Yarra, Vic 3141. Tel. (03) 26 5519.

Artbank, 50c Roseberry Avenue, Roseberry, NSW 2018. Tel. (02) 662 8011.
A programme of building up a collection of work of contemporary Australian artists. Funded by the Federal Government.

Arts Council of Australia, 5th Floor, 117 York Street, Sydney, NSW 2000. Tel. (02) 264 2500.
The council has representation in each state and aims to develop the arts in country regions and throughout each capital city. A non profit organistion.

Arts Law Centre of Australia, 1st Floor, 11 Randle Street, Surry Hills, NSW 2010. Tel. (02) 211 4795.
Outside Sydney area free call (008) 22 1457. The centre provides legal assistance and education on arts related matters.

Art Museum Association of Australia, PO Box 284, Kingston, ACT 2606.

Australia Council, 168 Walker Street, North Sydney, NSW 2060. Tel. (02) 923 3333.
Aim: to foster excellence in the arts, facilitate public access, promote international awareness and appreciation of Australian arts. The following boards are all located at 168 Walker Street and each offering specialist advice and awards grants. Providing art contacts throughout Australia for visiting art specialists.

Visual Arts Board of Australia
Theatre Board of the Australia Council
Music Board of the Australia Council
Literature Board of the Australia Council
Crafts Board of the Australia Council
Community Arts Board of the Australia Council
Aboriginal Arts Board of the Australia Council
Design Board of the Australia Council

Australian Film Commission, PO Box 3984, GPO Sydney, NSW 2001 or 8 West Street, North Ryde, NSW 2113. Tel. (02) 922 6855.

Australian Film Institute, 213–214 Palmer Street, Darlinghurst, NSW 2010. Tel. (02) 332 2111.
Aiming to foster a film culture within Australia.

Australian Film and Television School, 13–15 Lyon Park Road, North Ryde, NSW 2113. Tel. (02) 887 1666.

Australian Library Promotion Council, 328 Swanston Street, Melbourne, Vic 3000. Tel (03) 663 7194.

Australian National Gallery, Parkes, ACT 2600. Tel. (062) 71 2411.
Housing collection of contemporary and traditional Australian work with permanent collection of European work, **Australian Aboriginal**, sculpture, photography galleries and changing displays of major importance. (See gallery listings).

Australian Association for Dance Education, PO Box 287, Jamison, ACT 2614.

Australian Centre for Photography, Dobell House, 257 Oxford Street, Paddington, NSW 2021. Tel. (02) 331 6253.

Crafts Council of Australia, 100 George Street, The Rocks, Sydney, NSW 2000. Tel. (02) 241 1701.
The national non-governmental craft organisation representing Australia on the World Crafts Council. National Selected Slide Library available for public use and promotion. The council provides an information service, and a Craft Resources catalogue is available.

Design Institute of Australia, PO Box 21, Hawthorn, Vic 3122. Tel. (03) 819 1311.

International Cultural Corporation of Australia Ltd, Suite 102/103, 1st Floor, Scarborough House, 12 Playfair Street, The Rocks, Sydney, NSW 2000. Tel. (02) 241 1071.
Aims to promote, arrange and manage cultural exchange between Australia and other countries, in particular countries with whom Australia has a cultural agreement.

Industrial Design Council of Australia, 70 George Street, The Rocks, Sydney, NSW 2000. Tel. (02) 241 3392.
Exhibition areas and adjoining shop. Venue for Australian designers.

International Theatre Institute, Australia Centre, PO Box 137, Kings Cross, NSW 2011. Tel. (02) 38 2335.

Museums Association of Australia Inc., c/o Museum of Applied Arts and Sciences, PO Box K346, Haymarket, NSW 2000. Tel. (02) 217 0226.
Their aim is to promote within Australia the educational, cultural, aesthetic, scientific, archival and research value of both large and small museums.

NAVA—National Association for the Visual Arts, PO Box N296, Sydney, NSW 2000.
The association is an independent, self determining body that works to keep the interests of individuals and organisations in the visual arts in the minds of government, the commercial sector and the community. The National Board of NAVA is made up of two representatives from each state and territory in Australia. NAVA newsletter available.

National Library of Australia, Parkes, ACT 2600. Tel. (062) 62 1111. To make available a national record of library material including books, periodicals, manuscripts, pictures, films, photographs, music, maps and sound recordings.

Papermakers of Australia, Paper Mill, Centre for the Arts, University of Tasmania, GPO Box 252C, Hobart 7001. Contact Penny Wells. Newsletter available.

Print Council of Australia, 172 Roden Street, West Melbourne, Vic 3003. Tel. (03) 328 2140.
A national, non-profit arts organisation established in 1966, aiming to promote Australian prints and printmakers in all of their diversity. Regular exhibitions, publications and other activities. PCA's journal is called Imprint.

Power Institute of Fine Arts, Fine Arts Dept, University of Sydney, NSW 2006. Tel. (02) 326 2022.

The state contacts for NAVA are as follows:

NSW—2/107 Cremorne Road, Cremorne, NSW 2090. Tel. (02) 902 387

Vic—Crafts Council of Victoria, 7 Blackwood Street, North Melbourne. Tel. (03) 329 0133. Vic 3051.

SA—363 Esplanade, Henley Beach SA 5022. Tel. (08) 356 8511/354 6479.

Qld—32 Derby Street, Highgate Hill, Qld 4101. Tel. (07) 229 4355/846 3725.

WA—63 Mount Street, Perth, WA 6000. Tel. (09) 321 9464.

Tas—Centre for the Arts Gallery, Hunter Street, Hobart, Tas 7000. Tel. (002) 38 4300.

NT—185 Garden Circuit, Jingili, NT 5782. Tel. (089) 85 3357/81 4211.

ACT—c/o Canberra School of Art, (Chris Croft), PO Box 804, Canberra City, ACT 2601.

The Potter's Society of Australia, 48 Burton Street, Darlinghurst, NSW 2010. Tel. (02) 331 3151.
There are many organisations related to the visual arts and performing arts not able to be included in this listing due to available space and consideration for their national importance. I recommend contacting the Australia Council for comprehensive listings made available to the public in their newly updated **Ozarts directory**.

ABORIGINAL ART IN A CHANGING WORLD

Since 1788 traditional Aboriginal societies in many parts of the country have been devastated by white settlement. The invading Europeans looked at Aboriginal art and artifacts as being "primitive and crude". Until quite recently, Aboriginal art was confined to the ethnographic sections of museums. The pieces were regarded as relics of a lost, or disappearing world.

However, in parts of northern and central Australia, Aboriginal people were able to keep alive their complex social structure, religion and art. In Arnhem Land, for example, there are local artists working in traditions that are thousands of years old. The last two decades have seen great changes in the way Aboriginal art is now regarded. It is prized by collectors around the world both as art in itself and as the expression of a unique and sophisticated culture. This increased interest in Aboriginal art is especially shared by Aboriginal people both in the rural outback and the urban centres. In many communities the traditional arts are flourishing and have acquired a new and urgent emphasis—that of reinforcing Aboriginal identity and asserting traditional values. Art is, and always was, a way of teaching children the stories of their culture. The arts and crafts industry also offers economic benefits to the rural and remote communities existing throughout central Australia.

Traditions have been adapted for new media. The Tiwi people from Bathurst Island and neighbouring Melville Island are reproducing their abstract designs on textiles through the use of screenprinting. The women of Utopia and Ernabella in central Australia are producing brilliant batiks. But perhaps the most famous art comes from the Papunya Tula school where the symbols and motifs of ceremonial ground paintings have been translated on to canvas or board using acrylic paints. The desert painters are producing stunning contemporary works of art that have their roots in an ancient tradition which has evolved over the past 40,000 years of habitation.

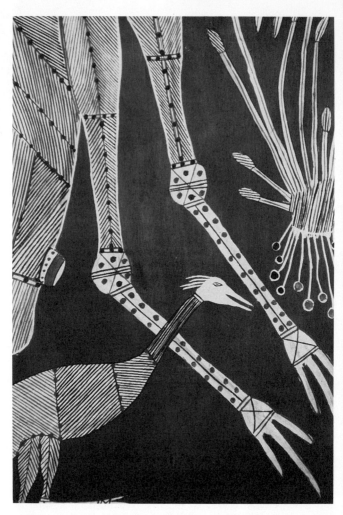

Detail from an Aboriginal bark painting (Hogarth Gallery Sydney)

I have attempted to list "Aboriginal Art Galleries" for each capital city. In the following chapters there are also several collections of Aboriginal works in public museums and galleries. The Aboriginal Arts and Crafts Organisation is a non-profit company of the Australian Government working amongst the Aboriginal people to help preserve and develop their culture by exhibiting and marketing their work. There are also many private dealers and galleries handling Aboriginal work.

Collections:

Australian National Gallery, Parkes Place, Parkes, ACT 2600. Tel. (062) 71 2411.
A special inner gallery houses fine examples of bark paintings, Tiwi bark paintings (language group) and general artifacts and items of great interest.

Australian Museum, 6 College Street, Sydney, NSW 2000. Tel. (02) 339 8111.
Large exhibition of Aboriginal and Pacific Islander bark paintings and artifacts. Well worth a visit.

Institute of Aboriginal Studies, 14 Jane Street, Balmain, NSW 2041. Tel. (02) 818 2255.
Collection, reference library and unpublished manuscripts.

Institute of Anatomy—Sydney University, Sydney, NSW 2006.
National ethnographic collection.

New South Wales Art Gallery, Art Gallery Road, Sydney, NSW 2000.
Permanent display of Aboriginal art with special exhibitions from time to time. Not to be missed.

Northern Territory Museum and Art Gallery, Darwin, NT 5790.
General collection of important Aboriginal artifacts.

South Australian Museum, Adelaide, SA 5000.
Excellent collection from the desert and Arnhem Land. Research facilities are available, reference library where researchers have worked throughout Australia.

Victorian Science Museum, National Museum Building, 304–328 Swanston Street, Melbourne, Vic 3000. Tel. (03) 669 9888.
Australian Aboriginal bark paintings and weavings.

CONTENTS
NEW SOUTH WALES

NEW SOUTH WALES

The state of New South Wales has a high degree of urbanisation with a population of 5½ million of which 3½ million live in the state's capital **Sydney**. **Newcastle** is the next largest city a commercial and industrial city and important as a major Australian port for the export of steel. **Wollongong**, known locally as the "Gong" is another major steel city and lies south of Sydney. Between the two major centres lie miles of beautiful coastline and national parks.

The **Blue Mountains** are within easy reach of Sydney and further north west from Newcastle, near Cessnock are the **Hunter Valley Vineyards**. **Broken Hill** is best known for its vast mineral deposits in zinc, silver and lead and if you manage to get that far west don't forget to visit Prohart's museum home and gallery. The holiday coast near the Queensland border situated around the town of **Coff's Harbour** is also known as the **Banana Coast**. The university town of **Armidale** has a university built around the old family home of Patrick White, the author. Nearby the lovely country town of Tamworth lies in the midst of lush farmland. The **Howard Hinton** and **Coventry art collections** are at Armidale's New England Regional Museum and were bequeathed by wealthy farming families from the region. Much further south near Canberra in the ACT, but still in NSW are the **Snowy Mountains** where winter skiing conditions are mostly ideal.

Sydney is Australia's largest city. Vying with Melbourne in Victoria as a cultural centre, it houses the world famous **Sydney Opera House** designed by Jørn Utzon and the magnificent (coathanger) Sydney Harbour Bridge, visible over most central bays and inlets. The wealth of cultural activities, restaurants, shops, lively city centre and the sheer beauty of the city's harbour, with its old colonial and modern verandahed houses nestling in the bays, makes it an enervating and beautiful city to live in. Sydney lifestyle with its vibrancy and colour and easy access to sailing, surfing, swimming, tennis, bush walking, cricket and horse riding is many a European's dream on long winter evenings.

Sydneysiders are stylish in dress, quick witted, cosmopolitan and fun. **Paddington** and **Woollahra** house many small commercial galleries. The **Art Gallery of New South Wales** is spreading in size with its new wing soon able to offer artist in residence programmes and other international attractions. Dynamic companies such as the **Sydney Dance Company** and **Sydney Theatre Company** are based in central Sydney at the new Wharf complex. The **Sydney Biennale**, a major

Scotland Island, Northern Sydney area, New South Wales

bi-annual art event held between May and July brings major overseas and Australian artists to the city and **Perspecta** every alternate year also attracts prominent artists. The **Festival of Sydney** for all the arts in late January—March brings together outstanding international theatrical, musical and artistic events to Sydney.

The dynamic **Sydney Dance Company** has been based at the Wharf Walsh Bay in its new studios since 1986. Graeme Murphy is artistic director and performances can be seen at the Opera House frequently. **The Australian Opera Company** is at the Opera House.

STATE ARTS ORGANISATIONS NEW SOUTH WALES

Aboriginal Artist Agency, 12 McLaren Street, North Sydney, NSW 2060. Tel. (02) 923 2366.

Aboriginal Training and Cultural Institute, 14 Jane Street, Balmain, NSW 2041. Tel. (02) 225 1700.

ANCAAA—Association of Northern and Central Australian Aboriginal Artists. Contact the **Aboriginal Board of the Australia Council**, 168 Walker Street, North Sydney NSW 2060.

Art Gallery of New South Wales, Friends of the Art Gallery of NSW, Art Gallery Road, The Domain, NSW 2000. Tel. (02) 221 2100/221 2656.

Artspace Visual Arts Centre, First Floor, 11 Randle Street, Surry Hills, NSW 2010. Tel. (02) 212 5031.
Contemporary visual art centre with gallery, membership available.

Arts Council of New South Wales Ltd, Toga House, 117 York Street, Sydney, NSW 2000. Tel. (02) 264 2500. PO Box Q98 Queen Victoria Building Post Office, Sydney NSW 2000.
The council is an independent, non-profit organisation dedicated to the development of the arts in country regions and part of the network forming the Arts Council of Australia. The council is a source of advice, information and organisational support. Application for financial assistance for arts projects can be made to the council. Information Officer: Tania Ursini; State development Officer: Bruce Dickson; General Manager: Helen Colman.

Artworkers Union, PO Box A509, Sydney South, NSW 2000.

Biennale of Sydney Ltd, First Floor, 100 George Street, The Rocks, Sydney, NSW 2000. Tel. (02) 27 3016.
The aim of the biennale is to mount an international exhibition of contemporary art in conjunction with current Australian work. The venues used for the exhibition have been the Art Gallery of NSW and Pier 2/3 at Millers Point. Known as the Australian Biennale in 1988.

Bondi Pavilion Community Centre, Queen Elizabeth Drive, Bondi Beach, NSW 2026. Tel. (02) 30 3325.
The Pavilion has become a lively cultural and recreational centre for the local community with good exhibiting space for performances or installations.

Community Arts Centre Newtown, Victoria Street, Newtown, NSW 2042. Tel. (02) 519 8047.

Division of Cultural Activities, NSW, 6th Floor, Export House, 22 Pitt Street, Sydney, NSW 2000. Tel. (02) 27 7235.

Festival of Sydney, 175 Castlereagh Street, Sydney, NSW 2000. Tel. (02) 267 2311.
Held annually in central Sydney during January with lots of outdoor summer activities ranging from opera in the park to ferry racing on Sydney harbour, also excellent exhibitions and performing arts activities.

NSW State Management Committee of NAVA, PO Box N296, Grosvenor Street, Sydney, NSW 2000. Tel. (02) 27 7995.
The committee is setting up an exchange for artists and studio/clerical workers who could be employed on a casual part-time basis to assist visual artists. Send name and address and or expertise to NAVA and information will be forwarded to you with relevant listings.

Regional Galleries Association of NSW Ltd, 22 Pitt Street, Sydney, NSW 2000. Tel. (02) 27 7237.

Royal Art Society of NSW, 25 Walker Street, North Sydney, NSW 2060. Tel. (02) 920 5752.

Sculptors' Society (NSW), Albert Road, Strathfield, NSW 2135. Tel. (02) 76 8848.

Sydney Film Festival, 405 Glebe Point Road, Glebe, NSW 2037. Tel. (02) 660 3844.

Sydney Filmmakers Co-Operative Ltd, St Peters Lane, Darlinghurst, NSW 2011. Tel. (02) 33 0721.

Sydney Printmakers, c/o 2/6a McLeod Street, Mosman, NSW 2088.

Southern Printmakers Association, Details from Val Dunn. Tel. (02) 524 5263.
Workshops held regularly in all aspects of printmaking with annual exhibitions of members work.

Waverly-Woollhara Arts Centre Co-Operative Ltd, 138 Bondi Road, Bondi, NSW 2026. Tel. (02) 387 2461.

Goëthe—Institute, 90 Ocean Street, Woollahra, NSW 2025. Tel. (02) 328 7411.

New South Wales Community Arts Association, 4 Goulburn Street, Sydney, NSW 2000. Tel. (02) 261 2166.

Travelling Film Festival, 405 Glebe Point Road, Glebe, NSW 2037. Tel. (02) 660 3844.

NSW Council for Children's Films & Television, 40 William Henry Street, Ultimo, NSW 2007. Tel. (02) 660 3106.

STATE CRAFT ORGANISATIONS NEW SOUTH WALES

Aboriginal Arts and Craft Pty Ltd, 38 Harrington Street, Sydney, NSW 2000. Tel. (02) 27 8492.
Aiming at maintaining and developing Aboriginal arts and crafts industry by marketing and promoting goods both nationally and internationally.

Crafts Council of New South Wales, 100 George Street, The Rocks, Sydney, NSW 2000. Tel. (02) 241 1701.
Housed in one of Sydney's historic buildings, it shares premises with the Crafts Council of Australia. Also the Crafts Council Gallery is on the ground floor with additional exhibition space in the basement. The Crafts Council of NSW holds comprehensive listings of all registered craft organisations and in conjunction registered craftspeople with a reference slide library available to the public. Only a few of the vast number of organisations can be listed here, so I recommend contacting the Crafts Council for further information.

Hand Spinners and Weavers Guild of NSW, 12 Birrong Avenue, Birrong, NSW 2143. Tel. (02) 654 3431. GPO Box 67, Sydney NSW 2001.

New South Wales Leatherworkers Guild, PO Box 73, Northbridge, NSW 2063. Tel. (02) 85 5985.

Potters' Society of Australia, 48 Burton Street, Darlinghurst, NSW 2010. Tel. (02) 331 3151.

Society of Arts and Crafts of NSW, Shop 2, Metcalfe Arcade, 80–84 George Street, The Rocks, Sydney, NSW 2000. Tel. (02) 21 1673.

The Embroiderers Guild of NSW, 175 Elizabeth Street, Sydney, NSW 2000. Tel. (02) 267 8211.

The Quilters Guild Inc., PO Box 654, Neutral Bay Junction, NSW 2089.

The Craft Centre the Rocks, Sydney

STATE REGIONAL GALLERIES AND MUSEUMS NEW SOUTH WALES

Albury Regional Art Centre, 546 Dean Street, Albury, NSW 2640. Tel (060) 21 6384.
Regular changing exhibitions with a permanent display from the Sir Russell Drysdale collection, including paintings, drawings and etchings.

Art Gallery of New South Wales, Art Gallery Road, The Domain, Sydney, NSW 2000. Tel. (02) 225 1700.
Touring exhibitions local and overseas, the venue for the Sydney Biennale, public film and lecture programmes, permanent exhibitions of the galleries collection and on completion of the massive extensions the gallery should become a focal point nationally and for Sydney as a centre for the contemporary arts. The bookshop and restaurant are both open normal gallery hours, Monday–Saturday 10–5, Sunday noon–5.

Bathurst Regional Art Gallery, First Floor, Civic Centre, Russell Street, Bathurst, NSW 2795. Tel. (063) 33 6283.
Permanent collection of contemporary Australian ceramics, small contemporary sculpture and touring changing exhibitions.

Bowral Paper Place Gallery, 376 Bong Bong Street, Bowral, NSW 2576. Tel. (048) 61 3214.
Continuing mixed media exhibitions by contemporary artists. Open Monday–Friday 9–5, Saturday 9–12.

Broken Hill City Art Gallery, Chloride Street, Broken Hill, NSW 2880. Tel. (080) 6602.
Changing touring exhibitions and gallery collections.

Burns-Kaldy Gallery, 10 Wood Street, Newcastle, NSW 2300. Tel. (049) 69 2958.
Large warehouse gallery presenting contemporary Australian art. Open daily 11–5.

Cottage Gallery, Victoria and Albert Guest House, Station Street, Mt Victoria, Blue Mountains, NSW 2786. Tel. (047) 82 2149.
Local fine art and crafts.

Gallery 460, 460 Avoca Drive, Green Point, Gosford, NSW 2250. Tel. (043) 69 2013.
Four exhibiting areas featuring traditional and contemporary fine art. Changing exhibitions, sculpture park spanning eight hectares. Open daily 10–5 or by appointment.

Art Gallery of New South Wales, Sydney

Griffith Regional Gallery, 167–185 Banna Avenue, Griffith, NSW 2680. Tel. (069) 62 5991.
Changing exhibitions of contemporary fine art and crafts.

Goulburn Regional Art Gallery, 260 Sloane Street, Goulburn, NSW 2580. Tel. (048) 21 1020.

Lake Macquarie Gallery, Old Council Chambers, Main Road, Speers Point, NSW 2284. Tel. (049) 58 5333.
New exhibitions monthly. Open Thursday & Friday 1–4, Saturday & Sunday 12–5 or by appointment.

Lismore Regional Art Gallery, 131 Molesworth Street, Lismore, NSW 2480. Tel. (066) 21 1536.
Changing exhibitions monthly. Open Wednesday–Saturday 10–4.

Maitland City Art Gallery, Brough House, Church Street, Maitland, NSW 2320. Tel. (094) 33 6725.
Permanent collection of Australian paintings, drawings and prints. Changing exhibitions every 4–5 weeks.

Manly Art Gallery and Museum, West Esplanade, Manly, NSW 2095. PO Box 82, Manly. Tel. (02) 949 1776.
Permanent collection of Australian paintings, drawings and watercolours with emphasis on the period 1900–1950. There is also a collection of modern Australian ceramics. There is usually a portion of a collection "Leisure time use of the beach" on display in the gallery. Open Tuesday–Friday 10–4, Saturday, Sunday & Public Holidays noon–5.

New England regional art museum, Armidale New South Wales with local school group

Newcastle Regional Art Gallery, Laman Street, Newcastle, NSW 2300. Tel. (049) 23 263.
Permanent collection of Australian painting, drawings and prints. Contemporary Australian and Japanese prints. Monthly changing exhibitions. Open Monday–Friday 10–5, Saturday 1.30–5, Sunday and Public Holidays 2–5.

New England Regional Art Musuem, Kentucky Street, Armidale, NSW 2350. PO Box 508. Tel. (067) 72 5255.
The museum houses the Howard Hinton Collection, the Chandler Coventry Collection and the Armidale City Collection. The Hinton Collection covers Australian art from the 1880s to 1940s, a unique Australian collection. The Coventry Collection is also one of Australia's most important contemporary collections. Open Monday–Saturday 10–5, Sundays 1–5.

Norman Lindsay Gallery and Museum, Norman Lindsay Crescent, Via Chapman Parade, Faulconbridge, Blue Mountains, NSW 2776. Tel. (047) 51 1067.
The home of Norman Lindsay displays a large collection of his oil paintings, etchings and watercolours. "The Magic Pudding" room portrays his characters from classic children's story. A scenic walk beyond the sculpture garden makes the drive well worth while. Open Friday, Saturday & Sunday 11–5 & Public Holidays. Group visits Wednesday & Thursday.

Orange Regional Gallery, Civic Square, Byng Street, Orange, NSW 2800. Tel. (063) 62 1755.
Mixed and varying exhibitions changing regularly, contemporary and traditional.

Penrith Regional Art Gallery and Lewers Bequest, 86 River Road, Emu Plains, NSW 2750. Tel. (047) 35 1448. Three gallery spaces with changing exhibitions monthly. Weekend films, performances and events, the gallery collection displayed regularly. Open Thursday–Sunday 11–5.

Tamworth City Art Gallery, 203 Marius Street, Tamworth, NSW 2340. Tel. (067) 66 2280. Permanent collection includes 19th century Australian and European paintings, silver and ivory, 20th century Australian paintings and the Tamworth Fibre Collection. Open Monday–Friday 9–11.30, Saturday & Sunday 2–5.

The Australian Museum, 6 College Street, Sydney, NSW 2000. Tel. (02) 339 8111. Australia's leading natural history museum with special exhibitions held. The museum has undergone major renovations and now presents lifesize displays to wander through. Open Tuesday–Sunday & Public Holidays 10–5, Monday noon–5.

The Nicholson Museum of Antiques, The University of Sydney, NSW 2006. Tel. (02) 692 1122 ext 2812. Open Monday–Thursday 10–4.45, Friday 10–3.30.

The Power Gallery of Contemporary Art, c/o The Power Institute of Fine Art, University of Sydney, NSW 1006. Tel. (02) 692 3170.

The Powerhouse, Museum of Applied Arts and Science, PO Box K346, Haymarket, NSW 2000. Cnr of Harris and Macarthur Streets, Ultimo, Sydney (nr Darling Harbour). Tel. (02) 217 0111. Powerhouse hotline, recorded information service. Tel. (02) 217 0111.

Norman Lindsay's house, Springwood, Blue Mountains

Power House Museum, Ultimo, Sydney

The newly opened museum displays the genius of modern technology, architecure and historical aspects of Australia in a venue which was once Sydney's powerhouse. Only a short walk from Darling Harbour and very close to a monorail stop.

The Mint and Hyde Park Barracks, Queens Square, Macquarie Sreet, Sydney, NSW 2000.
The recently restored buildings now open to the public recapture the charm of early settlement in Australia, touring exhibitions are held in the barracks while the mint houses gracious displays of Australian history with artifacts, costumes and coins.

The National Trust of Australia (NSW), Observatory Hill, Sydney, NSW 2000. Tel. (02) 27 5374.
Exhibition area and shop in the centre, S. Hervin Gallery with traditional exhibitions.

Sydney Textile Museum, 172 St Johns Road, Glebe, NSW 2037. Tel. (02) 692 8728.
Excellent display of textiles with changing exhibitions by Australian artists/designers.

Wagga Wagga City Art Gallery, 40 Gurwood Street, Wagga Wagga, NSW 2650. Tel. (069) 21 3621.
Regular changing exhibitions and the galleries contemporary collection.

Wollongong City Gallery, 85 Burelli Street, Wollongong East, NSW 2500. Tel. (042) 27 746/2.
Contemporary international exhibitions and national artists. Open Tuesday–Friday 10–5, Thursday 10–7, Saturday 10–7, Sunday noon–5.

COMMERCIAL AND NON-PROFIT GALLERIES SYDNEY

Sydney art scene

The Sydney art scene is very lively and colourful between February and November and much quieter over the hottest summer period before and after Christmas. The **Macquarie Galleries** are perhaps the most cosmopolitan galleries in Sydney with shows by prominent contemporary artists. **Paddington** and **Woollahra** house many of the important contemporary galleries such as **Roslyn Oxley, Rex Irwin, DC Art, Robin Gibson** and the **Australian Centre for Photography**. The **Surry Hills** area is attracting new galleries and the **Ray Hughes Gallery** is now in this area with exhibitions by dynamic Australian artists.

The **Art Gallery of New South Wales** is the centre for major touring exhibitions but also displays works by artists who have been successful in entering the **Archibald, Wynne, Sulman** and **Moët Chandon** prizes. The new extensions to the art gallery create an outstanding complex for the visual arts, with continual exhibitions of the highest quality both national and international. The artist in residence scheme helps bring alive gallery activities.

"Rainforest" paintings by Guy Warren

Inner City/Darlinghurst/Surry Hills/Pyrmont

Aboriginal Artist Gallery, Civic House, 477 Kent Street, Sydney, NSW 2000. Tel. (02) 261 2929.
Bark paintings, wood sculptures, canvas paintings by Aboriginal men and women.

Arthaus, 20 Palmer Lane, Darlinghurst, NSW 2010. Tel. (02) 33 4116.
Artist run gallery space.

Art Directors Gallery, 21 Nurse Walk, The Rocks, Sydney, NSW 2000. Tel. (02) 27 2740.
Exclusively the works of the now popular designer and artist Ken Done.

Artspace, 11 Randle Street, Surry Hills, NSW 2010. Tel. (02) 212 5031.
An interesting space for performance, installations and regular exhibitions.

AVAGO—Front Fence, Tin Sheds, University Art Workshop, 162 City Road, Darlington, NSW 2008. Smallest exhibition space in the southern hemisphere.

Beth Mayne, Cnr Palmer and Burton Streets, Darlinghurst, NSW 2010. Tel. (02) 357 6264.
Open Tuesday–Saturday 11–6. Contemporary Australian artist.

Bindi, Shop 2/24 Top Level, Queen Victoria Building, George Street, Sydney, NSW 2000.
Works by Australian Aboriginal artists. Open shopping hours.

Blaxland Gallery, 6 Floor, Grace Brothers Dept Store, Cnr Pitt and Market Streets, Sydney, NSW 2000. Tel. (02) 238 9390.
International and national contemporary and traditional fine art.

Bridge Street Gallery, 20 Bridge Street, Sydney, NSW 2000. Tel. (02) 27 9723.
Contemporary extensive selection of etchings, screenprints and lithographs by Australian and overseas artists. Exclusive representative for Christies Contemporary Art NSW, ACT & Qld. Open Monday–Friday 10.30–5.30, Saturday 2–5.

David Jones Art Gallery, 7th Floor, David Jones Dept Store, Elizabeth Street, Sydney, NSW 2000. Tel. (02) 266 5640.
International and national high quality fine art exhibitions. Open Monday–Friday 10–5, Saturday 10–3.

East Sydney Tech Cell Block, Forbes Street, Darlinghurst, NSW 2010. Tel. (02) 339 8666.
The old cell block of the former jail now serves as an interesting venue for the visual and performing arts.

First Impressions Fine Art Gallery, Ultimo Centre, 42 Wattle Street, Ultimo, NSW 2007. Tel. (02) 660 3340.
Original art works for business, hotels, foyers, councils, government and private homes. Leasing or direct sales. Open Tuesday–Saturday 10–6.30, Sunday and Monday by appointment only.

Gallery Lynch, Shop 15, Queen Victoria Building, Sydney, NSW 2000. Tel. (02) 29 1568.
Changing exhibitions of Australian artists. Open daily 10–5.

Garry Anderson Gallery, 102 Burton Street, Darlinghurst, NSW 2000. Tel. (02) 331 1524.
Open Tuesday–Saturday noon–6. A lively gallery with work by young contemporary artists.

Geo Styles Gallery, Shop 4, 50 Hunter Street, Sydney, NSW 2000. Tel. (02) 233 2628.
Open Monday–Friday 9–5.30. Australian and international contemporary painting.

Holdsworth Contemporary Galleries, 221–225 Liverpool Street, East Sydney, NSW 2011. Tel. (02) 32 1761.
Changing exhibitions by contemporary Australian artists in what must be Sydney's largest exhibiting gallery space. Open Monday–Saturday 10–5, Sunday noon–5.

Hyde Park Barracks, Queens Square, Macquarie Street, Sydney, NSW 2000. Tel. (02) 217 0111.
The recently renovated old barracks retain their charm of days long past and now serve as a major city centre exhibiting space for international and Australian work.

Kelly St Kolektiv, Kelly St, Ultimo, NSW 2007. Tel. (02) 281 1398.
The artist-run studios and gallery space provide an interesting alternative art venue for exhibitions and performances.

Lion Gate Lodge, Art Gallery Road, Sydney, NSW 2000.
Entrance near the Art Gallery of NSW, Botanic Gardens museum and exhibition area showing works from the Botanic Gardens collecting. Changing displays reguarly.

Macquarie Galleries, 204 Clarence Street, Sydney, NSW 2000. Tel. (02) 264 9787.
Open Monday–Friday 10–6, Saturday noon–6, Monday by appointment. Three gallery areas showing the works of leading Australian contemporary artists and craftspeople. Large stock room of paintings, works on paper and sculpture. Artists include: Alun Leach-Jones, Lloyd Rees, Victor Majzner, John Coburn, Brian Dunlop, Guy Warren, Graham Fransella, Jorg Schmeisset, Sydney Ball, Fred Cress, Alan Oldfield, Fiona Murphy, Richard Woldendorp, Bill Brown, Paul Hopmeier. The gallery offers the following services: commissions, sales, research valuations, restoration, framing, hanging, transport and packing.

Eileen Chanin of the Macquarie Galleries, Sydney

Milburn+Arte Galleries, 137 Pyrmont Street, Pyrmont, NSW 2009. Tel. (02) 660 7211.
Presenting contemporary Australian and overseas artists. Open Tuesday–Saturday 11–6.

Painters Gallery, 1st Floor, 137 Pyrmont Street, Pyrmont, NSW 2009. Tel. (02) 660 5111.
Changing exhibitions of leading contemporary Australian artists and craftspeople. Open Tuesday–Saturday 11–6.

Peter Lane, 14 Martin Place, Sydney, NSW 2000. (Cnr of Pitt Street). Tel. (02) 235 0136.
Primitive art and artifacts from overseas.

Pier 2/3, Hickson Road, Millers Point, NSW 2000.
The old piers are now a popular venue for exhibitions such as the installations at the biennale and other large scale contemporary work. The Sydney arts community are trying hard to retain this fabulous venue for continued use for the visual arts. Contact Art Gallery of NSW. Tel. (02) 225 1700.

Printfolio Gallery, Gallery Level, Westpac Plaza, 60 Margaret Street, Sydney, NSW 2000. Tel. (02) 27 6690.
International selection of printmakers work also a selection of fine art craft. Open Monday–Friday 8.30–6.

Ray Hughes Gallery, 270 Devonshire Street, Surry Hills, NSW 2010. Tel. (02) 698 3200.
Representing leading Australian contemporary artists. Director: Ray Hughes. Also owns a gallery in Brisbane. Artists include: Stephen Furlonger, Davida Allen, Ian Smith, John Dutruc, Tony Twigg. Stephen Furlonger and Davida Allen have both won major Australian art awards. Open Tuesday Saturday 11–6.

Richard King, 141 Dowling Street, Woolloomooloo, NSW 2011.
Incorporating The Print Room. Fine painting, master prints, sculpture, drawings and photography by Australian and European artists, contemporary and traditional. Open Tuesday–Saturday 11–5. Representing contemporary Australian artists.

S. H. Ervin Gallery and Museum, National Trust Centre, Observatory Hill, Sydney, NSW 2000. Tel. (02) 27 9222.
Changing exhibitions of Australian art and architecture with a historic emphasis. Open Tuesday–Friday 11–5, Saturday & Sunday 2–5, closed Monday except public holidays.

338 Gallery, 1st Floor, 338 Pitt Street, Sydney, NSW 2000. Te. (02) 267 6441.
Excellent space for installations.

The Wharf, Pier 4, Hickson Road, Millers Point NSW, 2000.
Foyer Gallery and exhibition area at the Wharf Theatre. Enquiries Tel. (02) 250 1777.

Victoria Rooms, Level 3, Queen Victoria Building, George Street, Sydney, NSW 2000. Tel. (02) 698 2557.
Open Monday–Friday 11–7, Saturday & Sunday 10–3. International contemporary art.

Watters Gallery, 109 Riley Street, East Sydney, NSW 2010. Tel. (02) 331 2556.
Representing contemporary Australian artists. Director: Frank Watters. Artists include: Robert Parr, John Delacair, Jenny Barwell, Peter Cripps, John Peart.

Woolloomooloo Gallery, 84–86 Nicholson Street, Woolloomooloo, NSW 2011. Tel. (02) 356 4220.
Changing exhibitions of work by Australian artists of promise and renown. Open Wednesday–Sunday 11–6.

Yuill/Crowley, 3rd Floor, 270 Devonshire Street, Surry Hills, NSW 2010.
Representing contemporary Australian artists.

Paddington/Woollahra and Eastern Sydney

Anna Art Studio and Gallery, 98 Oxford Street, Paddington, NSW 2021. Tel. (02) 331 1149.

Anthony Field, 38 Gruner Street, Paddington, NSW 2021. Tel. (02) 331 7378.
Drawings, pastels, watercolours and paintings by well known European artists of the past and present. Open Tuesday–Friday 11–7, Saturday 12–6 & Sunday 2–6.

Artmet, 124 Jersey Road, Woollahra, NSW 2025. Tel. (02) 32 9977.
Open Monday–Friday 9–5, Saturday 11–5. Contemporary paintings.

Australian Centre for photography, 257 Oxford Street, Paddington, NSW 2021. Tel. (02) 331 6253.
The centre has two exhibition galleries, studios and a book shop. Exhibitions and installations by Australian and overseas artists.

Barry Stern Exhibiting Gallery, 12 Mary Place, Paddington, NSW 2021. Tel. (02) 332 1875.
Regular changing exhibitions of work by contemporary Australian painters. Open Tuesday–Saturday 11.30–5.30.

Barry Stern Galleries Pty Ltd, 19 Glenmore Road, Paddington, NSW 2021. Tel. (02) 331 4676.
Gallery collection of traditional and contemporary painting. Open Monday–Saturday 11.30–5.30.

Bloomfield Galleries, 118 Sutherland Street, Paddington, NSW 2021. Tel. (02) 326 2122.
Open Tuesday–Saturday 10.30–5.30. Continuous exhibitions of contemporary Australian painting and sculpture and permanent gallery room of works by Norman Lindsay.

Bondi Pavilion, Queen Elizabeth Drive, Bondi Beach, NSW 2026. Tel. (02) 303 325.
An interesting gallery space in the famous beach side pavilion with exhibitions by local young contemporary artists.

Bonython—Meadmore Gallery, 95 Holdsworth Street, Woollahra, NSW 2025. Tel. (02) 327 5411.
Contact: Jim Baily. Regularly changing exhibitions of contemporary Australian painting, sculpture and works on paper. Artists include: John Martin, Leon Morocco, Oenpelli aboriginal artists, lively established contemporary artists. Nola Jones, Peter Crisp, Wendy Stokes. Gallery space is one large long room and one light small room, also sculpture courtyard. Open Tuesday–Saturday 10–5, Sunday 2–5.

Casey Gallery, 223 Glenmore Road, Paddington, NSW 2021. Tel. (02) 331 3350.

Collage Galleries, 210 Oxford Street, Paddington, NSW 2021. Tel. (02) 360 4003.
Selective arts from Papua New Guinea. Open Wednesday–Friday 11–4, Saturday & Sunday 2–5.

Contemporary Jewellery Gallery, 162a Queen Street Woollahra, NSW 2025. Tel. (02) 32 1611.
Representing recent and established Australian designers. Open Tuesday–Saturday 11–6.

Cooper Gallery, 3 Cooper Street, Paddington, NSW 2021. Tel. (02) 331 2060.
Contemporary Australian art. Open Tuesday–Saturday 11–5.30.

Coventry Gallery, 56 Sutherland Street, Paddington, NSW 2021. Tel. (02) 331 4338.
Contemporary works by prominent Australian artists. Open Tuesday–Saturday 11–5.

DC Art, 36 Jersey Road, Woollahra, NSW 2025. Tel. (02) 327 8626.
Representing prominent contemporary Australian and overseas artists. Open Monday–Saturday 10–5.30.

Edie Glastra, 44 Gurner Street, Paddington, NSW 2021. Tel. (02) 331 6477.
Contemporary paintings and prints and a continuous exhibition of impressionist, post impressionist works. Open Tuesday–Saturday 11–5.30, Sunday & Monday by appointment.

Elizabeth Street Gallery, 3 Elizabeth Street, Paddington, NSW 2021. Tel. (02) 331 2284.
Open Monday–Friday 10–6, Saturday & Sunday 12–6.

GAG—Graphics Art Gallery, 251 Oxford Street, Paddington, NSW 2021. Tel. (02) 387 4436.
Displays of Australian printmakers. Also Cnr Hollywood Avenue & Oxford Street, Bondi Junctin NSW 2026. Exhibitions of contemporary printmakers.

Four Winds Gallery, Shop 12, Bay Village, 28 Cross Street, Double Bay, NSW 2028. Tel. (02) 328 7951.
Specialists in fine American Indian Collectables. Open Monday–Saturday 10–5.

Galerie Anne Gregory, 40 Gurner Street, Paddington, NSW 2021. Tel. (02) 360 2285.
Contemporary works.

Georgina Kinch, 58 William Street, Paddington, NSW 2021. Tel. (02) 360 4933.
Contemporary works.

Gallery No. 29, William Street, Paddington, NSW 2021. Tel. (02) 33 2650.
Specialising in contemporary Japanese prints. Open Tuesday–Saturday 10.30–5.30, Sunday 2–5.

Glenmore Gallery, 296 Glenmore Road, Paddington, NSW 2021. Tel. (02) 331 3092.
Works in all media by local and overseas artists.

Hogarth Gallery, Walker Lane, Paddington, NSW 2021. Tel. (02) 357 6839.
Open Tuesday–Saturday 11–6. Changing exhibitions of contemporary and avant-garde Australian and international art every three weeks.

Holdsworth Galleries, 86 Holdsworth Street, Woollahra, NSW 2025. Tel. (02) 32 1364.
Regular changing exhibitions of established Australian & international artists. Open Monday–Saturday 10–5, Sunday 12–5.

Painting on canvas by an Aboriginal artist (Hogarth Gallery, Sydney)

Ivan Dougherty Gallery, Cnr Albion Avenue & Selwyn Street, Paddington, NSW 2021. Tel. (02) 339 9526.
Administered by The City Art Institute exhibiting important contemporary Australian and international work.

Josef Lebovic Gallery, 34 Paddington Street, Paddington, NSW 2021. Tel. (02) 332 1840.
Open Monday–Friday 1–6, Saturday 11–5. Specialist in international early prints.

Lipscombe Fine Art, 40 New South Head Road, Vaucluse, NSW 1030. Tel. (02) 337 6663.
Open Monday–Friday 12–5, Saturday 10–1.

Naughton Naive Studio, 26 Queen Street, Woollahra, NSW 2025. Tel. (02) 327 6196.
Open Tuesday–Saturday 11–6.

Print Workshop, 73 Jersey Road, Woollahra, NSW 2025. Tel. (02) 328 7772.
Open Monday–Friday 9.30–5, Saturday 10–5 & Sunday 2–4. Contemporary prints.

Rex Irwin Art Dealer, First Floor, 38 Queen Street, Woollahra, NSW 2025. Tel. (02) 32 3212.
Paintings by important Australian artists. Open Tuesday–Saturday 11–5.30 or by appointment. Has also shown large scale photographs. Director: Rex Irwin.

Roslyn Oxley 9 Gallery, 13 Macdonald Street, Paddington, NSW 2021. Tel. (02) 331 2021.
Representing leading Australian artists, new generation art. Open Tuesday–Saturday 11–6. Artists include: John Nixon, Ken Unsworth, Bonita Ely, Liz Sterling, Lindy Lee and others. Director: Roslyn Oxley. The galleries are large and therefore unusual and avant-garde works are shown as well as painting and sculpture.

The Works Gallery, City Art Institute Campus, Albion Avenue, Paddington, NSW 2021. Tel. (02) 339 9555.
Works by students of the institute and visiting exhibitions. Open Monday–Friday 10–4 & Saturday 12–4.

Roslyn Oxley Gallery, Sydney

Wagner Art Gallery, 39 Gurner Street, Paddington, NSW 2021. Tel. (02) 357 6069.
Exhibitions changing every three weeks by varying Australian artists. Open Tuesday–Saturday 11–5.30, Sunday 1–5.

Windsor St Gallery, 118b Windsor Street, Paddington, NSW 2021. Tel. (02) 328 6013.
Investment paintings and leasing available.

Stadia Graphics Gallery, Tel. (02) 958 4118.
The gallery is continuing to specialise in fine art prints with viewing by appointment only.

Trevor Bussell Fine Art Gallery, 180 Jersey Road, Woollahra, NSW 2025. Tel. (02) 32 4605.
Dealing only in fine Australian investment paintings 1800 to 1960. Extensive range in stock.

Balmain/Glebe and the inner west

Access Art Gallery, 115–116 Mullins Street, Balmain, NSW 2041. Tel. (02) 818 3598.
Open Wednesday–Sunday 11–6. A new gallery with sculpture garden and contemporary exhibitions in fine art and excellent craft.

Artlook, 172 St Johns Road, Glebe, NSW 2037. Tel. (02) 692 0723.
Open Wednesday–Saturday 1–4 plus evenings Wednesday–Friday 6–9.

Balmain Loft, 371 Darling Street, Balmain, NSW 2041. Tel. (02) 810 0319.
An alternative venue in a popular late night coffee shop. Open Monday–Tuesday 10–4, Wednesday–Sunday 10–midnight.

BT–Art, 23 Glebe Point Road, Glebe, NSW 2037. Tel. (02) 660 7419.
A window space art gallery open 24 hours.

Colouring Set, 139 St Johns Road, Glebe, NSW 2041. Tel. (02) 660 0613.
Open Wednesday–Saturday 12–5. Cartoons and works on paper by contemporary artists.

Denison Sculpture Studio, 97 Denison Street, Rozelle, NSW 2039. Tel. (02) 818 1883.

Gallery X, 38 Montague Street, Balmain, NSW 2041.
Open Wednesday–Sunday 12–6. Lively new gallery showing local contemporary artists.

Fourteen Roses Gallery, 8 Evans Street, Balmain, NSW 2041. Tel. (02) 810 8293.
Open Tuesday–Saturday 11–6. A new gallery exhibiting the works of contemporary local artists.

Galaxy Gallery, 32 Beattie Street, Balmain, NSW 2041. Tel. (02) 555 1199.
A gallery workshop complex offering handpainted couture garments and furnishings in silk.

Glass Artists Gallery, 70 Glebe Point Road, Glebe, NSW 2037. Tel. (02) 552 1552.
Open Monday–Saturday 10–6. Specialising in fine art glass.

Irving Sculpture Gallery, 144a St Johns Road, Glebe, NSW 2037. Tel. (02) 692 0880.
Open Tuesday–Saturday 11–6 with specialisation in interior and exterior sculpture by leading Australian artists.

Mori Gallery, 56 Catherine Street, Leichhardt, NSW 2040. Tel. (02) 560 4704.
Open Tuesday–Saturday 11–6. Representing Australian contemporary artists, mostly young and established. Artists include: Carol Roberts, Deborah Vaughan, Clinton Garfane, Robin Stacey, Deborah Singleton, Debra Dawes, Dale Frank, Peter Cooley, Janet Burchill, Jeff Gibson. Director: Stephen Mori.

Redfern/Newtown and Chippendale

Camera Lucida, 317 Abercrombie Street, Chippendale, NSW 2008.
A lively venue for young photographers to exhibit in.

First Draft, 2/27 Abercrombie Street, Chippendale, NSW 2008. Tel. (02) 698 4439.
Open Thursday–Sunday 12–6. Exhibitions of contemporary Sydney artists.

Harrington St Gallery, 17 Meagher Street, Chippendale, NSW 2008. Tel. (02) 699 7378.
Open Tuesday–Sunday 10–4. Contemporary paintings by local Sydney artists.

Kelly Street Kilektiv, 2–8 Kelly Street, Ultimo, NSW 2007. Tel. (02) 281 1398.
Artist run studios and gallery suitable for paintings, performances, installations and sculpture.

Moore Park Gallery, 17 Thurlow Street, Redfern, NSW 2016. Tel. (02) 698 8555.
A new Ken Done affiliated gallery exhibiting contemporary painting, works on paper and sculpture.

Performance Space, 199 Cleveland Street Redfern, NSW 2016. Tel. (02) 698 7235.
A very active centre for artists' performances. Open

Wednesday–Friday 3–8, Saturday & Sunday 12–8. Discussions and talks often held with the artists.

Rondeau, Cnr Brown and Wilson Streets, Newtown, NSW 2042. Tel. (02) 550 3237.
Changing exhibitions of paintings, decor and photography by various artists. Open Thursday–Friday 12–7, Saturday & Sunday 11–6.

Northern Sydney region

Artarmon Galleries, 479 Pacific Highway, Artarmon, NSW 2064. Tel. (02) 427 0322.
Large collection of Australian art, early and contemporary paintings and drawings. Open Monday–Friday 10–5, Saturday 11–4.

Ashanti, 19 The Esplanade, Balmoral, NSW 2088. Tel. (02) 969 8138.
Exhibitions by local contemporary artists.

Beth Hamilton, Northbridge Plaza, Sailors Bay Road, Northbridge, NSW 2063. Tel. (02) 958 7366.

Etchers' Workshop, now merged with Mosman Gallery, 122 Avenue Road, Mosman, NSW 2088. Tel. (02) 960 1124.
A large selection of Australian fine art prints. Open Tuesday–Saturday 10–5, Sunday 2–6.

Grace Gallery, 3rd Floor, Grace Brothers Dept Store, Chatswood, NSW 2067.
Open normal shopping hours. Exhibitions of fine art and fine art craft.

Lavender Bay Gallery, 25–27 Walker Street, North Sydney, NSW 2060. Tel. (02) 920 5752.
Exhibitions by fellows of the Royal Art Society of NSW.

Miniature Gallery, Shop 1, 3 Myahgah Road, Mosman, NSW 2088. Tel. (02) 969 7292.
Open Tuesday–Friday 10–5, Saturday 10–1.

Mosman Gallery, 122 Avenue Road, Mosman, NSW 2088. Tel. (02) 960 1124.
Exhibitions of contemporary Australian artists. Open Tuesday–Saturday 10–5, Sunday 2–6.

Noella Byrne Gallery, 240 Miller Street, North Sydney, NSW 2060. Tel. (02) 92 6589.

North Sydney Contemporary Art Gallery, 65 Union Street, North Sydney, NSW 2060. Tel. (02) 922 7853.
Changing exhibition of contemporary Australian artists. Open Tuesday–Saturday 11–5.

St Leonards Studio, 62 Mitchell Street, St Leonards, NSW 2065. Tel. (02) 437 5059.
Works by gallery artists. Open Thursday–Saturday 10–6.

Workshop Arts Centre Gallery, 33 Laurel Street, Willoughby, NSW 2068. Tel. (02) 958 6540.
Exhibitions by local contemporary artists. Open Monday–Saturday 10–4.

Outer Metropolitan Sydney

Allegro Gallery, 1 Porters Road, Kenthurst, NSW 2156. Tel. (02) 654 1386.
Open Wednesday–Sunday 11–6. Representing Australian and international artists and displays of fine art crafts. Only 45 minutes from the city centre to beautiful bushland settings and an architect designed gallery.

Cooks Hill Gallery, 67 Bull Street, Cooks Hill, Newcastle, NSW 2300. Tel. (049) 26 3899.
Contemporary Australian artists.

Gallery 460, Gosford, 460 Avoca Drive, Green Point, NSW 2250. Tel. (043) 69 2013.
Open daily 10–5. Continuing exhibitions in the sculpture gardens and selections of work from leading Australian painters.

Kenthurst Galleries, 5a Nelson Street, Kenthurst, NSW 2156. Tel. (02) 654 2258.
Open Wednesday–Sunday 10.30–5. Works by contemporary Sydney painters and fine art craftspeople.

Rainsford Gallery, 328 Sydney Road, Balgowlah, NSW 2093. Tel. (02) 94 4141.
Open Tuesday–Friday 11–5, Saturday 10–12.

Von Bertouch Galleries, 61 Laman Street, Newcastle, NSW 2300. Tel. (049) 23 584.
Exhibitions of contemporary art and fine art crafts.

CRAFT GALLERIES
NEW SOUTH WALES

Allegro Gallery, 1 Porters Road, Kenthurst, NSW 2156. Tel. (02) 654 1386.
Open Wednesday–Sunday 11-6. Exhibitions of leading Australian and international fine arts and crafts. Changing exhibitions and stock on display in a most beautiful setting as the gallery sits on the edge of a gully full of natural bushland. Only 45 minutes from the city.

Argyle Centre, 18 Argyle Street, The Rocks, Sydney, NSW 2000. Tel. (02) 241 1853.
Open daily 10–5.30. A selection of various craft shops within the historic sandstone buildings.

Australian Craftworks, The Old Police Station, 127 George Street, The Rocks, Sydney, NSW 2000. Tel. (02) 27 7156.
Open Monday–Saturday 10–5. Selected exhibitions of Australian crafts. The old jail cells now used as exhibit spaces. National Trust Building.

Cloud 9 Gallery, Shop 48, Gallery Level, Lemon Grove, Chatswood, NSW 2067. Tel. (02) 412 1450.
Display works by leading Australian craftspeople. Open Monday–Saturday shopping hours.

Contemporary Jewellery Gallery, 162a Queen Street, Woollahra, NSW 2025. Tel. (02) 321 611.
Open Tuesday–Saturday 11–6. Contemporary exhibits from all over Australia.

David Jones Art Gallery, 7th Floor, Elizabeth Street Store, Sydney, NSW 2000. Tel. (02) 266 5544 ext 2109.
Exhibitions of both Australian and international fine art and crafts. Open Monday–Friday 9.30–5, Thursday till 8.

Breewood Galleries, 134 Lurline Street, Katoomba, NSW 2780. Tel. (047) 82 2324.
Open Monday–Friday 9–5. If you're in the Blue Mountains call in and see some local crafts.

Hamilton Design Glass Gallery, 156 Burns Bay Road, Lane Cove West, NSW 2066. Tel. (02) 428 4281.
Exhibitions of contemporary Australian glass artists. Open Monday–Friday 9.30–6, Wednesday 9.30–4 & Saturdays 10–4.

Glass Artists' Gallery, 70 Glebe Point Road, Glebe, NSW 2037. Tel. (02) 552 1552.
Open Monday–Saturday 10–6. Leading Australian glass artists.

Holdsworth Galleries, 86 Holdsworth Street, Woollahra, NSW 2025. Tel. (02) 32 1364.
Large galleries displaying fine arts and contemporary crafts. Open Tuesday–Saturday 11–6.

Manly Art Gallery and Museum, West Esplanade, Manly, NSW 1095. Tel. (02) 949 2435.
Mixed media from the permanent collection including contemporary crafts, also regular changing exhibitions.

Oceanfront Gallery, 4/49 North Steyne, Manly, NSW 2095. Tel. (02) 977 8871.
Open seven days 10–6. Representing leading Australian artists in the crafts.

Glass Artists' Gallery, Glebe, Sydney

Old Bakery Gallery, 22 Rosenthall Avenue, Lane Cove, NSW 2066. Tel. (02) 428 4565. PO Box 193 NSW 2066.
Monthly exhibitions by Australian artists and craftspeople. Permanent stockroom with an extensive range of work in all media. Open Tuesday–Saturday 10–5.

Piramid Art, **Craft**, **Design**, Shop 1, The Institute Arcade, 332 Darling Street, Balmain, NSW 1041. Tel. (02) 818 5597.
Furniture, glassware, ceramics, jewellery, turned and carved wood by contemporary Australian craftspeople.

Platypus Gallery, Shop 16, Argyle Street, The Rocks, Sydney, NSW 2000. Tel. (02) 27 2590.
Open 9–6 seven days a week. Australian crafts.

Printfolio Gallery, Gallery Level, Westpac Plaza, 60 Margaret Street, Sydney, NSW. Tel. (02) 27 6690.
Exhibiting a small selection of fine craft and international prints. Open Monday–Friday 8.30–6.

Seasons Gallery, 259 Miller Street, North Sydney, NSW 2060. Tel. (02) 957 2060.
Open Tuesday–Saturday 11–6. In an old terrace house exhibitions of domestic and exhibition ceramics.

Studioshop, 27a Grosvenor Street, Neutral Bay, Sydney, NSW 2089. Tel. (02) 909 3583.
Open Tuesday–Saturday 10–6. Changing exhibitions of contemporary Australian craft.

The Potters' Gallery, 48–50 Burton Street, Darlinghurst, NSW 2010. Tel. (02) 331 3151.
Monthly exhibitions by leading national and international pot-

ters. Stoneware, earthenware and porcelain pots by members of The Potters Society of Australia.

Many of the leading fine art galleries also represent Australian and international craftspeople so it's worth checking with listings such as the exhibition guide in the Sydney Morning Herald's Friday supplement called **Metro** or **Art Almanac**.

The Craft Council Gallery, 100 George Street, The Rocks, Sydney, NSW 2000. Tel. (02) 241 1701.
Within the historic building near Circular Quay, the gallery is a perfect venue for regular exhibits by leading Australian crafts people. Upstairs in the building is the office for the **NSW Crafts Council** and the **Australia Crafts Council**. Not to be missed when wandering around the old Rocks area.

GALLERIES DEALING IN PRE 1900 EXHIBITS SYDNEY

Antiquarian Prints and Maps, 247 Victoria Street, Darlinghurst, NSW 2010. Tel. (02) 331 2745.
Large gallery with permanent display of the gallery collection.

Antique Engravings, 742 Military Road, Mosman, NSW 2088. Tel. (02) 960 3495.

Bibliophile, 24 Glenmore Road, Paddington, NSW 2021. Tel. (02) 331 1411.
Prints and maps.

Josef Lebovic Gallery, 34 Paddington Street, Paddington, NSW 2021. Tel. (02) 332 1840.
Old and rare etchings, engravings and photos.

Re Entombed Galleries, 22 Queen Street, Woollahra, NSW 2025. Tel. (02) 327 8204.
An interesting collection of archaeology and fine art. Also in Melbourne.

Tony Palmer, 261 Underwood Street, Paddington, NSW 2021. Tel. (02) 328 7655.
Commonwealth Govt. appointed valuer of fine art and antiques. Tony Palmer was a curator for 10 years at the Australian National Gallery.

Woollahra Galleries, 160 Oxford Street, Woollahra, NSW 2025. Tel. (02) 327 8840.
Fine art and collectibles.

ABORIGINAL ART GALLERIES SYDNEY

Aboriginal Art Australia, 477 Kent Street, Sydney, NSW 2000. Tel. (02) 261 2929.
National Marketing Service, with a gallery in the office. Administration Tel. (02) 923 2366.

Aboriginal Art Centre, 7 Walker Lane, Paddington, NSW 2021. Tel. (02) 357 6839. Also at The Rocks, Argyle Centre, Argyle Street, Sydney, NSW 2000. Tel. (02) 27 1380.
Displaying bark paintings, canvas paintings and artefacts.

Aboriginal Art Gallery, Yumbarra, 1/5 Springfield Avenue, Kings Cross, NSW 2011. Tel. (02) 358 6796.
Specialists in contemporary Aboriginal art, paintings, sculptures, silkscreens, woodburnings, ceramics, artefacts, bark paintings and jewellery. Open Tuesday—Friday 12—8, Saturday 1—8, Sunday 3—8.

Aboriginal Arts Australia Pty Ltd, 243 Miller Street, North Sydney, NSW 2060. Tel. (02) 920 5983.
COO-EE Australian Emporium, 98 Oxford Street, Paddington, NSW 2021. Tel. (02) 332 1544.
Aboriginal artefacts, bark paintings, crafts abd fabrics, agent for TIWI Designs.

Dreamtime Aboriginal Art Centre, 18 Argyle Street, The Rocks, NSW 2000. Tel. (02) 27 1380.

Primitive Art and Artefacts, 46 Oxford Street, Paddington, NSW 2021. Tel. (02) 331 3737. Open Monday—Saturday 10.30—6.00. ''Ethnographics'' - work from Australia and New Guinea.

Gallery Primitif, 174 Jersey Road, Woollahra, NSW 2025. Tel. (02) 32 3115. Authentic art of Oceania.

Bindi Gallery, Shop 2/4, Top Level Queen Victoria Building, Sydney 2000. Tel. (02) 261 5402. Open seven days a week 9.00—7.00, Thursday 9.00—9.00 or by appointment. Australian Aboriginal art and artefacts.

WORKSHOPS, STUDIOS AND ART CENTRES NEW SOUTH WALES

Artspace, 11 Randle Street, Surry Hills, NSW 2012. Tel. (02) 212 5031.
Artspace is supported by the Visual Arts Board and provides an alternative space for lectures, video, performances, exhibitions, seminars, installations and photography. Art books on sale, art information available and membership (a non profit organisation).

Australian Centre for Photography, Dobell House, 257 Oxford Street, Paddington, NSW 2021. Tel. (02) 356 1455.
Weekend workshops, lectures, children's workshops and intensive instruction or 11 week courses. Monthly exhibitions in the centre's gallery; demonstrations and discussions, also a bookshop.

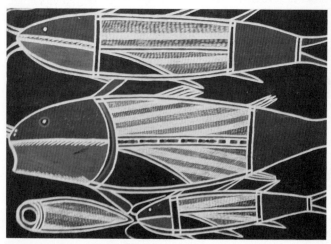

Aboriginal bark painting

Australia Japan Foundation, 50 Margaret Street, Sydney, NSW 2000. Tel. (02) 29 5653.
An interesting cultural organisation with much exchange between the two nations.

Glebe Hot Glass Studio, 136 Mitchell Street, Glebe, NSW 2037. Tel. (02) 660 3329.
Classes available in various techniques of glass.

Goëthe—Institute, 90 Ocean Street, Woollahra, NSW 2025. Tel. (02) 328 7411.
The German culture centre with events, film screenings, exhibitions and lectures.

Ian Hale's Etching Studio, 59 Kissing Point Road, Dundas, NSW 2117. Tel. (02) 638 4464.
Etching editions printed, monotone or colour, will work on the plate with the artist from start to finish.

Julian Ashton Art School, 117 George Street, The Rocks, Sydney, NSW 2000. Tel. (02) 241 1641.
Classes available in traditional drawing and painting.

Newcastle Printmakers Workshop, 27 Popran Road, Adamstown, NSW 2289. PO Box 102, Adamstown NSW 2289. Tel c/o (049) 43 1160.
Classes are run for members of the community and Fridays are open-workshop. The workshop aims to be self sufficient with membership allowing access to the facilities.

Nextu Art and Music Studios, 17 Regent Street, Redfern, NSW 2016.

Garage Graphix Community Arts Group, 24A Anderson Avenue, Blackett, Mt Druit, NSW. PO Box E30, Emerton NSW 2770. Tel. (02) 628 6897.
Garage Graphix is a community owned and managed design and screenprint workshop. They work with local people to make art which expresses their social and political concerns.

Primrose Papers, Primrose Park, Cammeray, NSW 2062.
Currently in the process of getting established and receiving grants to establish various workshops in papermaking including 3D work, Japanese techniques, colouring pulp, plant fibres and cotton rag fibres. At a later stage an exhibition space and shop are planned for. For information contact Tel. (02) 909 1277. Primrose papers will be the first open access hand papermaking facility in Australia.

Printworkshop and Gallery, 73 Jersey Road, Woollahra, NSW 2025. Tel. (02) 328 7772.
Open Monday–Friday 9–5, Saturday 10–5, Sunday 2–4. Limited open access for etching and lithography. Editioning in woodblock, etching and lithography. Night classes Thursday evening and Friday afternoon. Exhibitions given in graphics, free perspex framing available.

Printworkshop Zero, 68 Oxford Street, Darlinghurst, NSW 2010.
Facilities include etching, lithography, darkrooms, silkscreen printing, photography for printing.

Redback Graphix, PO Box 29, Westgate, NSW 2048. Tel. (02) 560 0066.
Providing high quality graphic art services including layout and design, printing on paper and T-shirts.

Royal Art Society Art School, 25–27 Walker Street, North Sydney, NSW 2060. Tel. (02) 92 5752.
Classes in landscape painting, life drawing, and painting, portrait, still life and watercolour painting.

Skull Printworks, 198 Queen Street, Woollahra, NSW 2025. Tel. (02) 326 2021.
Making prominent posters for Rock Banks and record companies.

Sturt Workshops, PO Box 34, Mittagong, NSW 2575. Tel. (048) 71 1279.
Established craft workshops in ceramics, screenprinting, woodcraft, weaving, metalcraft/jewellery and fibre. Summer schools also available.

The Cottage, Mosman, Mosman Community Centre, Short Street, Mosman, NSW 2088. Tel. (02) 960 2995.
Classes held in painting, drawing, calligraphy and the crafts.

The Griffith Workshop and Graphic Studios, 10 Hutchison Street, Bardwell Park, NSW 2207.
Etching and relief studio facilities, editioning under supervision. Workshop classes. Tel. (02) 502 1675.

The School of Colour and Design, Kendell Community Centre Hall, Cammeray Sydney, NSW 2062. Tel. (02) 95 5463/ 32 2014.
Specialised classes in the field of design and colour by two graduates from the Shillito Design School which closed in 1981.

The Tin Sheds—Art Workshop, Sydney University, City Road, Darlington, NSW 2006. PO Box 219, Wentworth Building, Sydney University NSW 2006.
The screenprinting workshop of the Tin Shed provides in the main workshop facilities for the production of art work and posters. A long standing history of work which has a political and social content is associated with the Tin Sheds. The facilities are available to artists for professional use and teaching.

Tom Bass Sculpture School, 159 Broadway, Sydney, NSW 2007 (rear access). Tel. (02) 212 3153.
Classes and workshops in various sculpture mediums.

Woollahra—**Waverly Art Centre**, 138 Bondi Road, Bondi Junction, NSW 2022. Tel. (02) 387 2461.
Workshops and classes in painting, drawing and the crafts.

Workshop Arts Centre, 33 Laurel Street, Willoughby, NSW 2068. Tel. (020 958 6540.
Classes and workshops in fine art and the crafts, also exhibition space in the centre. Individual tuition available and experimentation in the creative arts.

Workers Education Association, WEA House, 72 Bathurst Street, Sydney, NSW 2000. Tel. (02) 61 7449.
Day and evening classes in various aspects of the creative

arts, residential and non-residential workshops and summer schools.

Paddington Art School, 3 Elizabeth Street, Paddington, NSW 2021. Tel. (02) 331 2763.
Drawing and painting classes, 12 months part-time certificate and non-certificate course.

The Printworkshop, 73 Jersey Road, Woollahra, NSW 2025. Tel. (02) 328 7772.
Open Monday—Friday 9—5, Saturday 10—5, Sunday 2—4. Limited open access for etching and lithography, editioning done in lithography, etching and woodblock. Summer schools.

FINE ART COURSES AND COLLEGES NEW SOUTH WALES

City Art Institute—Sydney College of Advanced Education, Cnr Albion Avenue and Selwym Street, Paddington, NSW 2021. Tel. (02) 339 9555.
The Institute offers the wide range of courses in the following: Undergraduate degree (BA) in teaching; art & craft; design, painting, drawing, sculpture, printmaking, photography, ceramics, jewellery, textiles, film, television and cinema studies, professional writing/journalism/radio. Graduate Diploma in arts administration, painting, drawing, sculpture, printmaking, photography, ceramics, jewellery, textiles, film, television, cinema studies and professional writing/journalism/radio. Master's degree by research is offered in art history and theory, teaching; art & craft design, painting, drawing, sculpture, printmaking, photography, ceramics, jewellery, textiles and film, television and cinema studies.

Colleges of Technical and Further Education— **TAFE**. The Headquarters of the School of Art and Design is located at **East Sydney Technical College**, Forbes Street, Darlinghurst, NSW 2010. Tel. (02) 339 8666, with its annex at Avoca Street, Randwick NSW 2031. Tel. (02) 339 6677.
The venue of the old Sydney jail once housed The National Art School, which in its day was the only significant art school in Sydney. The location continues to house the art school with a continued feeling of being one of the more important of the TAFE college art schools and has recently been re-instated as **The National Art School** to stand along side both **The City Art Institute** and **Sydney College of the Arts** in importance.

The National Art School and the suburban **TAFE** college art schools offer the following: Associate Diploma (2 yrs) in art, ceramics, dress design, graphic design, interior design and jewellery design. A Fine Art Certificate is also offered in most subjects (1 yr) and a Single Subject Certificate sometimes varying with the individual school. The National Art School (East Sydney Tech.) is offering a diploma in art (3 yr). For detailed information contact the individual college.

Art students in a printmaking department

Gymea Technical College Art School, Hotham Road, Gymea, NSW 2227. Tel. (02) 521 4388.

Horsnby Technical College Art School, 205 Pacific Highway, Horsnby, NSW 2077. Tel. (02) 477 4999.

Liverpool Technical College Art School, College Street, Liverpool, NSW 2170. Tel. (02) 602 7133.

Meadowbank Technical College Art School, Constitution Road, Meadowbank, NSW 2114. Tel. (02) 808 0211.

Randwick Technical College Art School, Darley Road, Randwick, NSW 2031. Tel. (02) 398 7111.

Seaforth Technical Art School, Sydney Road, Seaforth, NSW 2092. Tel. (02) 948 0281.

St George Technical College Art School, Montgomery Street, Kogarah, NSW 2217. Tel. (02) 588 0200.

Strathfield College School of Textiles, Beresford Road, Strathfield, NSW 2135. Tel. (02) 764 4899.

Sydney Technical College School of Graphic Art, Broadway, Sydney, NSW 2000. Tel. (02) 217 3230.

Mitchell College of Advanced Education, Bathurst, NSW 2795. Tel. (063) 31 1022.
The college offers an Associate Diploma in painting, drawing, printmaking, photography and ceramics. An Undergraduate Degree (BA) is offered in professional writing/journalism/ radio and dance, drama and music.

Nepean College of Advanced Education, PO Box 10, Kingswood, NSW 2750. Tel. (047) 36 0222.
The college offers an Undergraduate Degree (BA) in painting, sculpture, printmaking, photography, ceramics and glass. An Associate Diploma is offered in graphic design and dance, drama and music.

New South Wales Institute of Technology—University, PO Box 123, Broadway, NSW 2007. Tel. (02) 20 930.
The institute offer an Undergraduate Degree (BA) in both film, television, cinema studies and professional writing/journalism/radio.

Newcastle College of Advanced Education, PO Box 84, Waratah, NSW 2298. Tel. (049) 67 1388.
The college offers an Associate Diploma in painting, drawing, photography, ceramics and textiles. A Graduate Diploma in painting, sculpture, printmaking, photography, ceramics, textiles and illustration. An Undergraduate Degree (BA) in teaching; art & craft; design, painting, sculpture, printmaking, photography, ceramics, textiles, illustration, film, television, cinema studies, professional writing/journalism/radio and dance, drama and music.

Northern Rivers College of Advanced Education, PO Box 157, Lismore, NSW 2480. Tel. (066) 21 2267.
The college offers an Associate Diploma in painting, drawing, printmaking, ceramics, film, television, radio and professional writing/journalism/radio. An Undergraduate Degree (BA) in teaching; art & craft; design and dance, drama and music.

Riverina—**Murray Institute of Higher Education**, PO Box 588, Wagga Wagga, NSW 2650.
The institute offers an Undergraduate Degree (BA) in painting, printmaking, ceramics, jewellery, textiles and graphic design. An Associate Diploma in film, television, cinema studies and dance, drama and music.

Sydney College of Advanced Education, see "City Art Institute" at the beginning.

Sydney College of the Arts, PO Box 226, Glebe, NSW 2037. Tel. (02) 692 0266.
The college offers an Undergraduate Degree (BA), a Graduate Diploma and a Master's by coursework in all the following: painting, sculpture, printmaking, photography, ceramics, jewellery, glass, industrial design, interior design, fashion design and graphic design.

The University of Wollongong, PO Box 1144, Wollongong, NSW 2500. Tel. (042) 27 0555.
The University offers an Associate Diploma, Undergraduate Degree (BA), Master's by coursework and Master's by research in all the following: painting, sculpture, printmaking, ceramics, textiles, professional writing/journalism/radio and dance, drama and music.

The University of Sydney, NSW 2006. Tel. (02) 692 2222.
The University offers both an Undergraduate Degree (BA) and Master's by research in art history & theory and film, television and cinema studies.

The University of New South Wales, PO Box 1, Kensington, NSW 2033. Tel. (02) 663 2804.
The University offers an Undergraduate Degree (BA), Master's by coursework and Master's by research in industrial design and interior design. A Master's by coursework and an Undergraduate Degree (BA) are offered in environmental/landscape design.

Macquarie University, North Ryde, NSW 2113. Tel. (02) 888 8000.
The University offers an Undergraduate Degree (BA) in film, television, cinema studies and professional writing/journalism/radio.

The Australian Film and Television School, PO Box 126, North Ryde, NSW 2113. Tel. (02) 887 1666. (and radio).
The school offers and Undergraduate Degree (BA) and Graduate Diploma in professional writing/journalism/radio and dance, drama and music.

ART SUPPLIES AND MATERIALS NEW SOUTH WALES

Alderson Art and Crafts, 264 Railway Parade, Kogarah, NSW 2217. Tel. (02) 587 2699.
"The department store for the fine arts".

Artistcare, 346 Kent Street, Sydney, NSW 2000. Tel. (02) 29 4151.
Specialist supplies for drafting, drawing and all graphic art needs. Also 4 other stores in Sydney.

Artist Supply Co., 152 Clarence Street, Sydney, NSW 2000. Tel. (02) 262 2477 and at Darlinghurst.
Huge selection of materials for the fine arts and crafts.

Asian Provisions, 166 Victoria Avenue, Chatswood, NSW 2067. Tel. (02) 411 2627.
Large selection of Chinese and Japanese inks and other speciality needs for the artist and calligrapher.

Deans—Four Art, 213 Oxford Street, Darlinghurst, NSW 2010. Tel. (02) 360 2599.

Dymock's, 424 George Street, Sydney, NSW 2000. Tel. (02) 233 4111.
Comprehensive range of artist materials within the main bookstore.

East Sydney Technical College Student Store, Forbes Street, Darlinghurst, NSW 2010. Tel. (02) 339 8666.
Student discounts given on all materials.

Elton Papers, A1 Wandella Avenue, Roseville, NSW 2069. Tel. (02) 406 4998.
Papers for art. Wholesale only. Specialist in imported Japanese papers.

Hunter Gallery and Art Supply, 14 Hunter Street, Hornsby, NSW 2077. Tel. (02) 476 3419.

Hurstville Art Supplies, 303 Forest Road, Hurstville, NSW 2220. Tel. (02) 570 4138.
Huge range of imported and local art materials for fine arts and crafts.

Oxford Art Supplies, 221 Oxford Street, Darlinghurst, NSW 2010. Tel. (02) 360 4066.
Discount art and drawing supply specialists on all leading brands of imported and national art materials.

Oxford Art Supplies, Darlinghurst, Sydney

Sussex Art Supplies Pty Ltd, 53 Liverpool Street, Sydney, NSW 2000. Tel. (02) 264 2088.

Tamarisque Fine Art Pty Ltd, 27 Albion Street, Surry Hills, NSW 2010. Tel. (02) 212 1223.
Specialist fine art papers from Europe, Japan and America and limited range of high quality artist material.

The Artists' Emporium, 40a Park Street, Sydney, NSW 2000. Tel. (02) 267 7972.
Fine art and graphic art specialists.

The Artist Warehouse Co., 401 Elizabeth Street, Surry Hills, NSW 2010. Tel. (02) 212 4622.
Large range of fine art, graphic art and drafting supplies.

S & S Wholesale Supplies, Unit 10, 9 Pioneer Avenue, Thornleigh, NSW 2120. Tel. (02) 875 1155.
School supplies in most art materials. Importers of wood for relief printing etc.

ART BOOKSHOPS
NEW SOUTH WALES

Many art galleries and museums also sell fine art books and magazines.

All Arts Bookshop, 160 Oxford Street, Woollahra, NSW 2025. Tel. (02) 327 8840.
Fine arts and antiques.

Angus and Robertson Bookshop, City, Imperial Arcade, 168 Pitt Street, Sydney, NSW 2000. Tel. (02) 235 1188.
Excellent selection of performing and visual arts, international and Australian.

Ariel, Booksellers & Publishers, 42 Oxford Street, Paddington, NSW 2010. Tel. (02) 332 4581.
Excellent selection of fine art books with specialisation in the performing arts. The bookshop also has an exhibiting space, a great atmosphere and worth a visit if in the area. Open 7 days a week 10am–midnight.

Art Gallery of NSW Bookshop, Art Gallery Road, The Domain, Sydney, NSW 2000. Tel. (02) 221 2100.
Extensive selection of fine arts and crafts. Catalogues, art journals and reproduction prints of the gallery collection. Open gallery hours.

Co-op Bookshop Ltd, 80 Bay Road, Broadway, Sydney, NSW 2007. Tel. (02) 212 2211.
Also located in major institutes and universities.

Dymocks', 424 George Street, Sydney, NSW 2000. Tel. (02) 233 4111.
Large selection of fine art, craft and technical books.

Ariel Bookshop, Darlinghurst, Sydney

Lamella art bookshop, Sydney

The Feminist Bookshop, 315 Balmain Road, Lilyfield, NSW 2040. Tel. (02) 810 2666.

Lamella Art Books, 333 South Dowling Street, Darlinghurst, NSW 2010. Tel. (02) 331 4501.
A specialist art bookshop with imports on all aspects of the visual and performing arts.

Mary Martin Bookshops Pty Ltd, 47 York Street, Sydney, NSW 2000. Tel. (02) 29 1891.
Wide selection of art books often discounted.

New Editions Bookshop and Tea Rooms, 328 Oxford Street, Paddington, NSW 2021. Tel. (02) 357 6913.
Open 7 days. Speciality books in the arts, architecture and performing arts. Great atmosphere on Saturdays with the market opposite and musicians playing.

Performing Arts Bookshop, 265 Elizabeth Street, Sydney, NSW 2000. Tel. (02) 267 2257.

Powerhouse Shop, Powerhouse Museum, Harris Street, Ultimo, NSW 2000. Tel. (02) 217 0111.
The shop has an interesting selection of applied design and art books.

The Bookshop Darlinghurst, 207 Oxford Street, Darlinghurst, NSW 2010. Tel. (02) 331 1103.
Literature, gay & feminist, photography, film & video, the performing art & magazines.

The Bookshop Newtown, 186 King Street, Newtown, NSW 2042. Tel. (02) 51 4244.
As above.

The Building Bookshop, 525 Elizabeth Street, Surry Hills, NSW 2021. Tel. (02) 699 5435.
Open Monday–Saturday 9–5, Sunday 12–5. Fine and decorative arts, architecture and technical books.

The Australian Heritage Bookshop, 81 George Street, The Rocks, Sydney, NSW 2000. Tel. (02) 27 7401.
If you're driving to Canberra from Sydney just before historic Berrima (after Mittagong) on the Federal Highway, you can brake the journey with a stop at **Books Berkelow**, a unique barn converted into an enormous second hand bookstore. Specialists in quality books covering the arts, film, travel, literature and out of print scholary books. Look for the big white sign. Tel. (008) 04 6240.

PHOTOGRAPHY, FILM AND VIDEO NEW SOUTH WALES

Australian Film and Television School, PO Box 126, North Ryde, NSW 2113. Tel. (02) 887 1666.
Melbourne representative (03) 328 2683. Offering Diplomas in film and television and a Graduate Diploma in media.

Macquarie Street Parade 200 year celebration, Sydney

Australian Broadcasting Commission, 150 William Street, Kings Cross, NSW 2011. Tel. (02) 339 0211.

Australian Film Studios Ltd, 1 Barr Street, Balmain, NSW 2041. Tel. (02) 555 1555.

Image East—Video Productions, 7 West Street, North Sydney, NSW 2060. Tel. (02) 92 0807.

Sydney University Filmmakers, Science Road, Sydney University, Sydney, NSW 2006. Tel. (02) 660 3079.

The Film Services Group, 303 Bourke Street, East Sydney, NSW 2000. Tel. (02) 331 2158.

The Sydney Film Co., 100 Bay Road, Waverton, NSW 2060. Tel. (02) 922 5533.

The Video Record Co. Pty Ltd, 10 Renwick Street, Redfern, NSW 2016. Tel. (02) 319 1873.

The NSW Film Corporation, 45 Macquarie Street, Sydney, NSW 2000. Tel. (02) 241 1245.

Schmeling Artvideo Australia. Melbourne. Contact Tel. (03) 750 1372.
Specialists in Australian art and craft films.

PHOTOGRAPHIC SUPPLIES

Fletchers Photographic, 317 Pitt Street, Sydney, NSW 2000. Tel. (02) 267 6146.
One of the leading photographic suppliers for the semi professional and amateur. Secondhand and new equipment. Colour and black & white developing available.

G & V Photographics, Victoria Plaza, 369 Victoria Avenue, Chatswood, NSW 2067. Tel. (02) 419 7060.

Jadonn-Colour Laboratory Pty Ltd, 1st Floor, 400 Kent Street, Sydney, NSW 2000. Tel. (02) 267 8119.
The transparency processing specialists.

Kolor Kraft, 51 Berry Street, North Sydney, NSW 2060. Tel. (02) 922 7116.
Complete processing services for colour and black & white.

Paxton's Photographic, 283 George Street, Sydney, NSW 2000. Tel. (02) 2 0225 (nr Wynyard Station).
Complete processing service available, new and secondhand equipment and trade-ins taken.

Rabbit Express, 151 Clarence Street, Sydney, NSW 2000. Tel. (02) 29 6312.
1 hour processing service, 34 shops throughout Sydney, reliable.

Ted's Camera Store, 238 Pitt Street, Sydney, NSW 2000. Tel. (02) 264 1687.
Camera equipment and accessories for the darkroom, duty free shop upstairs.

The Camera Service Centre, 2nd Floor, 203 Castlereagh Street, Sydney, NSW 2000. Tel. (02) 264 7091.
Professional repairs. Deal direct with the technicians.

FINE ART FRAMING
NEW SOUTH WALES

Most fine art galleries can offer a framing service, but often you can save some of the expense by going direct to the framing studios used by the galleries.

Bedford Framing Studios, Lower Avon Street, Glebe, NSW 2037. Tel. (02) 660 6886.
Large selection of local and imported mouldings. Restorations on water colours, oils, drawings and prints. Also at 21 Atchinson Street, St Leonards NSW 2065. Tel. (02) 439 4944.

Carat Framing Studio, 36 Chelsea Street, Redfern, NSW 2016. Tel. (02) 698 7150.
Fine art custom framing and restoration.

Frameworks, 283 Elizabeth Street, Sydney, NSW 2000. Tel. (02) 267 1212.
Large selection of imported and local mouldings.

Geometrics, Cnr Fig and Wattle Streets, Ultimo, NSW 2007. Tel. (02) 660 8699.
Personalised framing service for any requirements, retail and wholesale. Willing to work to artists needs.

Modern Framing, 99 Jones Street, Ultimo, NSW 2007. Tel. (02) 212 5444. Retail and wholesale, contract framing, archival mounts and artists exhibitions welcomed.

Pochoir Gallery, 77 Berry Street, North Sydney, NSW 2060 (in North Sydney Shopping World). Tel. (02) 922 2843.
Custom framing service.

ART SERVICES
NEW SOUTH WALES

Art consultants

Art Incorporate, 15–17 Buckingham Street, Surry Hills, NSW 2010. Tel. (02) 699 4219.
Experts in corporate sales with a large showroom representing the works of leading Australian artists. Offering a full consultancy service from a very active young team. Open Monday–Friday 9–5.

Conservation

Fine Art Conservation Pty Ltd, Tony Chadwick, 5 Bungay Street, Leichhardt, NSW 2040. Tel. (02) 569 6223.
Conservation, restoration and consultancy service for paintings.

Printers

Arcadia Press, 108 Arcadia Road, Arcadis, NSW 2159. Tel. (02) 653 1656.
A new concept in publishing, creative projects welcomed.

Port Jackson Press, 370 Pacific Highway, Crows Nest, NSW 2065. Tel. (02) 439 3578.
Art publishers and printers.

Ideas Australia, Level 3, 47 Wentworth Avenue, Sydney, NSW 2000. Tel. (02) 281 2385.
Suppliers of international quality graphics and corporate design services, catalogues, advertising materials etc.

Transport

Redleg, Sydney Tel. (02) 698 5118.
Professional art services dealing with galleries interstate and regional. Based in Melbourne, 20 Guildford Lane, Melbourne, Vic 3000. Tel. (03) 602 4071.

T.E.D. Fine Art Australia, 23 Luland Road, Botany, NSW 2019. Tel. (02) 666 5225.
Packaging and handling of all type of fine art.

Grace International Removals, Carter Street, Lidcombe, NSW 2141. Tel. (02) 648 4244.
Experts for all kinds of freighting interstate and international, packaging available.

Woollahra Art Removals, 200 Coward Street, Mascot, NSW 2020. Tel. (02) 669 2688.
Specialised in art removals throughout Australia.

Sydney art gallery tours

Art Tours, 55 Pentecost Avenue, St Ives, NSW 2075. Tel. (02) 498 6776/443 463.
Art Tours offers a unique service of personalised guided tours of the Sydney galleries for either a half day or full day. Plan the tour to suit the size of your group, smaller groups preferred and the types of galleries of major interest can be catered for.

Legal service

The Arts Law Centre, 1st Floor, 11 Randle Street, Surry Hills, NSW 2010. Tel. (02) 211 4033 or toll free outside of Sydney (008) 221 457.
Free legal advice on any arts related matter. Phone for an appointment or discuss over the phone.

THEATRICAL ORGANISATIONS NEW SOUTH WALES

Australian Elizabethan Theatre Trust, 153 Dowling Street, Potts Point, NSW 2011. Tel. (02) 357 1200.

Clovelly Puppet Theatre. Performances each month. Tel. (02) 665 9675 for details.

Ensemble Theatre, 78 McDougal Street, Milsons Point, NSW 2061. Tel. (02) 929 8877/929 0644.

Ensemble Studios, Theatrical School, 269 Miller Street, North Sydney, NSW 2060. Tel. (02) 929 6840.

Griffin Theatre Company, 10 Nimrod Street, Darlinghurst, NSW 2010. Tel. (02) 33 3817.

Marion St Children's Theatre, and Marionette Theatre of Australia Ltd, at The Rocks Theatre, 106 George North Street, Sydney, NSW 2000. Tel. (02) 241 1391, Box Office 27 3274.

Nida, the National Institute of Dramatic Art, PO Box 1, Kensington, NSW 203.

Nimrod Theatre Company, Cleveland Street, Cnr City Road, Darlington, NSW 2008. Tel. (02) 692 0555.
The Seymour Centre Box Office (02) 692 3511.

Northside Theatre Company, and Restaurant, 2 Marion Street, Killara, NSW 2071. Tel. (02) 498 3166.

One Extra Dance Company, 199 Cleveland Street, Redfern, NSW 2016. Tel. (02) 690 1870.

Pact Theatre—Youth Theatre, 173 Sussex Street, Sydney, NSW 2000. Tel. (02) 29 8239.
Workshops held during vacation time in drama for youngsters and teenagers.

Sydney Dance Company, Pier 4/5, Hickson Road, Millers Point, NSW 2000. Tel. (02) 221 4811.
Now internationally recognised for their contemporary dance productions.

Sydney Theatre Company Ltd, The Wharf, Pier 4, Hickson Road, Millers Point, NSW 2000. Tel. (02) 250 1700. Box Office 250 1777.
Now an interesting venue after restoration of the original old harbour side shipping wharfs.

Writers in the Park, you can catch them at Harold Park Hotel, 115 Wigram Road, Glebe, NSW 2037. Tel. (02) 692 0564.
Sydney has an ever increasing and changing number of small theatrical groups performing throughout the inner city. The **Sydney Morning Herald's** Friday supplement "**METRO**" will give you a good guide to all groups performing weekly with many small companies now performing in coffee shops such as The Loft in Balmain.

Theatrical venues—Sydney

Australian Theatre for the Young People, 106 George Street, Sydney, NSW 2000. Tel. (02) 251 3900.

Bondi Pavilion Theatre, Queen Elizabeth Drive, Bondi Beach, NSW 2026. Tel. (02) 30 7211.

Downstairs Theatre, Seymour Centre, City Road, Darlington, NSW 2006. Tel. (02) 692 3511.

Drama Theatre, Sydney Opera House, Bennelong Point, Sydney, NSW 2000. Tel. (02) 20 588.

Ensemble Theatre, 78 McDougal Street, Milsons Point, NSW 2061. Tel. (02) 929 8877. Box Office 929 0644.

Everest Theatre, Seymour Centre, City Road, Darlington, NSW 2006. Tel. (02) 692 3511.

Footbridge Theatre, Parramatta Road, Glebe (Sydney Uni), NSW 2037. Tel. (02) 692 9955.

Genesian Theatre, 420 Kent Street, Sydney, NSW 2000. Tel. (02) 267 6646.

Her Majesty's Theatre, 107 Quay Street, Railway Square, NSW 2000. Tel. (02) 212 3411.

Kinselas, 383 Bourke Street, Darlinghurst, NSW 2021. Tel. (02) 331 6200.

Nida Theatre, High Street, Kensington, NSW 2033. Tel. (02) 663 3815.

Theatre Royal, MLC Centre, King Street, Sydney, NSW 2000. Tel. (02) 231 6111.

The Performance Space, 199 Cleveland Street, Redfern, NSW 2016. Tel. (02) 698 7235.

The Rocks Theatre, 106 George North Street, Sydney, NSW 2000. Tel. (02) 241 1391.

The Seymour Centre, Theatre Complex, Cnr City Road & Cleveland Street, Sydney University, Darlington, NSW 2006. Tel. (02) 692 0555.
Housing the York Theatre, Everest Theatre and the Downstairs Theatre.

MUSICAL ORGANISATIONS AND VENUES NEW SOUTH WALES

Australian Institute of Eastern Music, 219 Victoria Avenue, Chatswood, NSW 2067. Tel. (02) 411 3709.

Australian National Folk Trust, 38a Oxford Street, Paddington, NSW 2021. Tel. (02) 33 3980.

Flute Society of NSW, 32 Warringah Road, Cammeray, NSW 2062. Tel. (02) 929 2118.

Hornsby Concert Band, Pennant Hills Road, Normanhurst, NSW 2076. Tel. (02) 487 2018.

Jazz Action Society, 74 Pitt Street, Sydney, NSW 2000. Tel. (02) 232 1419.

Jazz Club Co-op Ltd, 11 Milham Crescent, Forestville, NSW 2087. Tel. (02) 452 5831.

New South Wales State Conservatorium of Music, Macquarie Street, Sydney, NSW 2000. Tel. (02) 230 1222.

Opera House—Concert Hall—Opera Theatre—Drama Theatre and Music Room, The Sydney Opera House, Bennelong Point, Sydney, NSW 2000. Tel. (02) 205 88. PO Box 4274, GPO Sydney NSW 2000.
Home for the **Australian Opera Company** also. Address for admin. Australia Opera, 480 Elizabeth Street, Surry Hills NSW 2010. Tel. (02) 699 1099.

Sydney Entertainment Centre, Harbour Street, Haymarket, NSW 2000. Tel. (02) 211 2222.
Recorded information 24 hours 1 1582.

Sydney Symphony Orchestra, Victoria Avenue, Chatswood NSW, 2067. Tel. (02) 410 3500.

Sydney Youth Orchestra Association, 2 Stanley Street, Darlinghurst, NSW 2010. Tel. (02) 331 3444.

The Great Hall, Sydney University all enquiries Tel. (02) 692 222. For bookings contact the A.B.C. Box Office, Queen Victoria Building. Tel. (02) 264 9466.

The Sydney Town Hall, Sydney Square, George Street, Sydney, NSW 2000. Tel. (02) 265 9333.
There are many lively venues for popular music and rock, far too many for listing here. Most hotels in the inner city have live bands playing mid week and weekends. The most inexpensive and comprehensive coverage is found in METRO, the liftout supplement in the Friday issue of the Sydney Morning Herald, and many radio stations give mention to where live music is happening.

Australian Music Centre, Smail Street, Broadway, NSW 2000.
Access library of scores of professional musicians, organisations listed and publications available.

Music Performed Composers' Association, PO Box 97, Newtown, NSW 2042. Tel. (02) 969 4331.

Sydney Opera House from the harbour (Heather Waddell)

PLACES OF INTEREST
NEW SOUTH WALES

Sydney is a city full of wonderful outdoor locations all year round, there are many inner city parks and those lining the harbour foreshores are always a pleasant retreat, where you can watch the various harbour activities from small sailing craft, ferries, luxury yachts and the occasional cargo ship all adding to the spectacle of Sydney Harbour. Below is a selected list of just a few of the more popular inner city venues worth visiting.

Sydney Taronga Zoo, situated at Mosman, 12 minutes by ferry from Circular Quay No. 5 wharf. Open daily 9.30–5. Tel. 969 2777. Overlooking Sydney harbour it has spectacular views and is one of the world's finest zoos.

Ashton Park—Sydney Harbour. Anyone who enjoys walking through natural bushland shouldn't miss this famous walk. The walk begins to the right of Taronga Park Zoo and follows the harbour around to Clifton Gardens. Enjoy the views along the $4\frac{1}{2}$ kilometres which were painted by our famous Australian artists such as Tom Roberts, Arthur Streeton, Condor, McCubbon and Conrad Martin. Many of these paintings now hang in the Art Gallery of New South Wales and the National Gallery. Easiest access is to take a 12 minute ferry ride from the city to the Zoo.

The Rocks, Argyle Street, Sydney. Walking tours are available around the Rocks to explore Sydney's birthplace (1 hour tour), daily. For information Tel. 27 6678, 10–3. More fun to explore it by yourself possibly. Magnificent old colonial houses. Now a tourist centre around George Street.

Sydney Harbour Cruises. Cruises are available daily leaving No. 6 jetty almost hourly, at Circular Quay. Tel. (02) 27 9408 for information. Also the Sydney Urban Transit Authority offer various cruises leaving from Circular Quay Ferry Centre (02) 29 2622.

Manly. Manly's attractions are generally of a family nature; good surfing beach and pool, picnic areas, the art gallery. The ferry ride from Circular Quay makes a very enjoyable day's outing.

Elizabeth Bay House, 7 Onslow Avenue, Elizabeth Bay. Australia's finest remaining colonial "Stately Home", built between 1835 and 1838. The house has 19th century Greek revival detailing with a magnificent oval staircase covered by a dome. Special changing exhibitions are held in the house. Open Tuesday–Sunday 10–4.30. Tel. (02) 358 2344 for exhibition details.

Sydney Opera House, Bennelong Point, Sydney. Tel. (02) 20 588 for 1½ hour backstage tours of the Opera House. Originally designed by Danish architect Jørn Utzon who did not remain to see the completion of the building, completed by local architects. It was opened in 1973 by the Queen and cost a staggering A$ 102 million, some 15 times more than originally planned.

There is an unusual mural in the northern foyer of the main concert hall by John Olsen called "Salute to Five Bells". It is based on a poem by Australian poet Kenneth Slessor "Five Bells", an elegy for Joe Lynch, Slessor's friend, who was drowned when he fell off a ferry on his way to a party on the north side of the harbour. With a backdrop of vibrant blue/purple there are lively shapes leaping about the water in oranges, yellows, green and black like shapes out of a Joan Miro painting. It is a good introduction to contemporary Australian painting for visitors, although the tour guide is very disparaging about the mural sadly, obviously not interested in art.

Darling Harbour. Originally the tradesman's entrance to Sydney, the area now provides a huge expanse of entertainment area with Chinese Gardens, exhibition centre, casino, museums etc. with the now completed monorail operating from the Pitt Street area.

Australia Square Skywalk, George Street, the City, near Wynyard Station. From the fully enclosed level on top of Australia Square this is the second tallest observation tower in Sydney (Centre Point being the tallest). Enjoy the spectacular view of Sydney. Open daily 10–10.

Australian Pioneer Village. Authentic shops, houses and other buildings from the Hawkesbury settlement. Open from 10 Tuesday–Saturday, Rose Street, Wilberforce. Tel. (045) 751 457.

Katoomba Scenic Skyway and Railway. Soar 1,000ft above the beautiful Jamison Valley or ride the world's steepest railway. Coach tours operate daily between Katoomba and Sydney, also rail/coach tours or drive yourself in less than 2 hours.

Ride with Australia's last riverboat postman along the **Hawkesbury River**. Mail runs depart from Brooklyn at 9.30 and 11 Monday–Friday. Connecting trains leave Central Station at 8.08 and 9.10 respectively. Other cruises are available on Saturday, Sunday and public holidays. Tel. 455 1566.

Parks

Bondi Beach. This famous stretch of sand has excellent surf and is patrolled all year round. On the beach is Bondi Pavilion with its exhibition gallery and theatre, coffee shop and restaurant, and on selected summer days there are concerts in the courtyard with the music ranging from jazz, Latin American,

Sydney Harbour Bridge

pop and dance music. The area is also becoming known for its restaurants all year round with a very lively atmosphere at weekends. Sit on the lawns overlooking the surfing beach and admire the view. Catch the 380 bus from Elizabeth Street in the City (near Market Street).

Centennial Park. The park was opened in 1888 to celebrate the arrival of the First Fleet and today equally important as a large expanse of parkland, playing fields and avenues of various forms of plants. Popular sports here are bike riding and horse riding while a special track runs alongside for joggers. Bicycles are available for hire. Open from sunrise to sunset, Oxford Street, Paddington.

Neilson Park. Ideal for picnics, this small still-water, harbourside beach has a kiosk and adjoins a large park with picnic areas under the trees. The park is sheltered from the north east and southerly summer breezes. While swimming you can enjoy great views across the harbour. You can reach the park by driving along New South Head Road then turn left into Vaucluse Road and keep driving. Not far from here is another great swimming area, Parsley Bay, with its huge netted harbourside pool and suspension walking bridge.

Mrs Macquaries Point. A popular stopping place for visitors to Sydney with panoramic views of Sydney Harbour; looking west across to the Opera House and the Harbour Bridge and north over to Mosman and Taronga Zoo and east beyond Garden Island and the Australian Naval Base towards South Head and Vaucluse. Just a short walk from The Art Gallery of NSW or from the Opera House through the Botanic Gardens.

Royal Botanic Gardens. The gardens are on the harbour's edge at Farm Cove with a host of blooms in season, huge trees, tropical plants and luscious green lawns to relax on. There is a restaurant in the gardens.

Botanical Gardens, Sydney

Sydney Harbour National Park. This park circles the harbour foreshores in small individual sections. The park includes Shark and Clark Islands, Neilson Park, South Head, North Head, Dobroyd Head and Ashton Park. For information call (02) 337 5511/337 5432 (9–4).

Markets—Sydney

Annandale Market. The third Sunday of every month at the Annandale Neighbourhood Centre, 79 Johnson Street, Annandale from 10–4, new and secondhand items, everything from face painting to massaging.

Balmain Market. In the grounds of St Andrews Congregational Church, Cnr Darling Street & Curtis Road, every Saturday 7.30–4. Bric-à-brac, new and secondhand clothes, antiques etc. Lots of fun and entertainment.

Bankstown Market. In the grounds at Bankstown Showground, Milperra Road, every Sunday 9–4. About 200 stalls under cover with an extensive range of new goods at low prices.

Chatswood Market. The third Saturday of every month, open air market with a wide range of arts and crafts. 38 Devonshire Street, Chatswood.

Darlinghurst Market. Found in Albert Sloss Reserve on the second Saturday of each month. Genuine bargains, bric-à-brac, books and food.

Drummoyne—Birkenhead Point Markets. Open seven days a week, large indoor complex on the waterfront off Victoria Road, near Iron Cove Bridge, Drummoyne.

Flemington Markets. A Paddy's Market with the same range of goods as the new Paddy's Market at Darling Harbour. Operates on Fridays 11–4.30 and an even bigger market day on Sundays 9.30–4.30 without fruit or fish. Over 300 stands inside and out, even a car market. Off the Parramatta Road at Flemington.

Kings Cross Flea Market, 9.30–6.30 daily, mostly Eastern goods. Rosslyn Street, Kings Cross.

Kirribilli Market. The last Sunday of every month in the grounds of the Kirribilli Neighbourhood Centre, with a wide range of crafts, secondhand goods, clothing, books, records and food. 16–18 Fitzroy Street, Kirribilli.

Leichardt Market. Every Sunday 9–4 in the Kegworth School Playground, Tebbutt Street. Mixed market with 20–30 stalls.

Paddington Market—Village Bazar, Oxford Street, Paddington. Still remains the most popular market in Sydney attracting many young tourists and Sydney weekend visitors. A huge array of crafts, secondhand and new designer clothing, Eastern goods, jewellery, bric-à-brac and lots of interesting creations and musicians. Open 9–5 each Saturday with all

Paddington Market, Paddington, Sydney with young busker

the neighbouring shops staying open all day helping create a great atmosphere.

Paddy's Market. Sydney's oldest and most famous market now at a lower end of Liverpool Street, near Darling Harbour. Operating all day Saturday and Sunday with a huge range of goods and bargains to be found.

Surry Hills Market. The first Saturday of every month, 9–4 at Shannon Reserve opposite the Clock Hotel in Crown Street, Surry Hills. Seventy stalls with new and secondhand everything.

Sydney Dance Company, Graeme Murphy's Shining (Branco Gaica)

Waterloo Market. Every Saturday with up to 200 stalls, a wide range of most things you could imagine from 8–4. Pitt Street, Waterloo, which is closed to traffic.

The Queen Street Fair. An annual fair which takes place along the entire length of Queen Street, Woollahra. The street becomes a hive of activity for the day with over 200 stalls, entertainment, live bands and plenty of bizarre costumes to keep you amused for hours. Usually held on the last weekend of November annually.

RESTAURANTS SYDNEY

Sydney has an excellent selection of restaurants reflecting the city's cosmopolitan population. Restaurants with unusual or attractive interiors are **Il Fiasco**, Kings Cross, (post modern, designed by architects Furio Valich and Robert Griff), **La Colonna** in East Sydney with its Romanesque columns, **The Wharf Restaurant** at Walsh Bay with its vast bare space next to the water, **Kable's** at the Regent Hotel suspended in space on a floating gallery, **Kinsela's**, Darlinghurst which used to be a funeral parlour, the **Incinerator** designed by Walter Burley Griffin as a 1930s municipal rubbish incinerator and finally the **Oasis**, Paddington which has a shapely girl's leg at the reception table. Outside Sydney the **Berowra**

101

Waters Inn run by Gay Bilson is well worth a visit, known for its setting and excellent food.

The **Sydney Morning Herald** and Australian magazines run features on some of the best and most interesting restaurants regularly. **Leo Schofield** is Sydney's food connoisseur and restaurant expert. The following is a list of restaurants for artists and the art world, for visitors and for locals.

Art Gallery Restaurant, Art Gallery of New South Wales, The Domain, Sydney. Tel. (02) 232 5425.
Set on the first floor of the gallery looking down on the main foyer you can have a variety of attractively presented salads and inexpensive dishes amongst the Sydney art world or visitors from overseas. Open Monday–Saturday 10.30–4.30, Sunday noon–4.30.

Badde Manors, 37a Glebe Point, Glebe. Tel. (02) 660 3797.
Vegetarian meals, cakes and coffee. It is always busy with artists, students, writers and young inner city dwellers. Well worth a few minutes wait for a table. Open Monday–Thursday 8–1, Friday until 5, Saturday 9.30–5, Sunday 9.30–2.

Bagel Coffee House, 5 Flinders Street, Taylors Square. Tel. (02) 332 1106.
Delicious bagels with original fillings. Also tasty soups and delicious cakes.

Bill and Toni's, 74 Stanley Street, East Sydney. Tel. (02) 360 4702.
A favourite with artists. Noisy, entertaining, limited Italian menu with speedy service.

Boyd's, 184 Military Road, Mosman. Tel. (02) 969 2181.
An old dance hall now converted into an attractive restaurant with Thai, Cajun, Japanese, Italian and contemporary French dishes in the suburb of Mosman, North Sydney.

Chez Oz, 23 Craigend Street, Darlinghurst. Tel. (02) 332 4866.
Run by the well known Helen Spry and family, it has mainly French, some Asian and Italian dishes. Speciality smoked salmon crème fraîche with dill. A chic place to eat and you might even bump into Elton John or Ian Botham if they are in Australia.

Watson's Bay

Doyles on the Beach, Marine Parade, Watson's Bay. Tel. (02) 337 2007.
Situated next to the beach at Watson's Bay the restaurant can be reached from central Sydney, at Circular Quay, by the restaurant's own speed boat. Fresh seafood and enormous helpings, too large for most people.

The Tea Gardens Restaurant also at Watson's Bay is right at the edge of the water, also with good harbour views and light meals.

Doyles seafood restaurant, Watsons Bay, Sydney

The Watson's Bay Hotel is a good place to take a large crowd and the garden has magnificent sunny harbourside views. Seafood and smorgasbord.

Gianni's Beach House, Bondi Pavilion, Queen Elizabeth Drive, Bondi Beach. Tel. (02) 300 09137.
Bondi beach atmosphere and ideal to take children to.

Harbour Watch Restaurant, Cnr Hickson Road & Lower Fort Street, The Rocks West (Pier 1). Tel. (02) 241 2217.
Breathtaking views across the harbour. Speciality seafood of course. Queensland mud crabs and lobster. Booking preferable.

Sorrento's, 7 Elizabeth Street, Sydney. Tel. (02) 27 1419.
Serves the best John Dory in town. A popular place before rusing on to performances at the Opera House. Seafood a speciality.

The Cafe Opera, 117 Macquarie Street, Sydney. Tel. (02) 230 0200.
Stylish decor and set within the Intercontinental Hotel.

La Colonna, 117 Riley Street, East Sydney. Tel. (02) 331 1559.
In the heart of Sydney's Little Italy. Authentic Roman cuisine. Striking Romanesque columns and sky-blue interior.

Il Fiasco, 38 Bayswater Road, Kings Cross. Tel. (02) 358 1881.
Designed by architect Furio Valich and owner Robert Griff, a post-modern interior. Italian cuisine. Open Tuesday–Sunday.

The Akuna Bay restaurant, Sydney

The Rocks Push Restaurant, 107 George Street, Sydney.
Tel. (02) 241 3548.
In the heart of the Rocks and features jazz music five nights a
week. An open courtyard for summer time.

Tai Yuen, 110 Hay Street, Haymarket. Tel. (02) 211 3782.
One of Sydney's oldest Chinese restaurants. Unimpressive
decor but good Chinese food.

Paddington
There are numerous coffee shops on Oxford Street from
Whitlam Square through Taylor Square towards Paddington.
Paddington is at its liveliest on Saturdays when the market is
open and you can combine a visit to the many galleries in the
area, colourful shops and bookshops with lunch or coffee at
local cafes and restaurants.

Rowntrees Australian Restaurant, 188 Pacific Highway,
Hornsby. Tel. (02) 476 5150.
An original Aboriginal diner where tourists can munch bush
delicacies or even witchity grubs. A unique experience.

CONTENTS
VICTORIA

Victoria

Victoria, although a small state has a large population and **Melbourne** with three million inhabitants is the country's second largest city. **The Australian Ballet Company** and school are based in Melbourne and the major **Victorian Arts Centre** next to the river Yarra.

   Geelong, **Bendigo** and **Ballarat** are also sizeable cities. The **Dandenong Mountains** outside Melbourne offer spectacular views of the city and the nearby beaches to the city include 20 mile beach, a paradise of surf and sand. **Phillip Island** has koalas, penguins and a variety of birds.

   Historically Victoria has always had gold finds, once at **Walhalla**, now a ghost town and in the 1850s near Bendigo and Ballarat, where at the latter the famous **Eureka Stockade**, a miner's revolt took place. The state is rich in forests, parkland and the **Grampians** are famed for bushwalking, rock climbing and the variety of birds and wildflowers. There are also vineyards near the **Murray River** and these can be visited by paddle steamer.

STATE ARTS ORGANISATIONS VICTORIA

Arts Access Society, 109 Sturt Street, South Melbourne, Vic. 3205. Tel. (03) 699 8299.

Arts and Craft Society of Victoria, 37 Hardware Street, Melbourne, Vic. 3000. Tel. (03) 670 4063.

Arts Centre, 100 St Kilda Road, Melbourne, Vic. 3000. Tel. (03) 617 8211.

Australian Centre for Contemporary Art, Dallas Brooks Drive, The Domain, Melbourne, Vic. 3004. Tel. (03) 63 6422/63 4264.
A centre focusing on 20th century art with galleries, events and services.

Beaumaris Art Group, Reserve Road, Beuumaris, Vic. 3193. Tel. (03) 589 4917.

Contemporary Arts Society, Joan Gough Studio Gallery, 326 Punt Road, South Yarra, Vic. 3141. Tel. (03) 26 1956.

Contemporary Melbourne Women Printmakers, c/o The Bookshelf Gallery, 116 Bridge Road, Richmond, Vic 3121. Tel. (03) 428 2011.

Cosmopolitan Art Group, 39 Panorama Avenue, Lower Plenty, Vic. 3093. Tel. (03) 439 8334.

Victorian Arts Centre, Melbourne

Design Institute of Australia, PO Box 21, Hawthorn, Vic. 3122. Tel. (03) 819 1311.

Folk Lore Council of Australia, 68 Adelaide Street, Armadale, Vic. 3143. Tel. (03) 20 4136.

Goëthe Institute—German Cultural Centre, 606 St Kilda Road, Melbourne, Vic. 3000. Tel. (03) 51 8838.

Melbourne Art Directors Club Inc., 319 Lennox Street, Richmond, Vic. 3121. Tel. (03) 428 8226.

Moomba Festival—Melbourne, 2nd Floor, 191 Collins Street, Melbourne, Vic. 3000. Tel. (03) 63 7111.

National Gallery of Victoria, 180 St Kilda Road, Melbourne, Vic. 3004. Tel. (03) 62 7411.

National Gallery Society of Victoria, 180 St Kilda Road, Melbourne, Vic. 3004. Tel. (03) 618 0208.

PAGAM—Public Art Galleries Association of Melbourne, Information from George Paton Gallery, 2nd Floor, Union House, University of Melbourne, Parkville, Vic. 3052. Tel. (03) 344 6961.

Regional Galleries Association of Victoria, 180 St Kilda Road, Melbourne, Vic. 3004. Tel. (03) 618 0261.

Victorian Arts Centre, 100 St Kilda Road, Melbourne, Vic. 3004. Tel. (03) 617 8211.
Information and enquiries (03) 11 566.

Victorian Arts Council, 4 Prospect Hill Road, Camberwell, Vic. 3124. Tel. (03) 813 3199.

Victorian Art Jewellers Co-operative Pty Ltd, 4 Izett Street, Prahran, Vic 3181. Tel. (03) 51 2541.

Victorian Artists Society, 430 Albert Street, East Melbourne, Vic. 3002. Tel. (03) 662 1484.

Victorian Association of the Performing Arts Centre, 4 Prospect Hill Road, Camberwell, Vic. 3124. Tel. (03) 882 3472.

Victorian Council for Children's Film and Television, 17 St Andrews Place, East Melbourne, Vic. 3002. Tel. (03) 651 1919.

Victorian Print Workshop Inc., 188 Gertrude Street, Fitzroy, Vic. 3065. Tel. (03) 419 5820.

Warrandyte Arts Association, 15 Castle Road, Warrandyte, Vic. 3113. Tel. (03) 844 3206.

Print Council of Australia Inc., 172 Rode Street, West Melbourne, Vic. 3003. Tel. (03) 328 2140.

Multicultural Arts Victoria, State Offices, 232 Victoria Parade, East Melbourne, Vic. 3002. Tel. (03) 419 6700 ext 250.

Community Arts Network—Victoria, c/o Henderson House, 45 Moreland Street, Footscray, Vic. 3011. Tel. (03) 689 5677.

STATE CRAFT ORGANISATIONS VICTORIA

Arts and Craft Society of Victoria, 37 Hardware Street, Melbourne, Vic. 3000. Tel. (03) 670 4063.

Crafts Council of Victoria, 7 Blackwood Street, North Melbourne, Vic. 3051. Tel. (03) 329 8856.
The Crafts Council has many registered craft organisations operating in the regions of greater Melbourne. For more details about the various groups contact the Council.

Embroiderers Guild of Victoria, 170 Wattletree Road, Malvern, Vic. 3144. Tel. (03) 509 2529.

Meat Market Craft Centre, 42 Courtney Road, North Melbourne, Vic. 3051. Tel. (03) 329 9966.
A centre providing a focus for the crafts in Victoria, aimed at providing research, practise and to encourage excellence in improving skills.

Hand Weavers and Spinners Guild of Victoria Inc., 3 Blackwood Street, North Melbourne, Vic. 3051. Tel. (03) 329 6191.

Leather Workers Guild of Victoria, 16 Lennox Street, Hawthorn, Vic. 3122.

Victorian Ceramic Group Inc., 7 Blackwood Street, North Melbourne, Vic. 3051. Tel. (03) 329 1919.

Victorian Tapestry Workshop, 260 Park Street, South Melbourne, Vic. 3205. Tel. (03) 699 7885.

Victorian Woodworkers, Melbourne State College, 757 Swanston Street, Melbourne, Vic. 3000.

STATE REGIONAL GALLERIES AND MUSEUMS VICTORIA

Ararat Gallery, Vincent Street, Ararat, Vic. 3377. Tel. (053) 52 2836.
Open Monday–Friday 11–4. The collection concentrates on works in fibre and textiles, mostly contemporary Australian. It has a second collection of fibre and paper packages from Japan.

City of Ballarat Fine Art Gallery, 40 Lydiard Street, North Ballarat, Vic. 3350. Tel. (053) 31 5622.
Open Tuesday–Friday 10.30–4.30, Saturday, Sunday & Public Holidays 12.30–4.30. A collection of the history of Australian art in all major media, especially known for the collection of Heidelberg School paintings. Also a most impressive collection of Australian prints dating back to Captain Cook's voyages up to the present day.

Banyule Gallery, 60 Buckingham Drive, Heidelberg, Vic. 3084. Tel. (03) 459 2535.
An extension of the National Gallery of Victoria housed in a renovated 1846 homestead.

Benalla Art Gallery, Bridge Street, Benalla, Vic. 3672. Tel. (057) 62 3027.
Open daily except Wednesdays, 11–5, Saturdays 10. Housing a fine collection of Australian paintings. The Ledger collection contains works from the Colonial period and the Heidelberg School. Also a collection of contemporary post-1968 Australian work.

Bendigo Art Gallery, 42 View Street, Bendigo, Vic. 3550. Tel. (054) 43 4991.
Open Monday–Thursday 10–5, Friday–Sunday 2–5, Public Holidays 2–5. The largest regional gallery in Australia housing paintings from 1855–1970. The collection contains many works by Louis Buvelot and Barbizon School paintings and 19th century English and European Academy/Salon paintings.

Castlemaine Art Gallery, Lyttleton Street, Castlemaine, Vic. 3450. Tel. (054) 72 2292.
Open Monday–Friday 10–5, Saturday & Sunday 10–noon & 1–5. Major areas of work on display features Australian pictorial art, especially the period 1860–1960 and a selection of Australian crafts.

City of Caulfield Art Centre, 441 Inkermann Road, Caulfield North Vic. 3161. Tel. (03) 524 3227.
Permanent art collection of over 200 works by established Australian artists.

Geelong Art Gallery, Little Malop Street, Geelong, Vic. 3320. Tel. (055) 64 9832.
Open Tuesday–Friday 10–5, Saturday & Sunday and Public Holidays 1–5, closed Mondays. Australian paintings of all periods with a large component of contemporary work.

City of Hamilton Art Gallery, Brown Street, Hamilton, Vic. 3300. Tel. (055) 73 0460.
Open Tuesday–Friday 10–5, Saturday 10–noon & 2–5, Sunday 2–5. A famous collection of watercolours by English artist Paul Sandby (1731–1809) also decorative arts including an extensive glass collection.

Horsham Regional Gallery, Town Hall Building, 80 Wilson Street, Horsham, Vic. 3400. Tel. (053) 82 5575.
Open Tuesday–Friday 12–5, Sunday 2–5.30, closed Monday & Saturday. The collection consists of Australian photographs and paintings.

La Trobe Valley Arts Centre, 138 Commercial Road, Morwell, Vic. 3840. Tel. (057) 34 1364.
Open Tuesday–Friday 10–5, Sunday 1.30–4.30, closed Monday and Saturday. The galleries collection of works on paper as well as ceramics and glass by Australian artists. A large contemporary print collection.

Mildura Arts Centre, 199 Cureton Avenue, Mildura, Vic. 3500. Tel. (050) 23 3733.
Open Monday–Friday 9–4.20, Saturday & Sunday 2–4.20. The art collection includes contemporary sculpture and English paintings of the late 19th and early 20th century. Also some contemporary prints and paintings.

Mornington Peninsula Arts Centre, 4 Vancouver Street, Mornington, Vic. 3931. Tel. (059) 75 4395.
Open daily 2–5. The Biennale "Spring Festival of Drawing" is the largest drawing exhibit of its kind in Australia.

National Gallery of Victoria, 180 St Kilda Road, Melbourne, Vic. 3004. Tel. (03) 62 7411.
Open Tuesday–Sunday 10–5. Housing the State's art collection containing major works of European, Oriental and Australian art. The Australian school is well represented with works from the 1830s, colonial artists, golden age, impressionists and moderns. The gallery has an active programme of changing of changing and special exhibitions. Large car park behind the gallery.

National Museum, 285 Russell Street, Melbourne, Vic. 3000. Tel. (03) 69 9988.
On display is a large collection of Australian as well as the great Australian race horse Phar Lap. Open Monday–Saturday and Public Holidays 10–5, Sunday 2–5.

Sale Regional Arts Centre, Civic Centre, Macalister Street, Sale, Vic. 3850. Tel. (057) 44 2829.
Open Monday–Friday 10–5, Sunday & Public Holidays 2–5, closed Saturday. The gallery collects on the theme "Gippsland and the Environment" and also hold large groups of historical photographs.

Shepparton Arts Centre, Civic Centre, Shepparton, Vic. 3630. Tel. (058) 21 6352.
Open Monday–Friday 1–5, Sunday 2–5 and open by appointment. Australian ceramics, prints and paintings with the ceramics the most notable.

Swan Hill Art Gallery, Pioneer Settlement, Swan Hill, Vic. 3585. Tel. (050) 32 1403.
Open daily 9–5. The nucleus of the collection is "Naive" painting, also obtaining contemporary Australian prints and drawings under the Annual Pioneer Purchase Award.

Warrnambool Art Gallery, Leibig Street, Warrnambool, Vic. 3280. Tel. (055) 64 9832.
Open Tuesday–Friday 10–5, weekends and Public Holidays 2–5. Features Australian prints from 1970 and through the annual Henri Worland and Memorial Print Award the gallery continues to expand its collection, now approximately 500 prints. Also local art.

INTERVIEW WITH CHRISTINE ABRAHAMS

The Richmond district of Melbourne might be equated to London's Fulham. Here, in a very desirable warehouse conversion, the **CHRISTINE ABRAHAMS GALLERY** is located. Named after its vivacious owner Christine, the gallery operates on many levels, involving itself in adivising corporate collections and initiating the newly launched **Australian Contemporary Art Fair (ACAF1)**. During private views it is the gallery custom to allow guests free access to the stock room, enabling them to browse through the range of artworks currently available. The atmosphere might be relaxed but the director runs a tight ship.
Reproduced from Artline magazine, September 1988 issue. Interview by Mike von Joel.
Art Line: How do you see the role of a dealer in Australia?
Christine Abrahams: The dealer is very important. The dealer has access to major collectors so he is able to introduce the work to these people; also, it is an educational role as well. He can pick out new artists and is able to show them.

Artists in Melbourne and Sydney tend to move galleries frequently whereas in Europe they usually contract to one gallery. Is that a problem?

I think it is. It is such a young country and it is only in the last five years that we have had a real onslaught of artists and new galleries. None of the galleries are really long established so they don't have quite the same reputation, and a lot of the artists are new as well. We haven't got the history and tradition of galleries elsewhere.

What about a collector base, do you share the collectors too?

Yes, because if a collector is collecting contemporary art, which is what my gallery specialises in, he obviously goes to all the galleries that specialise in contemporary art—otherwise he would be most uninformed.

The only collectors who use one particular gallery director to collect for them are the corporations, like a Bank, where there is no one in the corporation with the appropriate knowledge. They appoint someone from outside to do the collecting for them. Very rarely you find a private individual having someone who will act for them, they usually go round themselves and they ask different people for advice.

One can invest quite substantial amounts of money and time in building an artist's career up. It must be rather irritating if they then move?

If it is someone from overseas, because of the distance, we usually do have a contract. But with people that are literally on your doorstep and who you see very frequently it is really a verbal agreement—which in fact is a contract. I am very fortunate in having my son, who is a lawyer, join the gallery in the last year and he is looking after all of that. He has just come back from overseas.

Is there much competition between individual galleries in Melbourne?

I don't feel very competitive about it at all, I think the more people who generate interest in the art the better it is for me...and the more people that go round to galleries the better it is for me. It is better for everybody, and it is crazy to think that you can monopolise...

What about the polarity between Melbourne and Sydney—this sort of competitiveness. Do you feel isolated from Sydney?

No, I go to Sydney very often. Sydney is a wonderful city and is vast. I really enjoy going there and quite a few of my artists live in Sydney, so it doesn't worry me. I find that it is a whole different clientele. I can't possibly look after everybody...

Is there a possibility of you having an extension to this gallery there?

There is a possibility I suppose, but I find that running a gallery is very personal and I just don't think I could divide my time up between the two places. If I had to rush up to Sydney and do that as well I would be too exhausted to do it properly.

You entrust your artists to another dealer in Sydney, does this worry you at all?
No, because as I said, it is a different clientele and they *are* very large cities. The people in Sydney don't know all the people in Melbourne and vice versa, so we are catering for a different audience. It doesn't worry me, no!

Let's look at the potential for expanding a gallery like this. One assumes that the next serious move for you is into the international arena, what plans do you have for the gallery?
I hope to do a show with a group of my artists in America and Europe also. This year I am going to have an exhibition in Los Angeles, prior to the Fair (LA88) and we are going to participate in the Fair. It is at a gallery run by Susan Kay, it is a new gallery. She visited Australia and was very keen on the artists here—she advises big interior designers.

Do you feel that this is the future. Not to establish galleries with your own name but to twin with a gallery you like elsewhere?
Yes, I think it is a great idea, because they are already established and they know the local scene, so you are already slotted into a ready market. Also you don't have to do all that groundwork which takes years and years...

Do you think it is essential that the market base is expanded here in Australia?
I do think that is really necessary. The art in Australia is wonderful and the scene is very buoyant. There are marvellous things being done but I think it is a very limited market here.

You mean the number of collectors is limited?
Yes, I mean the population is very small to! The whole of Australia's population is 16 million.

The collectors aren't expanding at the same rate as the number of artists making art are they? One can see a big boom in the number of people making art.
That's true.

How advanced are your plans to bring overseas art and artists here?
Last year I had a French artist here and this year I am actually having some Picasso works, which will be great.

Where do these originate from?
From Marina Picasso's estate, New York...from Jan Kruger.

When we talk about overseas you invariably refer to America?
No, that is not true. Monique Friedman was from Paris and I have shown an Italian artist from Venice. I showed two of my artists one of whom was Fred Cress in Venice.

How are the Australian artists perceived in those overseas locations?
With much curiosity but not much commercial success. That is because they are unknown and it is the same problem we have in Australia when we show contemporary European or American artists here. There is interest and they are curious but collectors are dubious...until they have seen it in a Museum.

This does come back to the idea of an art work being a Eurobond with similar sort of trading values. Do you think this is inevitable?
It *is* inevitable. It is unfortunate but people here just go by their gut instincts and when they like something buy it—without having that critical understanding and knowledge of the international establishment behind them.

Artists in the modern world are very much aware of the value of their painting and the sales potential?
There are material artists who really expect their price to go up gradually as they mature—but not really in the sense of wanting one to double their prices each year. I admit there are some artists who are like that.

Can you detect an element in the younger people that they want fame and the rewards now—rather than waiting for 20 years to go by?
Yes, I think so—and I think it is a big trap.

It can be very rewarding. Julian Schnabel was reputedly offered $1,000,000 to transfer to *Pace Gallery* **at 32 years of age...**
Yes, but it is one in a million and you don't hear of the others who have nervous breakdowns and drop out. I think very fast success can be incredibly damaging.

What is the position your gallery takes on recruiting new members. Do they show you slides or do you just hear on the grapevine.
It is a bit of both. I usually go, at the end of the year, to the college graduate shows and if I see anyone interesting I follow it up and go to their studio. Some of my artists are teachers and they tell me of someone who I can expect a lot out of.

I look at the slides or photographs and then decide whether I will visit a studio, I don't just go without having any indication.

You have instigated an Art Fair in Australia (*ACAF-1*** July 23–31 1988) which is happening this year, the result of three years groundwork, if it takes off and becomes a major thing is it going to become an annual...?**
Yes. If it is a success. We have been doing all this work on a voluntary basis and it really needs someone at it full time.

There are people in Australia for the Sydney Biennale. Could there be some relationship there...?

We were slotted in by this wonderful and generous patron who was organising an international trade fair. He was particularly keen that there should be an art component in this so that is where we came in. The trade fair was only a one-off event so in the future we are going to be on our own...

The Biennale does help and it would be a good idea to actually start it when the Biennale is on—when you get curators, historians and critics coming out in any event. They could do both things.

Do you think there is a big affinity with Australian painting in Los Angeles?
There is that very casual easy going attitude that we find there, not in New York, where it is very tough to survive. But I would love to find a gallery and have an East Coast liaison because I think New York is very important, it certainly has wonderful collections and there's so much good art it generates...

I understand that you are involved in corporate art in an advisory capacity?
I have been very fortunate to be the art consultant for the Hyatt Hotel here in Melbourne and the owner was very keen to have the best of contemporary art whether Australian or international. I nominated Paladino who did a wonderful sculpture which is outside the Hyatt. He has a considerable collection of Australian contemporary artists throughout the hotel.

Supplied by the Abrahams Gallery?
That is right yes. People like John Walker and Fred Cress and it is all original work...

You have placed these artists in a really high profile location?
It is a first! It is one of the few hotels I know that has got that sort of standard of art work.

That must cause quite a bit of envy amongst your fellow dealers?
They see it in the same way as I do—it generates more interest in all of us.

Your answer there is symbolic of Australia—this feeling of fellowship, which is sadly lacking in Europe.
We still can afford to be relaxed...

INTERVIEW WITH STUART PURVES OF THE AUSTRALIAN GALLERIES

The **AUSTRALIAN GALLERIES** are situated in a quiet side road in the Collingwood area of Melbourne. If they were well known in the past it was because, having been established in 1945 their very age made them, by Melbourne standards, noteworthy. If the organisation causes comment today it is most likely to be as a result of the antics of the managing

Stuart Purves, director Australian Galleries

director, Stuart Purves, who has brought a little bit of Manhattan to Australia and is enjoying every minute of! **MIKE VON JOEL** discusses the aggressive marketing policies and expansion plans of one of Australia's most senior venues...

Reproduced from Artline magazine. September issue 1988.

Art Line: **There has been, up until very recently, an easy going freemasonry amongst gallerists. This appears to have subtly changed...**

Stuart Purves: Originally my father and my mother, Ann, had been out trying to buy a painting and were dissatisfied with the service provided by the art business. They decided to open a gallery and to put the buying of pictures on a business like basis. I think it is still exactly the same today. I know that, in the main, artists never start out to entertain the bourgeoise for money. To the ones that really believe in themselves the money is secondary. Since we are non-creative people in a creative field, we do our job extremely well by making their base run as smooth as possible.

Your marketing policy might be regarded as aggressive by some other agencies...

First of all I haven't really got a 'marketing policy', it is a sort of day by day thing. I use my antenna. I feel that the art business is run by what it can afford. That is—the money that they earn from what they sell can either be spent on their private lives or the business. I put it back into the business.

Australia has got an awful lot of catching up to do to be on an international level and it ought to do it! There is an abundance of good artists in this country and we are crazy if we don't take the opportunity. I think that really successful contemporary art belongs, in a sense, to younger countries. They have a chance to buy and the artists have a chance to paint, the clients have a chance to buy works that are really quite culturally important. I say to myself, here is Australia which has international airports, jumbo jets, television etc., so it can learn the lessons very rapidly from older countries.

The gallery that you are used to be half the size and we have doubled it. We have got it in departments almost; you are sitting in a mini-gallery, which is my office, surrounded by a small one man show. Outside on the floor board areas we can have our exhibitions, the public area. Then we can have stock fed from the stock room, plus works on paper at the same time. We are building another gallery down the road specifically for works on paper because we feel that is in the air, and Australia has got great stockpiles of work on paper. We are giving sculpture an airing although that is the most difficult thing in this country by far. Then we go onto the next idea, because it arouses all of us so much: one that says Australia is the story of Sydney and Melbourne. It is extraordinary that a country like this with such a small population can maintain two major cities that are as equally important as one and other. When you think say New York has put every other city to death in America, as has Paris and London in their respective countries, it is not the case here.

You simply can't ignore Sydney if you are in Melbourne,

117

and if you are in Sydney you can't ignore Melbourne, I say why not take the facilities that one has and extend it to both! We are embarking on that right now and I think the single representation that we can offer to artists where they only have to deal with one set of personalities, formulate their ideas and instruct only one dealer, will cause us to wonder why we didn't do it a decade ago.

It seems a very obvious thing to do but why is there a reluctance by one set of people to trespass on the area of another?
It is difficult. It takes great energy and a great amount of devotion. It is really a bit like keeping two wives in different houses to balance it and make it work. I would rather do the galleries, incidentally. We are not finding it as smooth as we thought, but we will make it work. The cities are very different, they have different attitudes, so it is up to us to try and find some common ground. Without either city feeling deserted.

But, take the case of a successful artist, who might have had three shows in this city starting off at low prices building up to high prices. We have really worked for that. He rushes off to Sydney and has a show with someone else at high price; perhaps we should be taking that share of the market rather than giving it away! It is a very selfish and internal decision from that point of view, but it is a good one, because it will work for *all* of us in the long term.

Have you found actual resistance to your arrival in Sydney?
Yes, of course. I have had resistance from people I don't think matter and I have had a lot of encouragement from people that I think do. But each of us see things differently, we will just decide to block one ear and listen with the other...

Once you are established in Melbourne and Sydney, is the next step overseas representation?
I think there are far more people chasing the far fewer works that are available and almost always have been since the mid '60s. This is one of the things that has forced prices up, it is cause and effect if you like. But it *is* getting out of control! Far too many bad pictures are being sold at high prices and there is too much promotion of what isn't good enough. One really needs to listen to the good artists, go to the National Gallery and travel overseas as much as you can to re-set your eye, as it were.

This goes back to the thing I said about young countries that produce these pioneers who literally squeeze culture out because they are bursting at the seams. It has long been my view that if an artist wants to go overseas it is his job to do that. We would help where we can, but he ought then to pack his bags and go and live in whichever country he is attracted to. It might be Germany or America but usually it is England. Actually, I think it is more interesting if they go to places like Spain where they can get another sense of a country that has battled with its own history. It's that easy thing of language and that is really why England and American are so popular. I don't see us picking up, at this stage anyway, a whole lot of Australian artists and taking them overseas. I don't think we are ready for it, I don't think Europe is ready for it! Australia is still relatively unknown around the world and I just don't think that it is as important as all that either. I am not ready and I haven't beengiven the callby my artists to do it yet.

The quality of youthfulness that you describe as being inherent in artists must surely have parallels amongst the colector base...?
So far the collectors *have* been pioneers as well!. I don't suppose you can say there are a lot of them...and they could'nt answer why they have done it. It is just that people have worked hard and made good money, they buy good pictures because they feel good about it. They like the fact that they can be involved with a successful fellow like themselves. Then they have to meet the artist...! The other area is people who have inherited money, who are less of a strain in some ways. They are more considered about it but they are still collecting for themselves. There are a very few people in this country that I know and deal with who have got curators looking after their private collections. They are still very personal collections—a very personal challenge. Now there have been some big names that have begun to have curators looking after their work—so it is emerging and that probably announces another way of coming into the game in this country.

Is there a class of people that traditionally buys art?
Nobody traditionally buys art in Australia.

Don't the wealthy families buy old views of Sydney Harbour— that sort of thing?
No...some do. I find that the collectors who have curators are much more conservative than those who don't. The very fact that you have a curator means that you are setting out to do something by proxy. Whereas a wealthy person who is vitally involved, who may take the advice of certain people, the experience between the picture and his eye belongs to him...

In England the 'new money' comes from financial risk taking, advertising, rock 'n roll—these sort of extrovert fields. These high rollers are obviously a 'type' of person and there is evidence of the emergence of an artist who is that 'type' of person too. There is a relationship in attitude, style of dress etc. Is this apparent in Australia?
The only thing I would say is that I am 41 years of age. In a sense we have had a dream run: no war, appreciating economies...we have had what we wanted. We have really had it a bit easy. Now I can see there is a group who call themselves 'artists' and make works of 'art' whereas in actual fact it is not art at all but a very sophisticated form of commercial design. The people who buy that are equally inhabiting a situation they might not enjoy if times had been tough. I don't want times to be tougher! This is just the way it is and the way it has been dealt to us. We are very lucky.

I often think of how many artists went down the slippery dip either side of Van Gogh, you can't name one that painted the same week as him...

Given that you are a second generation dealer, do you see yourself to be working within a tradition?
Absolutely. My father was a genius for starters—he left me something to do! The intriguing thing is that my mother, still very active in this business and a joint founder of it, has the most experience of the commercial art world in this country, and has had a gallery for the longest time. I have had physical experience of this gallery for 23 years! There is no other major gallery that has been at the same address or owned by the same people for that length of time...!

Will Australia ever be able to enter the European arena, culturally, and be seen as an equal?
Australia is a very young country. It is beginning to a degree and I think Sydney is ahead of Melbourne in this area. Europe hasn't sent the good pictures to Australia—why should it? Why should they go through an educating process and subsidise us, it is better to let the young child, Austrlia, find its own. I think it is just the simple fact that place is a hell of a long way away from somebody—24 hours in an aeroplane. You don't come *through* Australia, you are in Australia because you've *come here*. I think also that Australians will travel. Only 10% of Australia's population has ever been on an aeroplane—but that 10% flies a hell of a lot—and about 1% of the 10 will be interested in art and they will visit the good shows...

Perhaps in 10 years, when our Australian base is stable, we might package an exhibition of our better artists and send it to America and possibly some galleries in London—the old traditional outposts in fact. I think Australia will be a long time in cracking a huge world market, I think we will creep up quietly in certain areas but will never ever be big...

COMMERCIAL AND NON-PROFIT GALLERIES MELBOURNE

Melbourne art scene

The **National Gallery of Victoria** near the Yarra River is part of the **Victorian Arts Centre** which also houses a theatre and concert hall. The national gallery contains major historical and Australian art, objets d'art and includes many famous Australian painters such as **Streeton**, **McCubbin** and other members of the **Heidelberg School**. There are significant collections from the Orient and Europe also. The gallery is a major venue for touring exhibitions from overseas and within Australia and for contemporary art events, the 1988 Australian Biennale was also held there.

The city of Melbourne has a large selection of commercial contemporary art galleries and the citizens are enthusiastic collectors of contemporary art, especially works by local Australian painters and sculptors. There are many art schools within the State of Victoria with the present government planning to amalgamate many of the schools into larger centres, but not every one is in agreement. The art community is

Realities Gallery, Toorak, Melbourne

generally very active in Melbourne with dynamic work not only in the visual arts but in film, theatre, dance and music.

The first **Australian Contemporary Art Fair—ACAF1**, was held in Melbourne during July 1988 when 23 leading contemporary art galleries combined in one massive exhibition to show the latest in Australian art. The event offered the unique opportunity for the public to view over 150 of Australia's top artists. Participating galleries were from all over the country each showing a selection of exciting works including paintings, sculpture, photography, prints and video. The event was a milestone in the development of contemporary art in Australia.

Inner city

Australian College of Photography, Art and Communication, 3 Oliver Lane, Melbourne, Vic. 3000. Tel. (03) 654 7966.
College gallery open Monday–Friday 10–5, Sundays 2–5. Student works and visiting exhibitions.

70 Arden Street, 70 Arden Street, North Melbourne, Vic. 3061. Tel. (03) 328 4949.
Open Tuesday–Saturday 12–6. Contemporary Australian artists.

Gallery Gabrielle Pizzi, 141 Flinders Lane, Melbourne, Vic. 3000. Tel. (03) 654 2944.
Open Monday–Friday 10–5, Saturday 11–5, Sunday by appointment. Exhibitions of Aboriginal art and Australian painting.

George Paton Gallery, 2nd Floor, Union House, University of Melbourne, Parkville, Vic. 3052. Tel. (02) 344 6961.
Open Monday, Tuesday, Thursday 10–6, Wednesday 12–7.30, Friday 1–6. Contemporary Australian artists and touring exhibitions.

Joshua McClelland Print Room, 2nd Floor, 15 Collins Street, Melbourne, Vic. 3000. Tel. (03) 654 5835.
Open Monday–Friday 10–5. Early Australian paintings and prints. Chinese and Japanese porcelain and lacquer. Closed through January.

Performing Art Museum, Melbourne Concert Hall, 100 St Kilda Road, Melbourne, Vic. 3004. Tel. (03) 617 8211.
Open Monday–Saturday 11–5, Sunday 12–5. Exhibitions related to the history of the performing arts.

Photography Studies College Gallery, 65 City Road, South Melbourne, Vic. 3205. Tel. (03) 62 3191.
Open Monday–Friday 9–5. Exhibitions daily, multi vision audio visual presentations. Groups welcome by appointment.

RAJA S2DO Gallery, Queen Victoria Arts and Crafts Centre, 120 Franklin Street, Melbourne, Vic. 3000. Tel. (03) 328 1768. (a/h 527 8157).
Open Tuesday–Sunday 11–5.30. Exhibitions of contemporary fine art prints, drawings and paintings.

RMIT Faculty Gallery, Faculty of Art Building 2–B8 RMIT, 124 Latrobe Street, Melbourne, Vic. 3000. Tel. (03) 660 2218.
Open Monday–Friday 9.30–4.30, closed January. Regular changing contemporary fine art exhibitions.

State Library of Victoria, The Queens Hall, State Library, 328 Swanston Street, Melbourne, Vic. 3000 Tel. (03) 669 9932.
Open 7 days 10–6 with exhibitions of the past and present.

Tribal Arts Gallery, 126 Franklin Street, Melbourne, Vic. 3000 (Queen Victoria Antique Arts and Crafts Centre). Tel. (03) 329 6734.
Open Tuesday–Sunday 10–5. Original artifacts from Papua New Guinea.

City Gallery, 45 Flinders Lane, Melbourne, Vic. 3000. Tel. (03) 654 6131.
Open Tuesday–Saturday 11–5, closed January. Exhibitions by leading contemporary Australian artists in painting, drawing, sculpture, installations etc. One of Melbourne's important contemporary venues.

Westpac Gallery, The Theatre, Victorian Art Centre, 100 St Kilda Road, Melbourne, Vic. 3004. Tel. (03) 617 8211 ext 324.
Open Monday–Saturday 9–9, Sunday 9–5. Touring and local fine art exhibitions from the visual to performing arts.

William Mora Galleries, First Floor, 19 Windsor Place, Melbourne, Vic. 3000. Tel. (03) 654 4655.
Open Tuesday–Saturday 10.30–5.30, closed January. Contemporary Australian and international artists.

Capricorn Gallery, 213 Franklin Street, Melbourne, Vic. 3000. Tel. (03) 328 2802.
Open Tuesday–Friday 10–5, Saturday & Sunday 11–4. Exciting new contemporary gallery.

Greater city

Acland Street Art Gallery, 18 Acland Street, St Kilda, Vic. 3182. Tel. (030) 534 2818.
Open Wednesday–Sunday 12–6 or by appointment. A lively gallery showing contemporary Australian artists.

Andrew Ivanyi Galleries, 262 Toorak Road, South Yarra, Vic. 3141. Tel. (03) 241 8366.
Open Monday–Saturday 11–5, Sunday 2–5. A continuous mixed exhibition of selected works by prominent Australian artists past and present.

The Art Gallery, 142 Greville Street, Prahran, Vic. 3181. Tel. (03) 529 2433.
Open Tuesday–Friday 10–5, Saturday 11–4. Major new contemporary Art Gallery.

Artist Space, 150 Park Street, North Fitzroy, Vic. 3068. Tel. (03) 489 2749.
Open Wednesday–Saturday 1–5. Local Melbourne and inter-state artists showing paintings, video and photography.

Artist Touch Gallery, 2/149 Upper Heidelburg Road, Ivan-hoe, Vic. 3079. Tel. (03) 49 6250.
Open Tuesday–Friday 10–5, Saturday 9–5 or by appoint-ment. Mixed exhibitions of contemporary local and interstate artists.

Australian Galleries, 33–37 Derby Street, Collingwood, Vic. 3066. Tel. (03) 417 4303.
Open Monday–Friday 10–6, Saturday 10–4. Representing prominent Australian artists.

Avant Galleries, 579 Punt Road, South Yarra, Vic. 3141. Tel. (03) 266 2009.
Dealers in fine art Australian and Aboriginal paintings.

Bay Gallery, 335 Beaconsfield Parade, St Kilda West, Vic. 3182. Tel. (03) 534 1287.
Open Saturday–Sunday 11–6 or by appointment. Australian contemporary original prints, hand coloured etchings, seri-graphs and lithographs by leading artists.

Bridget McDonnell Gallery, 130 Faraday Street, Carlton, Vic. 3053. Tel. (03) 347 1700.
Open Tuesday–Saturday 11–6, Sunday 2–5, closed Janu-ary. Paintings and prints by leading Australian artists.

Charles Nodrum Gallery, 292 Church Street, Richmond, Vic. 3121. Tel. (03) 427 0140.
Open Tuesday–Saturday 11–6. Modern Australian paintings, single and group shows.

Chowringe, King Arcade, 974 High Street, Armidale, Vic. 3143. Tel. (03) 509 2670.
Open Wednesday–Friday 10–6, Saturday & Sunday 2–5. Specialists in antique and modern Indian fine art and books.

Christine Abrahams Gallery, 27 Gipps Street, Richmond, Vic. 3121. Tel. (03) 428 6099.
Open Tuesday–Friday 10.30–5, Saturday 11–5. A major venue for leading contemporary Australian artists in all media. Artists include: Lesley Dumbrell, Lenton Parr, Helen Geier amongst others. Director: Christine Abrahams.

Community Arts Network, 18 Andrew's Place, East Mel-bourne, Vic. 3002. Tel. (03) 650 9172.
Seminars, workshop and services for the artist.

David Ellis Fine Art, 37 Bedford Street, Collingwood, Vic. 3066. Tel. (03) 417 3716.
Open Tuesday–Saturday 11–5. Dealing in Australian paint-ings with particular reference to contemporary artists and early modernists work of the 1930s and 1940s.

Christine Abrahams Gallery, Richmond, Melbourne

Dempsters Gallery and Book Barn, 181 Canterbury Road, Canterbury, Vic. 3026. Tel. (03) 830 4464.
Exhibitions of works on paper by Australian artists. Antiquarian books.

Devise Gallery, 263 Park Street, South Melbourne, Vic. 3205. Tel. (03) 690 6991.
Open Tuesday–Friday 11–5, Saturday 2–5. Contemporary works.

Distelfink Gallery, 432 Burwood Road, Hawthorn, Vic. 3122. Tel. (03) 818 2555.
Open Monday–Saturday 10–5. Exhibitions of fine arts and fine art craft.

Deutscher Fine Art, 68 Drummond Street, Carlton, Vic. 3053. Tel. (03) 663 5044.
Specializing in 19th and 20th century Australian art.

East and West Art, 1019 High Street, Armidale, Vic. 3141. Tel. (03) 20 7779.
Open Monday–Friday 10–6, Saturday 9–1. Exhibitions by Asian, European and Australian contemporary artists.

Editions Gallery, Roseneath Place, (off Market St), South Melbourne, Vic. 3205. Tel. (03) 699 8600.
Open Monday–Friday 9.30–5.30, Sunday 2–6. Exhibitions of Australian and overseas artist printmakers.

Eltham Gallery, 559 Main Road, Eltham, Vic. 3095. Tel. (03) 439 1467.
Regular exhibitions of traditional and contemporary Australian paintings, jewellery, ceramics and wood. Open Wednesdays–Saturdays 11–5, Sunday 1–5.

Stuart Gertsman galleries, Richmond, Melbourne

Gallery Art Naive, 430 Punt Road, South Yarra, Vic. 3141. Tel. (03) 267 3348.
Open Wednesday–Friday 11–5, Sunday 1–5.30 or by appointment. Australian and overseas naive artists.

Gallery Max Honigsberg, 485 Nicholson Street, North Carlton, Vic. 3068. Tel. (03) 347 1483.
Open Wednesday–Saturday 2–7, Sunday 2–6 or by appointment. A mixed selection of contemporary Australian art by prominent and promising new Australian artists.

Stuart Gerstman Galleries, 29 Gipps Street, Richmond, Vic. 3121. Tel. (03) 428 5479.
Changing exhibitions of Australian and international painting, drawing and printing. Open Tuesday–Friday 10.30–5.30, Saturday 10.30–2.

Girgis and Klym Gallery, 342 Brunswick Street, Fitzroy, Vic. 3065. Tel. (03) 417 2327.
At Rhumbarallas. Open daily 12–11. Contemporary art by young local artists.

200 Gertrude Street, 200 Gertrude Street, Fitzroy, Vic. 3065. Tel. (03) 419 3406.
Open Tuesday–Friday 10–5.30, Saturday 1–5.30. Within Gertrude Street Studios, exhibiting studio artists and contemporary Australian artists.

G.O.M.—Gallery of Melbourne, 110 Punt Street, Windsor, Vic. 3181. Tel. (03) 529 2924.
Open Friday 11–6, Saturday & Sunday 2–6. Interesting collection of new generation Australian contemporary art. Young originals gallery located in the same building.

Gould Galleries, 270 Toorak Road, South Yarra, Vic. 3141. Tel. (03) 241 4701.
Open Monday–Saturday 11–5, Sunday 2–5. Continuous exhibition of fine oils and watercolours by prominent Australian artists from 1882–1987.

Gretz Gallery, 9 Victoria Avenue, Albert Park, Vic. 3206. Tel. (03) 699 2780.
Open daily 12–6. Excellent range of prints, etchings, lithographs and woodcuts by Australian artists.

Greythorn Galleries, 2 Tannock Street, North Balwyn, Vic. 3104. Tel. (03) 857 9920.
Exhibitions and one person shows by prominent Australian painters. Open Monday–Friday 11–5, Saturday 10–1, Sunday 2–5.

Gryphon Galleries, Melbourne College of Advanced Education, Cnr Grattan and Swanston Streets, Carlton, Vic. 3053. Tel. (03) 341 8587.
Open Tuesday–Friday 10–4, Wednesday 10–7.30, Saturday 1–4. Changing exhibitions by local and interstate artists.

Heide Park and Art Gallery, 7 Templestowe Road, Bulleen, Vic. 3105. Tel. (03) 850 1849.
Overseas and Australian touring exhibitions. Open Tuesday–Friday 10–5, Saturday & Sunday 12–5.

Il Punto Gallery, 267 Barkly Street, St Kilda, Vic. 3182. Tel. (03) 534 2004.
Open Wednesday–Sunday 12–6. Group exhibitions by local contemporary artists.
312 Lennox Street, 213 Lennox Street, Richmond, Vic. 3121. Tel. (03) 428 7192.
Open Tuesday–Saturday 11–5.30. Representing Australian contemporary painters and sculptors.

Linden Gallery, 26 Acland Street, St Kilda, Vic. 3182. Tel. (03) 534 2396.
Open Wednesday–Friday 1–6, Saturday–Sunday 11–6. Political and contemporary issues in Australia.

Joan Gough Studio Gallery, 326–328 Punt Road, South Yarra, Vic. 3141. Tel. (03) 266 1956.
Contemporary art exhibitions, solo shows, monthly contemporary art society meetings, workshops, studio lectures every week.

Little Gallery, 3 Village Walk, 493 Toorak Road, Toorak, Vic. 3142. Tel. (03) 241 0504.
Open Monday–Saturday 9.30–5.30, Sunday 2–5. Exhibitions of drawings, paintings and fine art craft.

Mission Arts Centre, Old Mission to Seamen Building, Cnr Beach Road and Swallow Street, Port Melbourne, Vic. 3207. Tel. (03) 646 4745.
Open Wednesday–Sunday 10–6. Regular exhibitions.

Makers Mark, 2 Sims Street, Sandringham, Vic. 3191. Tel (03) 598 2155.
Open Saturday–Sunday 1–5.30 (hours vary). Mostly works on paper by local contemporary artists.

McClelland Gallery, McClelland Drive, Studio Park, Langwarrin, Vic. 3910. Tel. (03) 789 1671.
Permanent collection with special selection on display.

Moorabbin Art Gallery and Rogowski's Antiques, 432 South Road, Moorabbin, Vic. 3189. Tel. (03).
Paintings by prominent Australian and European artists, also permanent collection on display.

Niagara Galleries, 245 Punt Road, Richmond, Vic. 3121. Tl. (03) 429 3666.
Representing leading contemporary Australian artists. Open Tuesday–Friday 11–6, Saturday 10–1.

Print Council of Australia Gallery, 172 Roden Street, West Melbourne, Vic. 3003. Tel. (03) 328 2140.
Group exhibitions by print council members, printmaking groups from Melbourne, interstate and major touring exhibitions.

Realities Gallery, 35 Jackson Street, Toorak, Vic. 3142. Tel. (03) 241 3312.
Open Tuesday–Friday 10–6, Saturday 11–4 or by appointment. The unique setting in a converted church makes an interesting venue for large contemporary paintings; a sculpture garden and smaller gallery in the garden for framed works on paper and small sculptures. Artists include: Paul Partos, Jon Cattapan, Kerry Gregan, Kevin Conner, Anthony Pryor. Director: Pauline Wrobel.

Reconnaissance, 72 Napier Street, Fitzroy, Vic. 3065. Tel. (03) 417 5114.
Exhibitions of young and established contemporary Australian artists.

Roar 2, 115a Brunswick Street, Fitzroy, Vic. 3065. Tel. (03) 419 9975.
Interesting and lively venue for Melbourne's young artists.

Powell Street Gallery and Powell Street Graphics, 20 & 20A Powell Street, South Yarra, Vic. 3141. Tel. (030 266 5519/266 3127.
Open Tuesday–Friday 10.30–5, Saturday 10–1. Contemporary painting downstairs and prints upstairs.

Print Guild, 227 Brunswick Street, Fitzroy, Vic. 3065. Tel. (03) 509 4233.
Contemporary original prints by Australian, Japanese, British and European printmakers.

Rathdowne Street Gallery, 550 Rathdowne Street, North Carlton, Vic. 3053.
Open Tuesday–Friday 10–5.30, Saturday 10.30–2. Paintings and works on paper.

Realities Gallery sculpture garden, Toorak, Melbourne

The Printed Image Bookshop Gallery, 1262 High Street, Armidale, Vic. 3141. Tel. (030) 509 4233.
Open Tuesday–Friday 11–6, Saturday 11–5, Sunday 1–5.

The University Gallery, University of Melbourne, Parkville, Vic. 3052. Tel. (03) 344 5148.

Powell Street Gallery, South Yarra, Melbourne

Tolarno Galleries, 98 River Road, South Yarra, Vic. 3141. Tel. (03) 241 8381.
Open Tuesday–Saturday 10–5.30. Exhibitions by Australian, American and European contemporary artists.

Stanfield Gallery, Wynard Place, 3 Wynard Street, South Melbourne, Vic. 3205. Tel. (03) 690 9307.
Open Tuesday–Friday 10–5, Saturday 3–5.

Sweet Jamaique Gallery, 127 Bridge Road, Richmond, Vic. 3121. Tel. (030 429 4801.
Open Monday–Sunday 12–12. Venue for contemporary Australian artists.

Scotchmer Gallery, 67 Scotchmer Street, North Fitzroy, Vic. 3068. Tel. (03) 486 2058.
Open Wednesday–Sunday 12–5. Representing contemporary Melbourne artists.

Ufitzi Galleries, 120 Johnston Street, Fitzroy, Vic. 3065. Tel. (03) 419 4575.
Open Tuesday–Sunday 12–7. Mixed exhibitions by established and emerging artists and designers in many of Ufitzi's ten gallery spaces.

Victorian Artists Society, 430 Albert Street, East Melbourne, Vic. 3002. Tel. (03) 662 2302.
Open Monday–Friday 10–5, Saturday & Sunday 1–4.

13 Verity Street, Michael Waddell, 13 Verity Street, Richmond, Vic. 3121. Tel. (03) 428 3799.
Open Wednesday–Sunday 10–6.

William Street Gallery, 10 William Street, South Yarra, Vic. 3141. Tel. (03) 824 1027.
Open Tuesday–Saturday 11–4. Contemporary Australian art.

Women's Art Register, Carringbush Library, 415 Church Street, Richmond, Vic. 3121. Tel. (03) 429 3644.
12,000 slides of women's art. 650 booklets. Available on loan. Open Monday–Wednesday 10–8, Thursday & Friday 12–6, Saturday 12–4 & Sunday 2–5.

Wattle Tree Gallery, 409 Wattle Tree Road, Malvern, Vic. 3144. (Opposite Central Park).
Open Tuesday–Saturday 11–6, Sunday 1–5. Selected works by contemporary Australian artists.

York Street Gallery, 36 Rae Street, North Fitzroy, Vic. 3068. Tel. (03) 489 0336.
Open Wednesday–Saturday 1–5. Local and interstate contemporary artists.

CRAFT GALLERIES MELBOURNE

Ararat Gallery, Town Hall, Vincent Street, Ararat, Vic. 3377. Tel. (053) 52 2836.
Specialising in contemporary fibre arts.

Devise Gallery, 263 Park Street, South Melbourne, Vic. 3205. Tel. (03) 690 6991.
Open Tuesday–Friday 11–5, Saturday 2–5.

Heathmere Gallery, Lot 1, Woolamai Beach Road, Newhaven, Vic. 3925. Tel. (059) 56 7270.
Open Thursday–Monday 11–5 or by appointment. A superb gallery exhibiting excellent 3 dimensional and 2 dimensional work.

Mariposa Gallery, 747 Glenferrie Road, Hawthorn, Vic. 3122.

Meat Market Craft Centre, 42 Courtney Street, North Melbourne, Vic. 3051. Tel. (03) 329 9966.
Open 10–5 daily except Sundays. The large and unique hall of the 19th century former meat market features a changing programme of exhibitions which surveys the whole field of contemporary Australian crafts. On the Blackwood Street side of the building, but with access into the main hall, are the

Victorian State Craft Collection Gallery and the Blackwood Street Gallery. The collection was started in 1977 and is added to regularly, with works always on display. The centre also accommodates access workshops in ceramics, glass, leather, metal, textiles and wood, a craft shop, a resource and information centre, meeting rooms, a hotel and snack bar. Well worth a visit.

The Post Office Gallery, Flinders Road, Red Hill, Vic. 3937. Tel. (059) 89 2245.
Many of the galleries previously listed under "Commercial and non-profit galleries" are handling fine art crafts, but the majority of Melbourne craft galleries are out of the city centre and in the region of the Dandenongs which is a good day trip to this area from central Melbourne.

ABORIGINAL ART GALLERIES MELBOURNE

Aboriginal Artist Gallery, 12 Liverpool Street, Melbourne, Vic. 3000. Tel. (03) 663 5716.
Changing exhibitions of Papunya and Tula bark paintings, sculpture, carvings, textiles, musical instruments and artifacts. Open Monday–Friday 9–5, Saturday 11–4.

Aboriginal and Pacific Art, 42 Hardy Terrace, Ivanhoe East, Vic. 3079. Tel. (03) 49 4699.
By appointment only.

Aboriginal Handcrafts, 9th Floor, Century Building, 125–133 Swanston Street, Melbourne, Vic. 3000. Tel. (03) 63 4717.

Tribal Art Gallery, 130 Franklin Street, North Melbourne, Vic. 3051. Tel. (03) 329 6734.

GALLERIES DEALING IN PRE 1900 EXHIBITS MELBOURNE

Deutscher Fine Art Pty Ltd, 68 Drummond Street, Carlton, Vic. 3053. Tel. (03) 663 5044.
Specialising in 19th and 20th century art.

Duvance Galleries, 131 Exhibition Street, Melbourne, Vic. 3000. Tel. (03) 654 2929.

Early Art, 25 Streeton Crescent, Ivanhoe East, Vic. 3079. Tel. (03) 497 2640.

Exotica Gallery, 1203 High Street, Armadale, Vic. 3143. Tel. (03) 209 7462.
Icons and religious sculptures of Europe, 17th–19th century. Open Tuesday–Saturday 10–5.

Joshua McClelland Art Gallery and Cultural Centre, McClelland Drive, Studio Park, Langwarrin, Vic. 3910. Tel. (03) 789 1671.
Permanent collection with specialised displays.

Print Room, Second Floor, 15 Collins Street, Melbourne, Vic. 3000. Tel. (03) 654 5835.
Australian topographical and historical prints and paintings. Open Monday–Friday 10.30–5.

Robert Douwma Fine and Rare Prints and Maps, 283–5 Toorak Road, South Yarra, Vic. 3141. Tel. (03) 241 1473. Open Monday–Friday 9.30–6, Saturday 9.30–1. Rare and interesting original prints and maps.

Spencer Scott Sandilands, 545 High Street, East Prahran, Vic. 3181. Tel. (03) 529 8011.
Rare prints, antique maps and antiquarian books.

The Etching Art Gallery, Shop 107, Jam Factory Shopping Centre, 500 Chapel Street, South Yarra, Vic. 3141.
Original 18th, 19th & 20th century etchings.

WORKSHOPS, STUDIOS AND ART CENTRES MELBOURNE

Bill Young Studio, 1st Floor, Tattersalls Lane, Melbourne, Vic. 3000. Tel. (03) 663 1971.
Artist/printmaker specialising in all intaglio techniques. Full custom plate preparation, platemaking and editioning service. Exhibition space in an open access gallery adjoining the studio.

Carlton Arts Centre—Pottery School, 227 Nicholson Street, Carlton, Vic. 3053. Tel. (03) 347 3065.

Caulfield Arts Centre, 441 Inkerman Road, Caulfield North, Vic. 3161. Tel. (03) 524 3277.

Footscray Community Arts Centre, 45 Moreland Street, Footscray, Vic. 3011. Tel. (03) 689 5677.

Meat Market Craft Centre, 42 Courtney Street, North Melbourne, Vic. 3051. Tel. (03) 329 9966.

Port Jackson Press, Fitzroy, Melbourne

Victorian Print Workshop, Fitzroy, Melbourne
134

Melbourne School of Art and Photography, 477 Glenhuntly Road, Elsternwick, Vic. 3185. Tel. (03) 528 2315.

Port Jackson Press, 236 Brunswick Street, Fitzroy, Vic. 3065. Tel. (03) 419 8141.
Publishers of fine art prints, working with many of Australia's contemporary artists.

Portland Community Workshop, c/o Municipal Office, Portland, Vic. 3305.
Community access studio for screenprinting with membership and studio hire.

200 Gertrude Street, 200 Gertrude Street, Fitzroy, Vic. 3065. Tel. (03) 419 3406.
Artists studio work spaces with a gallery in the complex.

Victorian Print Workshop Inc., 188 Gertrude Street, Fitzroy, Vic. 3065. Tel. (03) 419 5820.
Facilities for artists to work in lithography, screenprinting, relief and intaglio with professional assistance. Editioning arranged.

Victorian Tapestry Workshop, 260 Park Street, South Melbourne, Vic. 3205. Tel. (03) 699 7885.

The Field Workshop, 24 Emerald Hill Place, South Melbourne, Vic. 3205. Tel. (03) 690 4249.
Specialised printmaking workshop with editioning and classes available.

The Howdens Studio—Etchings, 30 Hughes Street, Upway, Vic. 3158. Tel. (03) 754 6527.

ART SUPPLIES AND MATERIALS MELBOURNE

Art and Craft Supply Co Ltd, 279 Flinders Lane, Melbourne, Vic. 3000. Tel. (03) 654 5182.

Art Papers (Australia), 160 Springvale Road, Nunawading, Vic. 3131. Tel. (03) 877 5779.

Art Stretchers Co, Queensbury Place, Carylon, Vic. 3053. Tel. (03) 347 2836.
Comprehensive range of fine art materials for both professionals and amateurs.

Artistcare, 60 Little Bourke Street, Melbourne, Vic. 3000. Tel. (03) 676 185.

Atsco Australia Pty Ltd, 49 Taunton Drive, Cheltenham, Vic. 3192. Tel. (03) 584 5444.
Quality art papers and materials.

Bayswater Studio, 13 High Street, Bayswater, Vic. 3153. Tel. (03) 720 2627.
Large range of imported and local art materials.

Deans Art, 368 Lonsdale Street, Melbourne, Vic. 3000. Tel. (03) 602 2184, also at 188 Gertrude Street, Fitzroy, Vic. 3065. Tel. (03) 419 6633.
Comprehensive range of quality art materials.

Melbourne Artist Supplies, 906 Nepean Highway, Moorabbin, Vic. 3189. Tel. (03) 553 3663.

Melbourne Etching Supplies, 138 Commercial Road, Prahran, Vic. 3181. Tel. (03) 517 797, also at 227 Brunswick Street, Fitzroy and 44 Greeves Street, Fitzroy, Vic. 3065. Tel. (03) 419 5559/419 5666.
Melbourne's leading supplier for artist supplies, especially for printmaking.

Victorian Artists Supplies, 715 Main Road, Eltham, Vic. 3095. Tel. (03) 439 8798.

Eckersley's Fine Art and Commercial Art Supplies, 55 Elizabeth Stret, Melbourne, Vic. 3000, also 116 Commercial Road, Prahran, Vic. 3181. Tel. (03) 62 5655/51 1418.

The Field Workshop, 388 Clarendon Street, South Melbourne, Vic. 3205. Tel. (03) 690 4249.
Large range of fine art materials and papers.

PHOTOGRAPHY, FILM AND VIDEO MELBOURNE

Australian Council for Children's Film and Television, 7 St Andrews Place, East Melbourne, Vic. 3002. Tel. (03) 651 1804.

Australian Film Commission, 185 Bank Street, South Melbourne, Vic. 3205. Tel. (03) 690 5144.

Australian Film Institute, 47 Little Street, Latrobe, Vic. 7307. Tel. (03) 662 1944.

Australian Film and Television School, 369 King Street, Melbourne, Vic. 328 2517.

Australian Film Theatre, 31 Victoria Street, Fitzroy, Vic. 3065. Tel. (03) 417 3300.

Film Victoria, 409 King Street, Melbourne, Vic. 3000. Tel. (03) 329 7033.

Melbourne Access Video and Media Co-operative Pty Ltd, 13 Victoria Street, Fitzroy, Vic. 3065. Tel. (03) 419 5111.

State Film Centre, 1 Macarthur Street, East Melbourne, Vic. 3000. Tel. (03) 651 1301.

The Melbourne Camera Club, 13 Bruce Street, Mt Waverly, Vic. 3149. Tel. (03) 277 3701.

The Melbourne Film Festival, 41A Beckett Street, Melbourne, Vic. 3000. Tel. (03) 663 2954.

Photographic Studies College, 65 City Road, South Melbourne, Vic. 3025. Tel. (03) 62 3191.

PHOTOGRAPHIC SUPPLIES MELBOURNE

Camera Action, 217 Elizabeth Street, Melbourne, Vic. 3000. Tel. (03) 67 6901.

Fletchers Photographics, 353 Lonsdale Street, Melbourne, Vic. 3000. Tel. (03) 602 1404.
Extensive range of darkroom equipment and accessories.

Foto Fast, 146 Exhibition Street, Melbourne, Vic. 3000. Tel. (03) 63 1727.

Foto First, Cnr Commercial Road & Cato Street, Prahran, Vic. Tel. (03) 51 7414.
One hour colour processing, for the professional and the public.

Latrobe Colourlab, 89 Trope Street, South Melbourne, Vic. 3205. Tel. (03) 699 2444.
Complete professional photographic colour services.

Mark's Photographics, 87–89 Queensbridge Street, South Melbourne, Vic. 3205. Tel. (03) 614 4744.
One of the largest showrooms of photographic equipment for both professionals and amateurs.

Michaels Camera and Video, Cnr Elizabeth and Lonsdale Streets, Melbourne, Vic. 3000. Tel. (03) 670 0241.
Cameras bought and sold, duty free, service and repairs, hire service and videos, colour processing, darkroom equipment, educational and professional sales.

Pics Australasia Ltd, 77 City Road, South Melbourne, Vic. 3201. Tel. (03) 62 1133.
Leading suppliers for professional and industrial photographic needs.

Ted's Camera Stores, 239 Elizabeth Street, Melbourne, Vic. 3000. Tel. (03) 67 8482.
Extensive range of photographic equipment, fast processing and duty free store.

The Camera Exchange, 364 Lonsdale Street, Melbourne, Vic. 3000. Tel. (03) 67 1929.
Buy and sell quality used cameras, excellent repair service.

ART BOOKSHOPS MELBOURNE

Angus and Robertson, 107 Elizabeth Street, Melbourne, Vic. 3000. Tel. (03) 67 8941.
Comprehensive coverage of the visual arts and practising artists. Also music, dance, photography, cinema, literature, crafts, graphics and video. Order service available.

Bookshop of Margaret Webber, 15 McKillop Street, Melbourne, Vic. 3000. Tel. (03) 67 2559.
One of Melbourne's leading bookshops with a large selection of performing and visual arts.

Collins Booksellers, 86 Bourke Street, Melbourne, Vic. 3000. Tel. (03) 654 3144.
Comprehensive range of fine art, film, cinema, Eastern art, architecture and performing arts. The bargain basement, full of remainder books is at Swanston Street, Melbourne. Many arts books and very cheap.

Fine Music (Aust.) (Pty Ltd, 20 McKillop Street, Melbourne, Vic. 3000. Tel. (03) 67 5391.
Specialists in music and literature.

Gaumont Book Co., 123 Little Collins Street, Melbourne, Vic. 3000. Tel. (03) 67 3217.
Specialists in music, cinema and memorabilia.

Hill of Content, 86 Bourke Street, Melbourne, Vic. 3000. Tel. (03) 654 3144. Telex 37396 COLBOK.
Specialised collection of fine art and crafts, an up to date collection of Australian art publications often not available elsewhere in Melbourne. Special orders welcome.

Literature Book Shop, 87 Collins Street, Melbourne, Vic. 3000. Tel. (03) 654 6173.

Mary Martin Bookshops, 269 Swanston Street, Melbourne, Vic. 3000. Tel. (030 663 1621.
Specialised in bargains, fiction and art.

McGills, 187 Elizabeth Street, Melbourne, Vic. 3000. Tel. (03) 602 5566.
A large art section with music, dance, cinema, photography and Australiana.

Myre Melbourne—Dept Store, Lonsdale Street, Melbourne, Vic. Tel. 6 6111.
A selection of contemporary art, classical art, and limited editions of fine art books, European and Oriental art, and a large selection of Australian art books.

New Mint Books, Shop 2, 459 Toorak Road, Toorak, Vic. 3142. Tel. (03) 241 4778.
Large range of Australian and overseas art books.

Readings, 710 Glenferrie Road, Hawthorn, Vic. 3122. Tel. (03) 819 1917.
Australian and overseas art books. Open 7 days a week.

The Arts Bookshop, 1067 High Street, Armadale, Vic. 3143. Tel. (03) 20 2645.
International and Australian coverage of specialists visual arts and craft books, new, rare, and old. Most contemporary art journals in stock, international exhibition catalogues, art magazines and journals, academic art text, architecture and pre 18th century. One of Australia's best art bookshops. Open Monday–Saturday 9–5.30, worth visiting.

The Gallery Bookshop, National Gallery of Victoria, St Kilda Road, Melbourne, Vic. 3004.
Limited edition art books, overseas exhibition catalogues, art journals national and international, extensive coverage of music, the crafts and photography.

Seafood Platter

The Printed Image, 1262 High Street, Armadale, Vic. 3143. Tel. (03) 509 4233.
Fine photographic books.

Whole Earth Bookshop, 83 Bourke Street, Melbourne, Vic. 3000. Tel. (03) 63 9292.
Large Eastern art section, comprehensive art selection with film, photography, cinema, theatre, crafts, graphics, video and books on individual artists.

FINE ART ART COURSES AND COLLEGES VICTORIA

Ballarat College of Advanced Education, PO Box 663, Ballarat, Vic. 3350. Tel. (053) 30 1800.
The college offers an Undergraduate Degree (BA) in teaching: art and craft; design, painting, sculpture, ceramics and graphic design. Graduate Diploma in teaching: art and craft; design and ceramics. An Associate Diploma in illustration.

Bendigo College of Advanced Education, PO Box 199, Bendigo, Vic. 3550. Tel. (054) 40 3222.
The college offers an Undergraduate Degree (BA) in painting, printmaking and ceramics. A Diploma in graphic design.

Chisholm Institute of Technology, Caulfied East, Vic. 3145. Tel. (03) 573 2000.
The institute offers an Undergraduate Degree (BA) in painting, sculpture, printmaking, ceramics, jewellery; gold and silversmithing, glass and graphic design. A Graduate Diploma in painting, sculpture, printmaking, ceramics and glass. An Associate Diploma in illustration.

Footscray Institute of Technology, PO Box 64, Footscray, Vic. 3011. Tel. (03) 688 4200.
The institute offers an Undergraduate Degree (BA) in dance, drama and music.

Gippsland Institute of Advanced Education, Switchback Road, Churchill, Vic. 3842. Tel. (051) 22 0287.
The institute offers and Undergraduate Degree in painting, drawing, sculpture, printmaking, photography, ceramics and woodcrafts. A Graduate Diploma in teaching: art and craft; design, painting, sculpture, printmaking and ceramics.

Hawthorn Institute of Education, 442 Auburn Road, Hawthorn, Vic. 3122. Tel. (03) 818 0631 ext 224.
Only offers a Graduate Diploma in teaching: art and craft; design.

Melbourne College of Advanced Education, 757 Swanston Street, Carlton, Vic. 3053. Tel. (03) 341 8624.
The college ofers both an Undergraduate Degree (BA) and Master's by research in teaching: art and craft; design.

School of Art and Design, Phillip Institute of Technology, Plenty Road, Bundoora, Vic. 3083. Tel. (03) 468 2215.
The institute offers both an Undergraduate Degree (BA) and Graduate Diploma in the following: painting, drawing, sculpture, printmaking, photography, ceramics, graphic design and film, television, cinema studies.

Royal Melbourne Institute of Technology, GPO Box 2476V, Melbourne, Vic. 3000. Tel. (03) 660 2260/1.
The institute offers both an Undergraduate Degree (BA) and Master's by research in painting, sculpture, printmaking, photography, ceramics, jewellery, industrial design, interior design, fashion design, textile, graphic design, environmental/landscape design, film, television, cinema studies and professional writing/journalism/radio. A Graduate Diploma is offered in painting, sculpture, printmaking, ceramics and jewellery.

Swinburne Institute of Technology, PO Box 218, Hawthorn, Vic. 3122. Tel. (03) 819 8444.
The institute offers both an Undergraduate Degree (BA) and Master's by research in graphic design, film, television, cinema studies and professional writing/journalism/radio. A Graduate Diploma in film, television, cinema studies.

Victoria College, Burwood Campus, 221 Burwood Highway, Burwood, Vic. 3125. Tel. (03) 285 3333.
The college offers an Undergraduate Degree (BA) in teaching: art and craft; design, painting, drawing, sculpture, printmaking, photography, ceramics, industrial design and graphic design. A Graduate Diploma in teaching: art & craft; design and a Master's by research in painting, drawing, sculpture, printmaking, photography and ceramics.

Victorian College of the Arts, 234 St Kilda Road, Melbourne, Vic. 3004. Tel. (03) 61 9300.
The college offers both an Undergraduate Degree (BA) and Graduate Diploma in painting, sculpture, printmaking and dance, drama and music.

La Trobe University, Bundoora, Vic. 3083. Tel. (03) 478 3122.
The university offers an Undergraduate Degree (BA) in art history and theory and film, television, cinema studies. Also a Master's by research or by coursework in film, television, cinema studies.

Deakin University, Victoria 3217. Tel. (052) 47 1111.
The university offers both an Undergraduate Degree (BA) and Master's by research in art history and theory.

The University of Melbourne, Parkville, Vic. 3052. Tel. (03) 345 1844.
The university offers BA Degree, Graduate Diploma and Master's by coursework and by research in art history and theory.

Monash University, Clayton, Vic. 3168. Tel. (03) 541 0811.
BA Degree in art history, theory, film, television and cinema studies.

FINE ART FRAMING VICTORIA

AABA—Picture Frames, 258 Park Street, South Melbourne, Vic. 3205. Tel. (030 690 2358.

Artists Picture Frames, 27 Banksia Street, Burwood, Vic. 3125. Tel. (03) 288 2083.
All types of quality custom framing.

B & P Picture Frames, 172 Lygon Street, Carlton, Vic. 3053. Tel. (03) 663 6050.

Balwyn Picture Frames, 469 Whitehorse Road, Balwyn, Vic. 3103. Tel. (03) 836 2546.
Quality custom framing for the artist.

Brighton Picture Framers, 301 Bay Street, Brighton North, Vic. 3186. Tel. (03) 596 4100.
1 hour service available, retail and wholesale framing, restoration and do-it-yourself kits.

Custom Framing Pty Ltd, 8 Hosken Street, Springvale South, Vic. 3172.
Retail and wholesale custom framing, large range of mouldings, framing while you wait.

Jarman the Picture Framer, 158 Burwood Road, Hawthorn, Vic. 3122. Tel. (03) 818 7751.
Manufacturers of ornamental, swept frames from the Colonial period to the present day.

J. Kosnar Pty Lltd, 550 Mt Alexander Road, Ascot Vale, Vic. 3032. Tel. (03) 370 5044.
Comprehensive range of Australian and imported mouldings, modern, contemporary and traditional styles. Conservation mounting and custom service for artists.

Perimetrics Pty Ltd, 1 Maples Lane, Prahran, Vic. 3181. Tel. (03) 51 8907.
Archival quality wood and aluminium framing for works on paper and canvases.

The Frameworks Picture Framing, 167 Victoria Avenue, Albert Park, Vic. 3206. Tel. (03) 699 8639, also at 12 Errol Street, North Melbourne, Vic. 3051. Tel. (03) 329 6896. Custom framing, exhibition framing, corporate framing, conservation work.

THEATRICAL AND DANCE ORGANISATIONS VICTORIA

Arena Theatre Company, 27a Cromwell Road, South Yarra, Vic. 3141. Tel. (03) 240 1937.

Athenaeum Theatre Company Lilydale, Castella Street, Lilydale, Vic. 3140. Tel. (03) 735 1777.

Australian National Memorial Theatre Ltd, Cnr Barkly and Carlisle Streets, St Kilda, Vic. 3182. Tel. (03) 534 0221.

The Australian Ballet and School, 11 Mt Alexander Road, Flemington, Vic. 3031. Tel. (03) 376 1400.

The Drama Project Trust, 240 Chapel Street, Prahran, Vic. 3181. Tel. (03) 51 3959.

FM Live Theatre Company, 51a Karnak Road, Ashburton, Vic. 3147. Tel. (03) 25 6659.

Handspun Theatre Ltd, 108 Gertrude Street, Fitzroy, Vic. Tel. (03) 417 5978.

Heidelberg Theatre Company, 37 Turnham Avenue, Rosanna, Vic. 3084. Tel. (03) 45 4117.

Melbourne Theatre Company, 129 Ferras Street, South Melbourne, Vic. 3205. Tel. (03) 699 9122.

The Mushroom Troupe, 240 Chapel Street, Prahran, Vic. 3181. Tel. (03) 51 3959.

Playbox Theatre Co. Ltd, 45 Collins Street, Melbourne, Vic. 3000. Tel. (03) 654 7644.

Sherbrooke Theatre Company, 58 Sandells Road, Tecoma, Vic. 3160. Tel. (03) 754 4575.

Toorak Players Theatre Group, 16a Coleridge Street, Kew, Vic. 3101. Tel. (03) 818 5612.

West Theatre Co. Ltd, 182 Holmes Road, Moonee Ponds, Vic. 3039. Tel. (03) 370 7034.

THEATRICAL VENUES VICTORIA

Albany Theatre, 232 Collins Street, Melbourne, Vic. 3000. Tel. (03) 654 7962.

Anthill Theatre, 199 Napier Street, South Melbourne, Vic. 3205. Tel. (03) 699 3253.

Athenaeum Theatre, 1 & 2, 188 Collins Street, Melbourne, Vic. 3000. Tel. (03) 63 3834.

The Comedy Cafe, 177 Brunswick Street, Fitzroy, Vic. 3065. Tel. (03) 419 2869.

Community Arts Centre Theatre, 45 Moreland Road, Footscray, Vic. 3011. Tel. (03) 68 3665.

Crazy Horse Theatre, 34 Elizabeth Street, Melbourne, Vic. 3000. Tel. (03) 654 3630.

Karralika Theatre, Mines Road, Ringwood East, Vic. 3135. Tel. (03) 870 2888.

La Mama, 205 Faraday Street, Carlton, Vic. 3053. Tel. (03) 386 3583.

Last Laugh, 64 Smith Street, Collingwood, Vic. 3066. Tel. (03) 419 8600.
Theatre restaurant.

Playhouse—Victorian Arts Centre, St Kilda Road, Melbourne, Vic. 3004. Tel. (03) 654 4000.

National Theatre, Cnr Barkly and Carlisle Streets, St Kilda, Vic. 3182. Tel. (03) 534 0221.

Open Stage, 757 Swanston Street, Carlton, Vic. 3053. Tel. (03) 347 7505.

Union Theatre, University of Melbourne, Parkville, Vic. 3052. Tel. (03) 347 4186.

The Court House, 329 Drummon Street, Carlton, Vic. 3053. Tel. (03) 347 7868.

St Martins Theatre, 1 & 2, St Martins Lane, South Yarra, Vic. 3141. Tel. (03) 267 2551.

MUSICAL ORGANISATIONS VICTORIA

Australian Society for Music Education, c/o The Secretary, State College of Victoria, Toorak. PO Box 224, Malvern, Vic. 3144.

Australian Guild of Music and Speech Ltd, 1194 Malvern Road, Malvern, Vic. 3144. Tel. (03) 20 4866.

British Music Society of Victoria, 32 Chapman Avenue, Glenmore, Vic. 3340. Tel. (03) 3000 2156.

Early Music Society, 36 Neerim Road, Caulfield South, Vic. 3162. Tel. (03) 211 5210.

Musicians Union of Australia, 65 Wellington Street, Windsor, Vic. 3181. Tel. (03) 51 7506.

Musicians Club of Victoria, 65 Wellington Street, Windsor, Vic. 3181. Tel. (03) 51 2196.

Victorian Education Music Library, Prospect Hill Road, Canterbury, Vic. 3126. Tel. (03) 836 3425.

Victorian Childrens Dance Theatre, 17 Landau Drive, Warranwood, Vic. 3134.

Victorian Music Theatre Pty Ltd, 84 Orange Road, Elsternwick, Vic. 3185. Tel. (03) 523 8348.

Victorian State Opera, 370 Nicholson Street, Fitzroy, Vic. 3065. Tel. (03) 417 5061.

MUSICAL VENUES VICTORIA

Lemon Tree Hotel, 10 Grattan Street, Carlton, Vic. 3053. Tel. (03) 347 3017.
Great piano bar.

Great Hall, **National Gallery of Victoria**, St Kilda Road, Melbourne, Vic. 3004.
A variety of interesting national and international performances.

Melbourne Town Hall, Swanston Street, Melbourne, Vic. 3000. Tel. (03) 658 9800.

Mietta's Lounge, 7 Alfred Place, Melbourne, Vic. 3000. Tel. (03) 654 2366.
Good jazz.

Myer Sidney Music Bowl, Kings Domain, Alexandar Gardens, Melbourne, Vic. Tel. (03) 617 8332.

Prince Patrick Hotel, 135 Victoria Parade, Collingwood, Vic. 3066. Tel. (03) 419 4197.
Variety of interesting music.

Station Tavern and Brewery, 96 Greville Street, Prahran, Vic. 3181.
Excellent live jazz.

Storey Hall, 340 Swanston Street, Melbourne, Vic. 3000. Tel. (03) 660 2437.

The Royal Hotel, Shensley Street, Clifton Hill, Vic. 3068. Tel. (03) 489 6867.
Country and Western and blues music.

The Fountain Inn Hotel, Cnr Bay and Crockford Streets, Port Melbourne. Tel. (03) 654 2503.
Very entertaining live jazz.

Victorian Arts Centre, 100 St Kilda Road, Melbourne, Vic. 3004. Tel. (03) 617 8211.
Melbourne's major concert hall.

Melba Memorial Conservatorium of Music, 45 York Street, Richmond, Vic. 3121. Tel. (03) 429 6151.

PLACES OF INTEREST MELBOURNE

Bicycle Hire, Yarra Bank opposite the Royal Botanic Gardens, central Melbourne. Tel. (03) 429 3049. An excellent way to see Melbourne, with not too many hills. Available weekdays 8–5.30, Saturday noon–dusk, Sunday 9.30–dusk. Approx $20 for four hours.

Cook's Cottage, Fitzroy Gardens, Melbourne. Tel. (03) 419 8742. Original home of the parents of the discoverer of the East coast of Australia, Captain James Cook. The house was purchased in 1933 and brought out to Australia from England and rebuilt in the beautiful Fitzroy Gardens. Open day 9–5.

Leisure River Cruises, Princess Walk, Melbourne. Tel. (03) 63 4694. A cruise on the Yarra with excellent views of the city, the parks and the inner suburbs. Weekends at 11.30 the "M.V. Yarra Princess", does daily 1 hour trips from No. 3 berth, Princess Walk.

Melbourne City Walk. A planned walk around the inner city with glimpses of early Melbourne life. A brochure is available which links the photographic panels on route and also points out features to look for on the way. For further information contact Melbourne Town Hall. Tel. (03) 658 9800.

Melbourne Tourism Authority, 80 Collins Street, Melbourne, Vic. 3000. Tel. (03) 654 2288. On the 20th level of Nauru House, you will find helpful information on interesting places to visit and day trips out of Melbourne, also seasonal events.

Old Melbourne Gaol, Russell Street, Melbourne. Tel. (03) 654 3628. The sight where the hanging of the famous bush ranger Ned Kelly took place. Open daily 10–5.

Vintage Tram Rides. Melbourne and the Metropolitan Tramways Board, 616 Little Collins Street, Melbourne, Vic. 3000. Tel. (03) 62 0291. A unique feature of Melbourne on Sundays, is the vintage "Toastrack" tram which appears in all its glory for passenger travel between Princess Bridge/Batman Avenue terminus to Riversdale Road, Hawthorn and return. Operating Sundays 10.50–5.30, allow 15 minutes each way.

Parks

Melbourne has numerous parks, far too many to mention here, but a short walk from the centre of the city in the direction of the National Gallery of Victoria will lead you to beautiful shady trees where you can escape the summer sun. The state of Victoria is known as **"The Garden State"** as you will soon discover on all car number plates. A short distance from Melbourne are **"The Dandenongs"** where bush walking is popular and the air much cooler and cleaner. The city of Melbourne was carefully planed with spacious parks, giving the city its lush green appearance.

The Royal Botanic Gardens, an excellent example of classical landscaping on the South Bank of the Yarra River.

Fitzroy Gardens, one of the most popular gardens in Melbourne.

Flagstaff Gardens, well worth a visit as they contain many historic memorials and statues, north west of the city area.

Treasury Gardens, on the eastern side of the city adjoining Fitzroy Gardens with Treasury House and a memorial to the late President J. F. Kennedy. Historic buildings surround the park including the Old Royal Mint (built 1972) & St James' Old Cathedral (built 1842).

Carlton Gardens, features elaborate fountains surrounding the Royal Exhibition Building.

Markets

Melbourne has numerous weekend markets usually held all day Saturday and Sunday but the most impressive is the **Queen Victoria Markets** at Queen Street, North Melbourne. Open Tuesday, Thursday and Friday mornings with produce and on Saturday 6–12noon and Sunday 9–4 selling produce, fish, meat, secondhand goods, new goods and bric-à-brac. Exciting atmosphere just for wandering around on a sunny day.

Croydon Market, 13 Kent Avenue, Croydon. Tel. (03) 723 2045. Open Sunday 8.30–4.30. Colourful market with 300–400 stalls. Everything possible is on sale.

Dandenong Market, at the Drive-In, Gippsland Highway, Dandenong. Saturday & Sunday 8–2.

Essendon Market, 1059 Mt Alexander Road, Essendon. Saturday 9–1. Crafts.

Footscray Market, Hopskin Street, Footscray. Tel. (03) 68 1205. Flourishing "one-stop" market, unique in concept. Primarily a food market with a variety of stalls handling general merchandise. Wednesday 8–6, Thursday & Friday 6am–9pm and Saturday 6–1.

Prahran Market, 177 Commercial Road, Prahran. Popular meeting place Saturday mornings with flowers, food, vegetables etc. Open Tuesday 7.30–5, Friday 6–6 and Saturday 6–12.30.

Preston Market, 19 Mary Street, Preston. Everything possible for sale. Thursday 8–6, Friday 8–9 and Saturday 8–1.

St Kilda Market, Art Bank, Upper Esplanade, St Kilda. Sunday 9–6.

South Melbourne Market, Cnr Cecil and Coventry Streets, South Melbourne. Sunday 9–4.

RESTAURANTS MELBOURNE

Barbarinos, 474 St Kilda Road, Melbourne. Tel. (03) 266 1681.
"The" place for spare ribs, smothered in a special sauce.

Batavia—Dutch Indonesian cuisine, 1183 High Street, Armadale. Tel. (03) 20 3199.
Exotic entrees, mild or spicy main dishes and delicious desserts with friendly service.

Carlton—an area of Melbourne full of Italian restaurants, "Little Italy". You can't go wrong with Italian food in this area.

Empress of India Restaurant, 466 Swanston Street, Melbourne. Tel. (030) 347 8555.
Live entertainment, Indian music Tabla—Sitar—Tapura. Excellent food, Tandoori and Curries.

Golden Terrace—Restaurant—Turkish Cuisine, 805 Sydney Road, Brunswick. Tel. (03) 386 6729.
2 course menu for $10. Belly dancers Friday & Saturday nights. Good food.

Italian coffee shops, Carlton, Melbourne

Jasons International—Restaurant, 329 Bayswater Road. Tel. (03) 729 2953.
Prime steaks, and finest seafood in town.

Parma Bistro, 454 St Kilda Road, South Melbourne. Tel. (03) 266 3788.
Specialists in BBQ spare ribs.

Piero's Cafe, 275 Lygon Street, Carlton. Tel. (03) 347 1562.
Excellent pastries and gelato.

Ruffle's, 148 Auburn Road, Hawthorn. Tel. (03) 818 7038.
One of the few places in Australia to eat freshly smoked fish and meats while you wait.

Seahorse Restaurant—French and Continental, 127 Lygon Street, Carlton. Tel. (03) 347 6041.
Large variety of delicious seafood and steaks.

Spaghetti Tree, 59 Bourke Street, Melbourne. Tel. (03) 63 4166.
Great atmosphere and food at affordable prices. Excellent range of pastas.

TC's Restaurant, 114 Main Road, Croydon. Tel. (03) 725 7002.
Specialising in steak and seafood.

The Vic, The Theatres, Victorian Arts Centre, 100 St Kilda Road, Melbourne. Tel. (03) 617 8180.
An extremely pleasant restaurant in the centre of the Victorian Arts Centre. Relaxing atmosphere and delicious salads, gourmet dishes and mouth watering gateaux. Extensive selection of Victorian wines.

CONTENTS
SOUTH AUSTRALIA

SOUTH AUSTRALIA

Adelaide, the capital city of South Australia, holds a major national **Arts Festival** every two years during March when international and national arts, literary, music, dance, drama, and other fringe events bring the city alive. The **Australian Dance Theatre** is based in Adelaide. The city population is about one million and the city is surrounded by beautiful scenery. The city itself with its attractive wrought iron-clad, neatly kept houses is a delight to wander around. The famous wine growing ares of the **Southern Vales** and the **Barossa Valley** to the north produce some excellent internationally recognised wines. Visiting the vineyards and enjoying wine tasting are a popular day's outing from Adelaide. **The Flinders Ranges** have attracted artists from Aboriginal times to the present day and further to the west **Coober Pedy** is the opal capital of Australia.

150

Cleland Park, Adelaide Hills (Heather Waddell)

STATE ARTS ORGANISATIONS SOUTH AUSTRALIA

Adelaide Dance Company Inc., Dance Centre, 25 Whitmore Square, Adelaide, SA 5000. Tel. (08) 212 1665.

Adelaide Festival Centre Trust, Festival Centre, King William Road, Adelaide, SA 5000. Tel. (08) 216 8600.

Adelaide Festival Fringe Inc., 40 Register Street, Adelaide, SA 5000. Tel. (08) 211 7899.

Adelaide Festival of Arts, King William Road, Adelaide, SA 5000. Tel. (08) 213 4600.

Art Gallery of South Australia, North Terrace, Adelaide, SA 5000. Tel. (08) 223 7200.

The Art Gallery of South Australia Foundation at the same address.

Arts Council of South Australia, 97 South Terrace, Adelaide, SA 5000. Tel. (08) 212 2644.

Australian Booksellers Association, 136 Rundle Mall, Adelaide, SA 5000. Tel. (08) 223 6669.

Australian Dance Theatre, 120 Gouger Street, Adelaide, SA 5000. Tel. (08) 212 2084.

Carlew Art Centre Incorporated, 11 Jeffcott Street, North Adelaide, SA 5006. Tel. (08) 267 1991.

Department for the Arts, Edmund Wright House, 59 King William Road, Adelaide, SA 5000. Tel. (08) 227 3911.

Experimental Art Foundation Inc., 68 North Terrace, Adelaide, SA 5000. Tel. (08) 211 7505.
Including workshops, library, flexible exhibition space, bookshop and coffee bar.

History Trust of South Australia, Institute Building, North Terrace, Adelaide SA 5000. Tel. (08) 223 8808.
Responsible for recording, preserving and promoting the history of South Australia. It also manages four museums including the Old Parliament House.

South Australian Media Resource Centre, 242 Pirie Street, Adeliade, SA 5000. Tel. (08) 223 1500.

South Australian Writers Center Inc., 265 Rundle Street, Adelaide, SA 5000. Tel. (08) 223 7662.

The Adelaide Centre for Photographic Studies, 9 Wallis Street, West Beach, SA 5024. Tel. (08) 353 5754.

The Jam Factory Workshops Inc., 169 Payneham Road, St Peters, SA 5069. Tel. (08) 425 661.
Guided tours of the workshops by appointment. A major centre where artists and craftspeople work and exhibit their specialised skills.

The Arts Dept for South Australia, 44 Pirie Street, Adelaide, SA 5000. Tel. (08) 237 3911.

The Living Arts Centre, 68 North Terrace, Adelaide, SA 5000. Tel. (08) 212 1258.

STATE CRAFT ORGANISATIONS SOUTH AUSTRALIA

Adelaide Potters Club, 15 Liston Street, Parkside, SA 5063. Tel. (08) 271 9459.

Craft Council of South Australia Inc., 169 Payneham Road, St Peters, SA 5069. Tel. (08) 42 4001.
Within the Jam Factory Workshops, listings of other smaller craft groups are available from the office.

The Craftsman Workshop, 2 Gray Street, Kilkenny, SA 5009. Tel. (08) 268 6195.

The Embroiderer's Guild of South Australia Inc., 16 Hughes Street, Mile End, SA 5031. Tel. (08) 234 1104.
Open Monday—Friday 10–3.

Hand Spinners and Weavers Guild of South Australia Inc., 4 Astrid Street, Christie Downs, SA 5164. Tel. (08) 384 3575.

Jam Factory Workshops Inc., 169 Payneham Road, St Peters, SA 5069. Tel. (08) 425 661.
General information on various craft groups available from here.

Mitcham Village Arts and Crafts Association, 33 Albert Street, Mitcham, SA 5062. Tel. (08) 272 4505.

STATE REGIONAL GALLERIES AND MUSEUMS SOUTH AUSTRALIA

Adelaide Festival Centre Foyer Gallery, King William Road, Adelaide, SA 5000. Tel. (08) 216 8600.
Interesting national and international exhibits on a regular basis in the gallery space. Also bookshop and coffee shop. Monday–Saturday 10.30–8.30, Sunday 12–6. A very lively venue in March during the biennial Adelaide Festival, worth visiting.

Adelaide Festival Centre, Adelaide

Art Gallery of South Australia, North Terrace, Adelaide, SA 5000. Tel. (08) 223 7200.
Excellent collection of early Australian and contemporary works. Also impressive collection of Aboriginal work. The Arts Bookshop is open 10–4.45 daily, the coffee shop 10.30–4.15 daily. The gallery opens Monday–Saturday 10–5, Wednesday 10–9 and Sunday 1.30–5. Guided tours are available daily at 11.

Flinders University Art Museum, Sturt Road, Bedford Park, SA 5042. Tel. (08) 275 2695.
Changing exhibitions of Australian and overseas art. Open Monday–Thursday 9.30–4.30.

Hahndorf Academy Gallery and Museum, 68 Main Street, Handorf, SA 5245. Tel. (08) 388 7250.
Just 25 minutes from the city of Adelaide in the Adelaide Hills is the small German town of Hahndorf. The area is a focal point for South Australian crafts with wonderful coffee shops and restaurants to make a day trip well worth while.

Migrant and Settlement Museum, 82 Kintore Avenue, Adelaide, SA 5000. (next to Childrens Library). Tel. (08) 223 8940.
Australia's first museum to tell the story of our migrants. Galleries and museums are in the superbly restored site of the historic Destitute Asylum. Open Monday–Friday 10–5, Saturday, Sunday & public holidays 1–5.

National Motor Museum, Main Street, Birdwood, SA 5234. Tel. (085) 68 5006.
Just over an hour's drive brings you to a collection of over 300 vehicles, housed on a beautiful 20 acres at historic Birdwood Mill. Tearooms and barbeques available. Open 9–5 daily.

Old Parliament House, North Terrace, Adelaide, SA 5000. Tel. (08) 212 6066.
The original Parliament House now superbly restored to be a prize winning museum with exhibitions and an excellent audio visual programme. A delightful garden and restaurant in the grounds. Open Monday–Friday 10–5, Saturday, Sunday & Public Holidays 1–5.

Performing Arts Collection Theatre Museum, Adelaide Festival Centre, King William Road, Adelaide, SA 5000. Tel. (08) 216 8767.

South Australian Maritime Museum, Lipson Street, Port Adelaide, SA 5015. Tel. (08) 240 0200.
Climb an 1869 lighthouse and visit historic ships in Adelaide's heritage area. Open Saturday–Wednesday 10–5.

South Australian Museum, North Terrace, Adelaide, SA 5000. Tel. (08) 223 8911. Open daily 10–5, except Wednesday 1–5 & Sunday 2–5. Largest Aboriginal collection in the world on display. Museum shop Tel. (08) 223 8956.

The Gallery, Level 6, Adelaide University, Union House, North Terrace, Adelaide, SA 5000. Tel. (08) 228 5834.
Open Monday–Friday 10–5, Saturday 2–5. Regular changing exhibitions of local and interstate artists.

COMMERCIAL AND NON PROFIT GALLERIES ADELAIDE

Adelaide art scene

The **Adelaide Arts Festival** held every two years (1988, 1990) has a literary, dramatic and musical stress although there are several important art exhibitions. Authors, actors and musicians come from all over the world as well as nationally to participate. The **South Australian Art Gallery** on North Terrace has an excellent art collection and one of the best Australian collections of Aboriginal work. It is the venue for many exciting touring contemporary exhibitions and events. It has an excellent arts bookshop and lively atmosphere. The **Bonython—Meadmore Galleries** show leading Australian artists and the **Jam Factory** holds quality craft exhibitions as the state of South Australia is highly respected for the quality of its crafts. **The Experimental Art Foundation** is an important venue for visiting international artists and holds regular avant garde events.

Anima Gallery, 239 Melbourne Street, North Adelaide, SA 5006. Tel. (08) 267 4815.
Regular exhibitions by leading contemporary Australian artists. Open Tuesday–Friday 10–5.30, Saturday & Sunday 2–5.

Aramis Gallery, 197 Payneham Road, St Peters, SA 5000. Tel. (08) 42 2584.

Artist Producer Australia, 29 Osmond Terrace, Fullarton, SA 5063. Tel. (08) 79 8385.

Art Zone, 80 Hindley Street, Adelaide, SA 5000. Tel. (08) 383 8672.
Regular changing exhibitions of contemporary art. Open Monday–Friday 1–5, Saturday & Sunday 10–5.

Barry Newton Gallery, 259 Unley Road, Malvern, SA 5061. Tel. (08) 271 4523.
Regular exhibitions of fine arts by prominent and emerging artists. Open Tuesday–Friday 11–5, Saturday & Sunday 2–5.

Bonython-Meadmore Gallery, 88 Jerningham Street, North Adelaide, SA 5006. Tel. (08) 267 4449.
Contact: Keith Woodward. Regular changing exhibitions by leading Australian and overseas artists. Artists include: James Willebrant, Bruce Anderson, Colin Lanceley, Inge King, Lawrence Daws, Philipe Lakeman, Ian Ferguson, Brian Westwood. Open Tuesday–Friday 10–5, Saturday & Sunday 2–5, closed January.

Coledale and Laurence, Colin Lanceley (Bonython-Meadmore Gallery)

Contemporary Art Centre of South Australia, 14 Porter Street, Parkside, SA 5063. Tel. (08) 272 2682.
Changing exhibitions of prominent Australian artists. Lively art centre with talks by visiting artists and membership for South Australian artists. Open Tuesday–Friday 11–5, Saturday & Sunday 1–5, gallery closed January.

College Gallery, South Australian School of Art, SACAE, Holbrooks Road, Underdale, SA 5031. Tel. (08) 352 0011.
Exhibits by students from the School of Art and contemporary Australian artists. Open Tuesday–Friday 11–5, Saturday & Sunday 1–5.

Cromwell Gallery, 120 Melbourne Street, North Adelaide, SA 5006. Tel. (08) 267 3093.

Elders Fine Art Gallery, 106 Melbourne Street, North Adelaide, SA 5006. Tel. (08) 239 0202.

Experimental Art Foundation Inc., 68 North Terrace, Adelaide, SA 5000. Tel. (08) 211 7505.
An alternative art space with lively exhibitions, performances and other events by Australian and overseas visiting artists. International collection of video tapes. An internationally recognised artists exhibiting space. Open Tuesday–Friday 11–6, Saturday 2–5. Now located in the Living Arts Centre.

Greenhill Galleries, 140 Barton Terrace, North Adelaide, SA 5006. Tel. (08) 267 2887.
Regular exhibitions by leading Australian artists. Open Tuesday–Friday 10–5, Saturday & Sunday 2–5, gallery closes December–January.

Hill Smith Fine Art Gallery, 113 Pirie Street, Adelaide, SA 5000. Tel. (08) 223 6558.
Continuous exhibitions of traditional Australian art. Open Monday–Friday 10–5.30, Saturday & Sunday 2–5.

Kensington Gallery, 39 Kensington Road, Norwood, SA 5067. Tel. (08) 332 5752.
Open Wednesday–Friday 11–5, Saturday & Sunday 2–5. Traditional works by Australian and overseas artists.

Kingston House Galleries, Resident Gallery, 148 Anzac Highway, Glandore, SA 5037. Tel. (08) 293 2287.
Traditional Australian paintings, watercolours, etchings and other works on paper. Open 1–53.0, closed Tuesdays.

Kintore Gallery, Royal South Australian Society of Arts, Institute Building, Cnr North Terrace and Kintore Avenue, Adelaide, SA 5000. Tel. (08) 223 4704.
Works by South Australian artists. Open Monday–Friday 11–5, Saturday & Sunday 2–5.

McLaren Vale Galleries, 146 Main Road, McLaren Vale, SA 5171. Tel. (08) 323 8572.

Multicultural Art Workers Committee, Morphett Street, Adelaide, SA 5000. Tel. (08) 212 4276.

North Adelaide School of Art Gallery, 42 Stanley Street, North Adelaide, SA 5006. Tel. (08) 267 4811.

Old Clarendon Gallery, Main Road, Clarendon, SA 5157. Tel. (08) 383 6151.

Photographic Art Gallery, 6 Yalpa Road, Marino, SA 5049. Tel. (08) 298 7777.

Reade Art, 101 Glen Osmon Road, Eastwood, SA 5063. Tel. (08) 272 3178.

Tete Gallery, Living Art Centre, Cnr North Terrace and Morphett Street, Adelaide, SA 5000. Tel. (08) 267 5936.
Contemporary Australian artists. Check with the gallery for opening times.

The Albert Mill Gallery, 2 Junction Street, Nairne 5252. Tel. (08) 388 6152.

The Bugle Galleries, Bonython Road, Bugle Ranges, SA. Tel. 391 0053.
Specialising in traditional Australian paintings for investment and directed by the well known dealer Hugh Bonython. By appointment only any time, an hour's drive from central Adelaide.

The Butcher's Hook, 734 Anzac Highway, Glenelg, SA 5045. Tel. (08) 295 5528.
Contemporary art space with regular changing exhibitions.

Eerie Mountain, Lawrence Davis (Bonython-Meadmore Gallery)

The Jam Factory Workshops Inc., 169 Payneham Road, St Peters, SA 5069. Tel. (08) 42 5661.
Gallery space within the centre. Fine art and crafts.

The Liston Street Gallery, 15 Liston Street, Parkside, SA 5063. Tel. (08) 271 9459.

Toorak Art Gallery, 375 Grenhill Road, Toorak Gardens, SA 5065. Tel. (08) 332 3597.

Tuominen Galleries Pty Ltd, 33 City Cross Street, Adelaide, SA 5000. Tel. (08) 212 5672.
Regular changing exhibitions of contemporary Australian artists.

Tynte Gallery, 83 Tynte Street, North Adelaide, SA 5006. Tel. (08) 267 2200.
Contemporary Australian and international art, limited edition fine art prints and conservation framing available. Open Tuesday–Friday 10–5, Saturday & Sunday 2–5.

CRAFT GALLERIES
ADELAIDE

Adelaide Hills Galleries are within half an hour's drive from central Adelaide and provide a unique centre for South Australian crafts. The historic buildings complement the fine quality of the local crafts and nestled amongst the galleries are excellent coffee shops and restaurants.

Aldgate Crafts, 4 Strathalbyn Road, Aldgate, SA 5154. Tel. (08) 338 6152.
Open Monday–Saturday 10–5, Sunday & Public Holidays 11–5. A wide selection of the best of South Australian crafts are available.

Birchgrove Fine Crafts, 50 Main Road, Hahndorf, SA 5245. Tel. (08) 388 7171.
Crafts on display by local craftspeople.

Budgeree Glass Studio, 20 William Street, Norwood, SA 5067. Tel. (08) 332 5167.
Some of the finest handmade glass in Australia, limited editions both functional and decorative.

Burnside Arts, Crafts and Hobby Centre, 427 Portrush Road, Toorak Gardens, SA 5065. Tel. (08) 31 9389.

Coach House Gallery 9 Walters Street, Tea Tree Gully, SA 5091. Tel. (08) 265 1182.

Cellar Cottage Crafts, Main Road, McLaren Vale, SA 5171. Tel. (08) 323 8537.

Elmswood Fine Crafts, 189 Unley Road, Unley, SA 5061. Tel. (08) 272 3198.
Regular changing exhibitions of leading Australian craftspeople. Open Monday–Saturday 10–5, Sunday & Public Holidays 2–5.

Jam Factory Crafts Centre, Workshops and Gallery, 169 Payneham Road, St Peters, SA 5069. Tel. (08) 42 5661.
Changing exhibitions by leading Australian craftspeople. Specialists in glass, leather, ceramics, textiles and jewellery. Guided tours of the workshops by appointment. Open Monday–Friday 9–5, Saturday 10–5, Sunday & Public Holidays 2–5.

LimeburnesArt Gallery and Coffee Lounge, 250 Main Road, McLaren Vale, SA 5171.

L'Unique, Shop 6, The Renaissance Arcade, Pulteney Street entrance, Adelaide, SA 5000. Tel. (08) 223 1328.
South Australian pottery be leading potters and other selected fine arts and crafts.

Mitcham Village Arts and Crafts Association Inc., 33 Albert Street, Mitcham, SA 5062. Tel. (08) 272 4504.

Once Upon a Time, 82 Rose Street, Mile End, SA 5031. Tel. (08) 354 0731.

Quality 5 Crafts, City Cross Arcade, Adelaide, SA 5000. Tel. (08) 212 3340. Tel. (08) 212 3340.
Selected fine crafts by leading Australian craftspeople.

Studio 20, 20 Coromandel Parade, Blackwood, SA 5051. Tel. (08) 278 7737.
Open Monday–Saturday 10.30–5.30, Sunday & Public Holidays 2–5. High quality Australian crafts.

Tea Tree Gully Steam Flour Mill Art Gallery, 1370 North Est Road, Tea Tree Gully, SA 5091.

The Albert Mill Gallery, 2 Junction Street, Nairne, SA 5252.

The Craft Gallery, John Fisher Avenue, Gumeracha, SA 5233. Tel. (08) 389 1084.
Fine art and crafts including wrought iron work, handspun garments and pottery.

Ratbags, 177 King William Road, Hyde Park, SA 5061. Tel. (08) 271 1658.
Individually designed leather goods including clothing.

Tuominen Galleries, City Cross Arcade, Adelaide, SA 5000. Tel. (08) 212 5672.
Studio and workshop is at 205 Magill Road, Maylands, SA 5069. Tel. (08) 42 5533.
Handcrafted stoneware pottery.
The region of Adelaide has numerous high quality craft galleries. For an extensive listing check with the South Australian Crafts Council and listings appear in the complimentary handbook available at tourist information centres.

ABORIGINAL ART GALLERIES ADELAIDE

Adella Gallery, 28 Currie Street, Adelaide, SA 5000. Tel. (08) 212 2171.
Authentic Aboriginal arts and crafts. Open 7 days, Sunday 1–4.30.

Adelaide Aboriginal Arts and Crafts, 185 Pirie Street, Adelaide, SA 5000. Tel. (08) 223 5001.
Genuine Aboriginal artifacts and bark paintings from the northern regions of Australia.

South Australia Museum Shop, North Terrace, Adelaide, SA 5000. Tel. (08) 223 8911.
Aboriginal and modern Australian art and craft now available.

The Australian Scene, 235 Henley Beach Drive, Torrensville, SA 5031. Tel. (08) 436 916.

GALLERIES DEALING IN PRE 1900 EXHIBITS ADELAIDE

Aldgate Book and Art, Mount Baker Road, Aldgate, SA 5154. Tel. (08) 339 2882.

Augusta Antiques, 166 Magill Road, Norwood, SA 5067. Tel. (08) 42 1076.
Specialist in folk art.

Investigator Gallery Antiques, 6 Gays Arcade, Adelaide, SA 5000. Tel. (08) 223 3010.
Manuscript paintings one area of fine specialisation.

Joe Orlando, 163 Glen Osmond Road, Frewville, SA 5063. Tel. (08) 79 8112.
Collector and restorer of old photographs.

Somewhere In Time, Shop 3, Bay Mall, 112 Jetty Road, Glenelg, SA 5045. Tel. (08) 295 3419.
Victoriana and specialists in advertising and movie collectables.

The Gold Brooch, 73 Grenfell Street, Adelaide, SA 5000. Tel. (08) 223 2040.
Various area of specialisation including objects d'art.

WORKSHOPS, STUDIOS AND ART CENTRES ADELAIDE

Contemporary Art Society of South Australia Inc., 14 Porter Street, Parkside, SA 5063. Tel. (08) 272 2682.

Contemporary Art Society Print Workshop, 315 Young Street, Wayville, SA 5034. Tel. (08) 271 4094.
The services of a professional workshop for fine art printmakers.

Central School of Art Adelaide, Bloor Court, Adelaide, SA 5000. Tel. (08) 516 714.

Adelaide Centre for Photographic Studies, 9 Wallis Street, West Beach, SA 5024.

North Adelaide School of Art, 42 Stanley Street, North Adelaide, SA 5006. Tel. (08) 267 4811.

The Bakery Women's Performance Centre. Contact the Arts Council of South Australia, 97 South Terrace, Adelaide, SA 5000. Tel. (08) 212 2644.

The Jam Factory Workshops Inc., 169 Payneham Road, St Peters, SA 5069. Tel. (08) 42 5661.
Access workshops for professional artists and craftspeople with a gallery space in the complex.

The Jay and Jay Film, Television and Theatrical Make-up Academy, 43b Woodville Road, Woodville, SA 5011. Tel. (08) 45 2947.

Slade School of Pottery, 21 Wycombe Road, Aldgate, SA 5154. Tel. (08) 339 2537.

Printmakers at work

ALTERNATIVE ART SPACES ADELAIDE

Roundspace Inc., 21 Blyth Street, Adelaide, SA 5000. Tel. (08) 212 4678.
An interesting gallery space available for any project.

Experimental Art Foundation, Living Arts Centre, North Terrace, Adelaide, SA 5000. Tel. (08) 211 7505.
A major centre for avant garde events, both national and international. International collection of video tapes built up over the years.

FINE ART COURSE AND COLLEGES ADELAIDE

Flinders University of South Australia, Sturt Road, Bedford Park, SA 5042. Tel. (08) 275 3911.
The following Undergraduate Courses are available in the areas of teaching: art and craft, design, painting, sculpture, printmaking, photography, ceramics, graphic design. Master's Degree by coursework is available in painting, sculpture, printmaking, photography and ceramics.

South Australia College of Advanced Education, (CAE), 46 Kintore Avenue, Kintore, SA 5000. Tel. (08) 223 6170.
The college offers Undergraduate courses in teaching: art and craft, design, painting, sculpture, printmaking, photography, graphic design, ceramics, jewellery, illustration, industrial design, interior design, dance, drama and music, film, television and cinema studies. Associate Diploma is available in ceramics, jewellery, textiles, graphic design. Post Graduate Degree is available in painting, sculpture, printmaking, and photography.

South Australia Institute of Technology, North Terrace, Adelaide, SA 5000. Tel. (08) 228 0376.
The institute offers a Graduate Diploma in arts administration and an Undergraduate Degree in interior design.

ART SUPPLIES AND MATERIALS ADELAIDE

Art Stretchers Co., 188 Morphett Street, Adelaide, SA 5000. Tel. (08) 212 2711.
Specialists in painting, drawing and printmaking supplies for artists, students and schools.

Artistcare (Australia) Pty Ltd, 21 Gouger Street, Adelaide, SA 5000. Tel. (08) 211 8883.
Suppliers of drafting materials, fine art equipment, mounting boards and educational materials.

Artland, 1 Princess Parade, Clovelly Park, SA 5042. Tel. (08) 276 9522.
Suppliers of quality imported ink, paints, brushes, art books and imported fine art papers for printmaking, watercolour and painting.

Deans Art, 210 Rundle Street, Adelaide, SA 5000. Tel. (08) 223 6590, also at 185 Pulteney Street, Adelaide, SA 5000. Tel. (08) 223 6199.
Artists materials, graphic supplies and a framing service.

Eckersley's, 21 Frome Street, Adelaide, SA 5000. Tel. (08) 223 4155.
Extensive range of fine art materials and suppliers for graphics.

Premier Art Supplies Pty Ltd, 43 Gilles Street, Adelaide, SA 5000. Tel. (08) 212 5922.
Comprehensive range of art materials for commercial or professional use.

Salisbury Art Supplies, Shop 5, 3 Church Street, Salisbury SA 5108. Tel. (08) 250 1056.
Professional oil paints, watercolours, acrylics, gouache, inks, etc., also extensive sculpture supplies.

South Australian Campus Supplies, City Student Union Inc., Holbrooks Road, Underdale, SA 5032. Tel. (08) 354 0833.
Wholesalers of artists' materials, technical drawing supplies, papers and boards, photographic equipment and general art goods.

Fine Art Papers, Robert Jones, 123 Drayton Street, Bowden, SA 5007.
Fine rag paper for printmakers, drawing and painting imported from Tuscany.

The Beehive Press, 123 Drayton Street, Bowden, SA 5007. Tel. (08) 46 7558.
Excellent selection of imported Japanese and European papers, sample booklet available.

PHOTOGRAPHY, FILM AND VIDEO SOUTH AUSTRALIA

Adelaide International Film Festival, GPO Box 354, Adelaide, SA 5001. Tel. (08) 51 0121.

Community Media Association Inc., 23 Henley Beach Road, Mile End, SA 5031. Tel. (08) 35 27150.

Lips Studio Pty Ltd, 67 Lipson Place, Adelaide, SA 5000. Tel. (08) 47 8266.

National Film Theatre of Australia, 358 Carrington Street, Adelaide, SA 5000. Tel. (08) 223 5850.

South Australia Media Resource Centre, 242 Pirie Street, Adelaide, SA 5000. Tel. (08) 223 1600.

State Film and Video Library of South Australia, 113 Tapleys Hill Rod, Henden, SA 5014.

The Adelaide Centre for Photographic Studies, 9 Wallis Street, West Beach, SA 5024. Tel. (08) 353 5754.

The Australian Institute of Professional Photography, Secretatiat, PO Box 136, North Adelaide, SA 5006. Tel. (08) 363 0671.
Office at 15 Leslie Avenue, Evandale, SA 5069.

PHOTOGRAPHIC SUPPLIES SOUTH AUSTRALIA

G.C.S. Photographic Industrial Sales, 212 Rundle Street, Adelaide, SA 5000. Tel. (08) 223 3449.
Suppliers of materials and equipment for the professional photographer.

Diamond Photographics, 165 Rundle Street, Adelaide, SA 5000. Tel. (08) 224 0665.
All popular photographic equipment, repairs and trade-ins.

Foto First, 34 King William Street, Adelaide, SA 5000. Tel. (08) 231 0660.
Same day service available for colour and black and white work, a one hour quality service available.

Gum tree

Photographic Wholesalers Pty Ltd, 153 Hutt Street, Adelaide, SA 5000. Tel. (08) 223 6777.
Photographic, video, optical equipment, print and slide film processing.

Pics Australasia, 113 Carrington Street, Adelaide, SA 5000. Tel. (08) 223 4655.
Photo finishing equipment, industrial, commercial and professional photographic equipment, audio visual and computor graphics equipment available.

South Australia Campus Supplies, City Student Union Inc., Holbrooks Road, Underdale, SA 5032. Tel. (08) 354 0833.
Photographic supplies and general art materials.

Technicolour and Film Lab, 89 Fullarton Road, Kent Town, SA 5067. Tel. (08) 31 6755.
Professional photographic processing and printing to suit your needs.

Ted's Camera Store, 212 Rundle Street, Adelaide, SA 5000. Tel. (08) 223 3449.
Retail, industrial, duty free, superby quality processing, repairs, repairs and trade-ins.

ART BOOKSHOPS
ADELAIDE

Adelaide Book Co., 136 Rundle Mall, Adelaide, SA 5000. Tel. (08) 223 5830.

Adelaide University Union Bookshop Pty Ltd, on campus off North Terrace, nr gate 9, Victoria Drive, Adelaide, SA 5000. Tel. (08) 223 4366.
Excellent international art section.

Angus and Robertson Bookshops, 41 Rundle Mall, Adelaide, SA 5000. Tel. (08) 212 6449.
Large selection of visual and performing arts. Orders welcome.

Art Gallery Bookshop, Art Gallery of South Australia, North Terrace, Adelaide, SA 5000. Tel. (08) 223 7200.
Excellent selection of art and craft books both national and international.

Blackwood Books, Hindmarsh Arcade, 336 Shep rds Hill Road, Blackwood, SA 5051. Tel. (08) 278 5094.
All types of books researched and ordered.

City Books, 108 Gawler Place, Adelaide, SA 5000. Tel. (08) 223 2773.
Extensive range of books including art, open 7 days a week.

Australian art books

Fables Bookstore, 65 Gawler Place, Adelaide, SA 5000. Tel. (08) 212 7449.
Fine and unusual books in the visual and performing arts. Open 7 days a week, worth visiting.

Flinders University Bookshop, Sturt Road, Bedford Park, SA 5042. Tel. (08) 276 8464.
General public and special orders welcome, excellent fine arts section.

Food in Print, 92 Unley Rod, Unley, SA 5086. Tel. (08) 272 8210.
South Australia's only specialist food and wine bookshop, worth a visit.

Mary Martin Bookshops Pty Ltd, 91 Gawler Place, Adelaide, SA 5000. Tel. (08) 212 7911.
Specialisation in art, remainder books and bargains. Open daily.

The Book Place, 57 Franklin Street and 8 Rundle Mall, Adelaide, SA 5000. Tel. (08) 211 7268.
A selection of high quality arts and books.

FINE ART FRAMING
SOUTH AUSTRALIA

Abacus Picture Framing, Factory/Workshop 4, 34 First Street, Brompton, SA 5007. Tel. (08) 46 9292.
Open Monday–Friday 9–5. Also at Tynte Gallery, 83 Tynte Street, North Adelaide, SA 5006. Tel. (08) 267 2200. Professional fine art framers for works on paper and paintings.

Advance Picture Framing, 615a Lower North East Road, Campbelltown, SA 5074. Tel. (08) 336 9787.
General custom framing with special rates for artists.

All Art Picture Framers and Gallery, 88 Pirie Street, Adelaide, SA 5000. Tel. (08) 223 3863.
Individual framing for artist exhibitions, kit service to assemble yourself, with an extensive moulding range.

Artland, Factory and Showroom, 1 Princess Parade, Clovell Park, SA 5042. Tel. (08) 276 9522.
Custom framing to order, or do it yourself framing and cutting service.

Golden International Picture Framers & Co. Pty Ltd, 288 Waymouth Street, Adelaide, SA 5000. Tel. (08) 212 1466.
Professional service for artists with a 24 hour service where possible.

Hooper's Picture Framers, 7a Gawler Place, Adelaide, SA 5000 (next to David Jones Car Park). Tel. (08) 212 4704.
Matt cutting and mounting, extensive range of mouldings with specialised service for artists, photographers and galleries.

R. Diamond and Sons Pty Ltd, 59 Beulah Road, Norwood, SA 5067. Tel. (08) 42 5002.
Fine art framing and restoration.

The Frame Factory, 197 Magill Road, Maylands, SA 5069. Tel. (08) 42 7875.
Specialising in custom built frames.

THEATRICAL ORGANISATIONS SOUTH AUSTRALIA

Adelaide Dance Company Inc., Dance Centre, 25 Whitmore Square, Adelaide, SA 5000. Tel. (08) 212 1665.

Australian Dance Theatre, 120 Gouger Street, Adelaide, SA 5000. Tel. (08) 212 2084.
A very lively company.

Adelaide Repertory Theatre Inc., 53 Angas Street, Adelaide, SA 5000. Tel. (08) 212 5777.

Arts Theatre, 53 Angas Street, Adelaide, SA 5000. Tel. (08) 212 5777.

Association for Community Theatre Inc., 1a Falcon Avenue, Mile End, SA 5031. Tel. (08) 43 6200.

Australian Elizabeth Theatre Trust, 28 Fifth Avenue, St Peters, SA 5069. Tel. (08) 42 9576.

Bunyip Children's Theatre, 134 Molesworth Street, North Adelaide, SA 5006. Tel. (08) 267 2684.

Henley Drama Group, 5 Hobart Road, Henley Beach, SA 5022. Tel. (08) 353 4314.

La Mama Theatre, 184 Port Road, Hindmarsh, SA 5007. Tel. (08) 46 4212.
Drama courses.

Paperbag Theatre Co., 26 Watson Street, Fullarton, SA 5063. Tel. (08) 79 8030.

S.A. Creative Workshops Inc., 72 Edmund Avenue, Unley, SA 5061. Tel. (08) 272 3036.

The State Opera of South Australia, 20 Rowlands Place, Adelaide, SA 5000. Tel. (08) 212 6080.

The State Theatre Company at the Playhouse, King William Road, Adelaide, SA 5000. Tel. (08) 51 5151.

Sheridan Theatre Group, 50 MacKinnon Parade, North Adelaide, SA 5006. Tel. (08) 267 3751.

Tea Tree Players Inc., 22 Kingford Smith Street, Modbury Heights, SA 5092. Tel. (08) 264 0516.

Troup Theatre Company, Unley Road, Unley, SA 5061. Tel. (08) 271 7552.

THEATRICAL VENUES
SOUTH AUSTRALIA

Adelaide Festival Centre, King William Road, Adelaide, SA 5000. Incorporating the **Adelaide Festival Playhouse**, the **Festival Theatre** and the **Festival Space**, the **Opera Theatre** and the **Foyer Gallery**. Within the complex there is a bistro, restaurant and kiosk. Also the museum and bookshop are open during normal business hours. **Festival Centre Information** for what is on Tel. (08) 211 8999.

Arts Theatre, 53 Angas Street, Adelaide, SA 5000. Tel. (08) 212 5777.

Mathew Flinders Theatre, Flinders University, Sturt Road, Bedford Park, SA 5042. Tel. (08) 275 2445.

Mayfair Theatre Company Inc., 22 Rutland Avenue, Unley Par, SA 5061. Tel. (08) 272 5206.

The Opera Theatre, 58 Grote Street, Adelaide, SA 5000. Tel. (08) 683.

The Parks Community Centre, Theatres 1 & 2, Cowan Street, Angle Park, SA 5010. Tel. (08) 268 5666.

Patch Theatre Company, 20 Tarlton Street, Sommerton Park, SA 5044. Tel. (08) 294 3287 (Box office).

Price Theatre Centre for the Performing Arts, 97 Grote Street, Adelaide, SA 5000. Tel. (08) 51 9521.

Regent Theatre, No. 1 & No. 2, 101 Rundle Mall, Adelaide, SA 5000. Tel. (08) 223 2233 for No. 1 and 223 6100 for No. 2.

Royalty Theatre, 65 Angas Street, Adelaide, SA 5000. Tel. (08) 223 5765.

S. A. Media Resource Centre, 242 Pirie Street, Adelaide, SA 5000. Tel. (08) 223 1600.
Cinema seating for 59 people.

Scott Theatre, 46 Kintore Avenue, Adelaide, SA 5000. Tel. (08) 228 1620 (Box office).

Therbaton Theatre, 114 Henley Beach Road, Torrensville, SA 5031. Tel. (08) 43 5255.

MUSICAL ORGANISATIONS SOUTH AUSTRALIA

Adelaide Boy's Band, 3 Donegal Street, Salisbury Downs, SA 5108. Tel. (08) 258 5859.

Adelaide Chamber Orchestra Inc., 97 South Terrace, Adelaide, SA 5000. Tel. 212 3877.

Adelaide Chorus Inc., 1 Hextall Avenue, Tranmere, SA 5073. Tel. (08) 31 4554.

Adelaide Classical Guitar Society Inc., 24 Harrow Road, Somerton Park, SA 5044. Tel. (08) 296 0561.

Adelaide Folkloric Society Inc., 13 Leigh Street, Adelaide, SA. Tel. (08) 212 6267.

Adelaide Rock Academy, 260 Franklin Street, Adelaide, SA 5000. Tel. 231 1467.

Australian Guild of Music, Speech and Drama, 362 Wright Road, Para Vista, SA 5093. Tel. (08) 264 8870.

South Australia Pipe Band Association Inc., 47 Osborne Road, North Haven, SA 5018.

Metropolitan Musical Theatre Co. of South Australia Inc., 8 Lloyd Street, St Marys, SA 5042.

MUSICAL VENUES SOUTH AUSTRALIA

Adelaide Festival Centre, Jazz on the Bistro Terrace, King William Road, Adelaide.

Amphitheatre Rock Concerts in the gardens of the Festival Centre, King William Road, Adelaide, SA 5000. For information Tel. (08) 211 8999, 24 hour service.

Adelaide Town Hall, King William Street, Adelaide, SA 5000.

After Dark Club, 63 Light Square, Adelaide, SA 5000. Tel. (08) 212 2066.

Grenfell Tavern, 25 Grenfell Street, Adelaide, SA 5000. Tel. (08) 212 5388.
Good for jazz.

International Society for Contemporary Music, c/o Dept of Music, University of Adelaide, SA 5000. Tel. (08) 223 4333 ext 2425.

National Music Camp Association, 19 North Terrace, Hackney, SA 5069. Tel. (08) 363 0722.

Pilgrim Church, 12 Flinders Street, Adelaide, SA 5000. Tel. (08) 212 3295. 9–4.

The Cumberland Arms Hotel, 205 Waymouth Street, Adelaide, SA 5000. Tel. (08) 51 3577.
Folk music.

The Royalty Theatre, 65 Angas Theatre, Adelaide, SA 5000. Tel. (08) 223 5765.

PLACES OF INTEREST SOUTH AUSTRALIA

Parks

Victoria Square is a spacious open area dominated by a variety of architecture. It was once the heart of the city.
Along the banks of the **Torrens River** and beneath the Adelaide Festival Centre are enormous parklands and lakes which have now become the heart of the city, since completion of the Festival Centre. Various other smaller parks are scattered throughout Adelaide and along the river, with the **Botanic Gardens** and the Botanic Park a short walk from King William Road.

Adelaide Hills provide **Mt Lofty Botanic Gardens** with exotic plants, open Sundays 10–4 autumn and spring only. **Gorge Wildlife Park**, **Cuddle Creek** is where you can wander among Australian wildlife, open daily. **Blackhill Wildflower Garden** off George Road, Adelaide has unique Australian flowers in its gardens, open Sunday–Friday 8.30–5. **Windy Point** is also in the Adelaide Hills and gives a spectacular panoramic view over Adelaide. **Wittunga Botanic Gardens**, **Blackwood**, provide excellent examples of Australian native and South African plants, open daily 10–4.
Recreation Parks around Adelaide include **Belair**, with the old Government House in the grounds, open Tuesday–Sunday 10–4, also plenty of natural bushland in the area. **Parra Wirra** has forests, steep gullies and rocky gorges. Kangaroos, other wildlife and native flowers can be found in the park. Enter by the Main North Road from Adelaide. Also **Cleland Park** where emus, koalas and kangaroos can be seen in the park.

Terraced houses, Adelaide, South Australia (Heather Waddell)

Markets

Antique Market, 32 Grote Street, Adelaide. Largest antique market in Australia.

The Central Market, Grote Street, Adelaide. Biggest produce market in the southern hemisphere. Open Tuesday 7–6, Friday & Saturday 7–1. Also craft work and auctions held with bargain prices, extensive meat and fish market included.

RESTAURANTS
ADELAIDE

The **Barossa Valley** vineyards and the **Southern Vale** vineyards are within easy reach of Adelaide, where good Australian wines can be tasted.

Many of the Adelaide restaurants are set in charming houses with ornate wrought-iron balconies, especially in the suburbs.

Arkaba Steak Cellar, 22 Gilbert Place, Adelaide. Tel. (08) 51 2221.
One of the largest steakhouses in Australia. A la carte menu is offered with chefs preparing the steaks in a century old wine cellar. Open for lunch Monday–Friday, dinner Monday–Saturday.

Angkor Wat Restaurant, 28 Regent Arcade, Adelaide. Tel. (08) 224 0186.
Possibly the only Cambodian restaurant in Australia with dishes prepared from authentic recipes. Lunch Monday–Friday, dinner Monday–Saturday.

Cafe Michael, 236 Rundle Street, Adelaide. (East end). Tel. (08) 223 3519.
Excellent seafood value, plus charcoal grilled steaks.

Hotel Adelaide, 62 Brougham Place, North Adelaide. Tel. (08) 267 3444.
The hotel has spectacular views of the city and surrounding gardens. The Brougham or the Garden Court Coffee Shop offer an interesting variety of dishes catering for breakfast, lunch and dinner.

Jasmin Indian Restaurant, 31 Hindmarsh Square, Adelaide. Tel. (08) 223 7837.
Open for lunch Tuesday–Friday 12noon–2.30 and for dinner Tuesday–Saturday. The best north Indian cuisine.

La Scala Restaurant, 172 Pulteney Street, Adelaide. Tel. (08) 223 1910.
Stylish surroundings and delicious Italian or creative French cuisine. Continuous service from noon till late.

Mezes Restaurant, 287 Rundle Street, Adelaide. Tel. (08) 223 7384.
Homestyle Greek cooking with daily speciality dishes. Greek music and cocktails till 2am.

Mona Lisa's Bistro, Cnr Hunt and Carrington Streets, Adelaide. Tel. (08) 223 3733.
Daily blackboard menus with Turkish dishes and other exciting creations. Live jazz and blues from 10pm till late on Friday & Saturday nights.

Quiet Waters, Lebanese Restaurant, 75 Hindley Street, Adelaide. Tel. (08) 51 3637.
Vegetarians catered for with Middle Eastern and Lebanese cuisine.

Rosanna's Vegetarian Restaurant, 137a Wright Street, Adelaide. Tel. (08) 51 2318.
Quality fresh and tasty home made bread and dishes. Special diets catered for.

The Botanic Hotel Basement Bistro, 309 North Terrace, Adelaide. Tel. (08) 223 4411.
Situated downstairs in one of Adelaide's oldest hotels, a mouthwatering menu and reasonable prices. After dinner there is live music. Open 7 days a week.

The Curry Queen Indian Restaurant, 253 Gouger Street, Adelaide. Tel. (08) 51 4920.
Authentic Indian cuisine with Australian dishes also available.

Tooraks Restaurant, 98 Melbourne Street, North Adelaide. Tel. (08) 239 0344.
Just like stepping into a typical New Orleans restaurant. Cajun Creole cuisine with extensive wine list and indoor and outdoor dining. Live jazz on Saturday and Sunday.

Zapata's Mexican Restaurant, 42 Melbourne Street, Adelaide. Tel. (08) 267 4653.
Favourite spicy dishes and tacos.

CONTENTS
QUEENSLAND

QUEENSLAND

The state of Queensland covers the north eastern corner of Australia with vast geographical differences from the blue waters of the **Great Barrier Reef** on its east coast to the red earth of the harsh outback of areas such as **Mt Isa** and beyond to the corners of central Australia. The east coast of Queensland continues to attract large numbers of tourists to such places as **Dunk Island**, **Fraser Island** and other islands of the Great Barrier Reef. The town of **Cairns** is the most popular northern town now servicing international flights at its new airport and becoming a new gateway for visitors to Australia. Other sizeable towns in the north are **Rock- hampton**, centre for the beef industry, **Townsville** with its mining and agricultural hinterland along with **Toowoomba**. Sugar, bananas, pineapples, citrus fruits, tropical fruits and seafood are all-important produce for Queensland. **Brisbane** and its neighbouring area **Surfers Paradise** are in the south east corner of the state with close proximity to rainforest regions on the **Great Dividing Range** which extends as far south as the state of Victoria.

178

Bushman's pub

STATE ART ORGANISATIONS QUEENSLAND

Artists Guild of Australia (Qld Branch), 45 Swan Street, Shorncliffe, Qld 4017. Tel. (07) 269 5236.

Arts On The Move, PO Box 155, Brisbane, North Quay, Qld 4002.
Arts On The Move is a radio programme produced fortnightly by the Division of Cultural Activities in the studios 4MBS–FM and is a broadcast in Brisbane, Townsville, Toowoomba and Cairns.

Aapley Art Group, c/o 56 Jacaranda Drive, Albany Creek, Qld 4035.

Australian Flying Art School at Kelvin Grove, c/o Brisbane College of Advanced Education, Kelvin Grove Campus, Victoria Park Road, Kelvin Grove, Qld. 4059. Tel. (07) 352 8400.
A service to outback lying regions, where the community has no regular arts training centre.

Brisbane Institute of Art Inc, 58 Latrobe Terrace, Paddington, Qld 4064. Tel. (07) 369 7290.

Brisbane Warana Festival Limited, 93 Queen Street, Brisbane, Qld 4000. Tel. (07) 229 2000.

Design Institute of Australia, Queensland, PO Box 317, Spring Hill, Qld 4000. Tel. (07) 221 4149.

Institute of Modern Art, 106 Edward Street, Brisbane, Qld 4000. Tel. (07) 229 5985.

Northside Creative Arts Association, 56 Leworthy Street, Bardon, Qld 4065. Tel. (07) 369 3113.

Queensland Art Gallery Society, PO Box 686, South Brisbane, Qld 4101. Tel. (07) 287 5582.

Queensland Arts Movement, 27 Allen Street, Hamilton, Qld 4007.

Queensland Art Teachers Association, Dept of Education, Kenny House, Cnr George and Charlotte Streets, Brisbane, Qld 4000. Tel. (07) 224 7563.

Queensland Wildlife Artists Society, 71 Empress Terrace, Bardon, Qld 4065. Tel. (07) 38 4270.

Regional Galleries Association of Queensland, Executive Officer/Exhibition Co-ordinator, PO Box 182, Brisbane North Quay, Qld 4002. Tel. (07) 221 7443.

Royal Queensland Art Society, GPO Box 1602, Brisbane, Qld 4001. Tel. (07) 831 3455.

University of Queensland Fine Arts Society, c/o University of Queensland Students' Union, St Lucia, Qld 4067.

STATE CRAFT ORGANISATIONS QUEENSLAND

Art in Bark Association, c/o Brisbane Grammar School, Gregory Terrace, Brisbane, Qld 4000. Tel. (07) 831 3091.

Australian Forum for Textile Arts, (Qld Division), 30 French Street, Paddington, Qld 4064. Tel. (07) 369 6409.

Australian Lace Guild (Qld Division), PO Box 338, South Brisbane, Qld 4101.

Crafts Council of Queensland, "School of Arts", 2nd Floor, 166 Ann Street, Brisbane, Qld 4000. Tel. (07) 229 2661.

Crafts Unlimited, 39 Jephson Street, Toowong, Qld 4066. Tel. (07) 371 4315.

Creative Glass Guild, GPO Box 1562, Brisbane, Qld 4000. Tel. (07) 398 9370.

Embroiders' Guild of Qld Inc., 149 Brunswick Street, Fortitude Valley, Qld 4006. Tel. (07) 52 8629.

Leathercraft Association of Queensland, 65 Trouts Road, Stafford, Qld 4053. Tel. (07) 355 4992.

Queensland Bookbinders' Guild, 110 Andrew Avenue, Tarragindi, Qld 4121. Tel. (07) 848 3774.

Queensland Jewellery Workshop, PO Box 199, St Lucia, Qld 4067. Tel. (07) 377 3430.

Queensland Potters' Association, 483 Brunswick Street, Fortitude Valley, Qld 4006. Tel. (07) 358 5121.

Queensland and Spinners Weavers and Dyers Group, PO Box 362, Toowong, Qld 4066.

Woodcraftsman's Guild of Queensland, 185 Ness Road, Salisbury, Qld 4107.

Woodturners Society of Queensland, 29 Outlook Crescent, Bardon, Qld 4065. Tel. (07) 369 3544.

STATE REGIONAL MUSEUMS AND GALLERIES QUEENSLAND

Brisbane Civic Art Gallery and Museum, City Hall, King George Square, Brisbane, Qld 4000. Tel. (07) 225 4355. Open Monday–Friday 10–4. Historical and contemporary fine arts collection. Admission free.

Buderim Art Gallery, on the Sunshine Coast, 52 Burnett Street, Buderim, Qld 4556. Tel. (071) 45 3722. Open Tuesday–Saturday 10.30–4.30.

Community Arts Gallery, Community Arts Centre, 107–109 Edward Street, Brisbane, Qld 4000. Tel. (07) 221 1913.

Gladstone Art Gallery and Museum, Cnr Goondoon and Bramston Strets, Gladstone, Qld 4680. Tel. (079) 72 2022. The public gallery is a community service of Gladstone City Council. Exhibitions change monthly and include the local artists and craftspeople. Open Monday, Wednesday & Friday 10–5, Thursday 10–8, Saturday 10–noon.

Gold Coast and Albert Museum, PO Box 88, Southport, Qld 4215. Tel. (07) 32 2539 for information about the museum.

City of Ipswich Art Gallery, Cnr Nicholas and Limestone Streets, Ipswich, Qld 4305. Tel. (07) 280 9246. Selections from the permanent collection on display as well

Queensland Art Gallery

as changing exhibitions from interstate and overseas. Open Tuesday–Friday 10–2, Thursday 7–9, Saturday 10–noon.

Noosa Regional Gallery, Noosa Shire Council Chambers, Pelican Street, Tewantin, Qld 4567. Tel. (071) 47 1464.
Changing exhibitions from interstate, local and overseas.

Percy Tucker Regional Gallery, Flinders Mall, Townsville, Qld 4810. Tel. (077) 72 2560.
Changing exhibitions from local artists to overseas.

Queensland Art Gallery, Queensland Cultural Centre, Melbourne Street, South Brisbane, Qld 4101. Tel. (07) 240 7333.
Housing Queensland contemporary art collection, holds changing exhibitions of major importance, gallery bookshop, sculpture court and a cafeteria with an outdoor setting overlooking the river. Open Monday–Sunday 10–5, Wednesday until 8pm.

Rockhampton Art Gallery, Victoria Parade, Rockhampton, Qld 4700. Tel. (075) 38 2121.
Changing exhibitions and displays from the permanent collection of paintings, sculptures and ceramics. Open Monday–Friday 10–4, Wednesday 7–8.30 and Sunday 2–4.

The Institute of Modern Art, 4th Floor, 106 Edward Street, Brisbane, Qld 4000. Tel. (07) 229 5985.
A lively centre for the visual and performing arts in Brisbane.

Townsville Museum, Material Cultural Unit, James Cook University, Townsville, Qld 4811. Tel. (077) 81 4111.

University Art Museum, Forgan Smith Building, University of Queensland, St Lucia, Qld 4067. Tel. (07) 377 3048.
The museum houses the University Art Collection and the Stuart-Holme Bohan collection with temporary exhibitions of interstate and overseas art. Open Monday–Friday 10–4, Sunday 2–5.

COMMERCIAL AND NON PROFIT GALLERIES BRISBANE

Brisbane arts scene

Although Brisbane is primarily known for its proximity to one of Australia's most favourite holiday resorts "**The Gold Coast**" and for the world **Expo '88** with its theme "Leisure in the Age of Technology", which was a great success, there is nevertheless an active arts community. The **Institute of Modern Art** encourages lively contemporary visual and performing art events with Australian and overseas artists often in residence. The **Ray Hughes Gallery** in Enoggera Terrace, Red Hill shows leading Australian artists and his stable of artists continue to win national art awards such as the Archibald Prize. The **Queensland Art Gallery** has a major historical art collection and holds major touring exhibitions from interstate and overseas. Tourism in the coastal regions of Queensland is contributing to the increasing success of arts and crafts in these centres, such as Surfers Paradise.

Adrian Slinger Galleries, 1st Floor, 230 Edward Street (Cnr Queen Street), Brisbane, Qld 4000. Tel. (07) 221 7938.
Changing exhibitions by Australian artists. Contemporary and traditional paintings. Monday–Friday 9–5.

Ardrossan Gallery, 1st Floor, Cnr Brookes and Gregory Terrace, Bowen Hill, Qld 4006. Tel (07) 52 3077.
Changing exhibitions by leading Australian artists. Contemporary and traditional drawing, painting, sculpture and Australian wildlife art. Open Monday–Friday 11–6, Saturday & Sunday 1–5, Thursday & Friday evenings 8–10.30.

Art Centre Hire Service, 18 Spence Street, Mt Gravatt, Qld 4122. Tel. (07) 349 6196.
Art hire for office, art carriers, art packing specialists, picture frame hire etc.

Barry's Art Gallery, 34 Orchid Avenue, Surfers Paradise, Qld 4217. Tel. (075) 31 5252.
Large selection of paintings by prominent Australian and overseas artists. Open Monday–Saturday 11–6, during tourist season extended hours. Viewing by appointment.

Cintra House Galleries, Cintra House, 23 Boyd Street, Bowen Hills, Qld 4006. Tel. (07) 52 7522.
Dealers in fine art and antique furniture in historic Cintra House. Open Tuesday–Sunday 10–5.30.

Creative 92 Gallery, 92 Margaret Street, Toowoomba, Qld 4350. Tel. (076) 32 8779.
Australian and overseas paintings and etchings. Also dealers in antique maps and prints. Open Monday–Friday 9–5, Sunday 11–4.30.

De Gruchy Gallery, 57 Jephson Street, Toowoong, Qld 4066. Tel. (07) 371 3636.
Dealers in fine art and crafts. Open Monday–Friday 9–5, Saturday 9–noon.

De Lisle Gallery, The Village Green, Montville, Qld 4555. Tel. (071) 45 8309.
Regular changing exhibitions of paintings and works on paper. Open daily 11–5.

Dimensions Art Galleries, 101 Adelaide Street, Brisbane, Qld 4000. Tel. (07) 229 9701.
Dealers in fine art, insurance and market valuation. Expert restoration.

Galerie Baguette, 150 Racecourse Road, Ascot, Qld 4007. Tel. (07) 268 6168.
Solo exhibitions by leading Queensland artists. Paintings, original prints, art glass and sculpture. Open Monday–Friday 9–noon and 3–6.

Gallery Peterson, 617 Seventeen Mile Rocks Road, Seventeen Mile Rocks, Qld 4073. Tel. (07) 376 1106.
Original graphics and other fine art.

Galloway Galleries and Fine Arts Centre, 34 Brookes Street, Bowen Hills, Qld 4006. Tel. (07) 852 1425.
Local, interstate and overseas artists. Open Monday–Friday 11–6, Saturday & Sunday 1–5.

Geoffrey Hoisser Galleries, 800–804 Zillmere Road, Aspley, Qld 4034. Tel. (07) 263 5800.
Continually changing mixed and one-man exhibitions of works by Queensland and interstate artists. Open Monday–Saturday 9–5.

Grafton House Galleries, Grafton House, 42 Grafton Street, Cairns, Qld 4870. Tel. (07) 51 1897.
Specialising in Australian fine art by north Queensland artists,

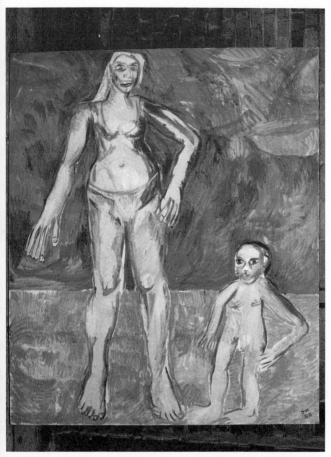

Mother and child, Joe Furlonger, (Ray Hughes Gallery)

also dealing in antique furniture and jewellery. Open Tuesday–Saturday 10–6.

Imagery Gallery, 89 Grey Street, South Brisbane, Qld 4101. Tel. (07) 844 8207.

Institute of Modern Art, 4th Floor, 106 Edward Street, Brisbane, Qld 4000. Tel. 229 5985.
One of Brisbane's leading venues for contemporary art with changing exhibitions.

John Cooper Eightbells Gallery, 3026 Gold Coast Highway, Surfers Paradise, Qld 4217. Tel. (075) 31 5548.
Continually changing exhibitions of paintings in stock by leading Australian artists past and present. Open Tuesday–Sunday 11–5.30.

Michael Milburn Galleries, 336–338 George Stret, Brisbane, Qld 4000. Tel. (07) 221 5199.
Representing contemporary Australian artists with changing exhibitions every three weeks. Open Tuesday–Saturday 10–5.30.

Phillip Bacon Galleries, 2 Arthur Street, New Farm, Qld 4005. Tel. (07) 358 3993.
Regular exhibitions by Australian artists, plus large collection of 19th century paintings. Open Monday–Saturday 10–5.

Ray Hughes Gallery, 11 Enoggera Terrace, Red Hill, Qld 4059. Tel. (07) 369 3757.
Representing leading Australian contemporary artists. Artists include: Davida Allen, Stephen Furlonger, Ian Smith, John Dutruc, amongst others. Director: Ray Hughes. An important Australian art gallery with a dynamic director. Gallery also in Sydney. Open Tuesday–Saturday 11–6.

Roz MacAllan Gallery, 1st Floor, 106 Edward Street, Brisbane, Qld 4101. Tel. (07) 229 4355.
Regular exhibitions by contemporary Australian artists.

Schubert Gallery, 34 Orchid Avenue, Surfers Paradise, Qld 4217. Tel. (075) 38 9599.

The Centre Gallery, Bundle Road, Surfers Paradise, Qld 4217. Tel. (075) 31 9517.

The Town Gallery and Japan Room, 4th Floor, Dunstan House, 236 Elizabeth Stret, Brisbane, Qld 4000. Tel. (07) 229 1981.
Contemporary Australian artists, and original Ukiyo-e and contemporary Japanese woodblock prints. Open Sunday–Friday 10–5.

Victor Mace Fine Art Gallery, 35 McDougall Street, Milton, Qld 4064. Tel. (07) 369 9305.
Changing exhibitions by leading Australian artists and tribal art. Open Saturday–Wednesday 11–5.

Young Masters Gallery, Ground Floor Entrance Foyer, Network House, 344 Queen Street, Brisbane, Qld 4000. Tel. (07) 229 5154.
Representing paintings, limited edition prints. Open Monday–Friday 10–6.

CRAFT GALLERIES
QUEENSLAND

Artisan—Gallery of Craft and Design, 10 Lambert Road, Indooroopilly, Qld 4068. Tel. (07) 371 1582.
A selection of work by Australian craftspeople.

Cottage Gallery, Unit 24, Mackie House, South Pine Road, Strathpine, Qld 4500. Tel. (07) 205 6953.

Craft—Interiors, 1122 Oxley Road, Oxley, Qld 4075.

Creation, 50 Musgrave Road, Red Hill, Qld 4059. Tel. (07) 221 3889.

Dabbles-On-Days Gallery, 185 Days Road, Grance 4051. Tel. (07) 356 7537.

Findhorn Gallery, 791 Sandgate Road, Clayfield, Qld 4011. Tel. (07) 262 6219.

Four Winds Ceramic Pty Ltd, 260 South Pine Road, Alderley, Qld 4051. Tel. (07) 354 3054.

Friary Pottery, The Friary, 131 Brookfield Road, Brookfield, Qld 4069. Tel. (07) 378 9878.

Gallery 88, Settlement Road, The Gap, Qld 4061.

Gallery Two, 98 Latrobe Terrace, Paddington, Qld 4064. Tel. (07) 369 7156.

Impressions Fien Art and Craft Gallery, 85 Latrobe Terrace, Paddington, Qld 4064. Tel. (07) 368 1685.
Leading Australian craftspeople.

Jaffron Crafts, 333 Waterworks Road, Ashgrove, Qld 4064.

Miskin Gallery, Cnr Wool and Miskins Streets, Toowong, Qld 4066. Tel. (07) 371 8671.
Quality Australian crafts available in ceramics, jewellery, glass, textiles. Open Tuesday–Friday 10–5.30, Saturday 10–5, Sunday 2–5.

Nundah Arts and Crafts, 1182 Sandgate Road, Nundah, Qld 4012. Tel. (07) 266 7177.

Plumridge Fine Craft Gallery, 123 Oxley Road, Chelmer, Qld 4068. Tel. (07) 379 8363.

Sherwood Village Arts and Crafts, 600 Sherwood Road, Sherwood, Qld 4075. Tel. (07) 379 6985.

The Potters' Gallery, The Queensland Potters' Association, 483 Brunswick Street, Fortitude Valley, Qld 4006. Tel. (07) 358 5121.

The Pottery Connection, 4 Carrara Street, Mount Gravatt, Qld 4122. Tel. (07) 343 7246.

Victor Mace Fine Art Gallery, 35 McDougall Street, Milton, Qld 4064. Tel. (07) 369 9305.
Exhibitions of leading Australian artists and craftspeople in various fields.

Virtu Craft Gallery, 57 MacGregor Terrace, Bardon, Qld 4065. Tel. (07) 369 9434.

Womens Creative Arts Centre, 651 Stanley Street, South Brisbane, Qld 4101. Tel. (07) 391 2556.

The Crafts Council of Queensland, "School of Arts", 2nd Floor, 166 Ann Street, Brisbane, Qld 4000. Tel. (07) 229 2661.
The Crafts Council has extensive and comprehensive listings of specialised craft centres, workshops and other organisations relating to the crafts in Queensland. Due to the size of Queensland it is impossible to list all the galleries and centres for the crafts. The Queensland Division of Cultural Activities has published a small handbook with numerous listings for regional areas **"Queensland Cultural Organisations"** covering both fine arts & crafts. Available from Division of Cultural Activities, Dept of the Arts, National Parks and Sport, PO Box 155, Brisbane North Quay, Qld 4002. Tel. (07) 227 4837.

ABORIGINAL ART GALLERIES QUEENSLAND

Aboriginal Artifacts, 135 George Street, Brisbane, Qld 4000. Tel. (07) 224 5730.

Native Arts and Crafts (Australia), 17 Elysium Road, Rochedale, Qld 4123. Tel. (07) 341 7065.

Queensland Aboriginal Creations, 135 George Street, Brisbane, Qld 4000. Tel. (07) 224 5730.

GALLERIES DEALING IN PRE 1900 EXHIBITS QUEENSLAND

Antiquarian Print Gallery, The Mansions, 40 George Street, Brisbane, Qld. Tel. (07) 221 7178.
Dealers in antique and rare maps, prints and early marine work.

Artifacts Gallery, Cnr Sandgate and Oriel Roads, Clayfield, Qld 4011. Tel. (07) 262 7552.
Dealers in Egyptian, Oriental, primitive South American art and Korean chests.

Creative 92, 92 Margaret Street, Toowoomba, Qld 4350. Tel. (076) 32 8779.
Contemporary Australian and overseas art, also dealers in antique maps and prints.

Decorators Gallery, 93 Musgrave Road, Red Hill, Qld 4059. Tel. (07) 369 3386.
Objets d'Art, antiques, primitive New Guinea art, Asian and Egyptian art.

Japan Room—Town Gallery, 4th Floor, Dunstan House, 236 Elizabeth Street, Brisbane, Qld 4000. Tel. (07) 229 1981.
The gallery exhibits 17th–20th century Japanese woodblock prints. Open Sunday–Friday 10–5.

Philip Bacon Galleries, 2 Arthur Street, New Farm, Qld 4005. Tel. (07) 358 3993.
Regular exhibitions of Australian artists plus large collection of 19th century paintings.

The Mansions, 40 George Street, Brisbane, Qld 4000. Tel. (07) 221 7178.
Antiquarian print gallery and mansions fine art and antiques. Hand coloured lithographs in the finest condition. Open 7 days 10–5 or by appointment. Catalogues available $3 each.

WORKSHOPS, STUDIOS AND ART CENTRES QUEENSLAND

Brisbane Community Arts Centre, 109 Edward Street, Brisbane, Qld 4000. Tel. (07) 221 1527.

Workshops in many different areas with life drawings classes available.

Performance and Promotional Club, 57 Hirschfield Street, Zillmere, Qld 4034.

Photography Workshops, Imagery Gallery, Cnr Grey and Melbourne Streets, South Brisbane, Qld 4001. Tel. (07) 844 8207.
Regular workshops held for both beginners and advanced students.

Pioneer Craft Guild Workshop, Primary Building, 281 Adelaide Street, Brisbane, Qld 4000. Tel. (07) 31 0291.

Queensland Film and Drama Centre, Griffith University, Nathan, Qld 4111. Tel. (07) 275 7414.
Workshops held in drama, music, mime, video, printmaking, ceramics and painting.

Queensland Fine Art Centre, "Androssan Hall", Cnr Gregory Terrace and Brookes Street, Bowen Hills, Qld 4006.
Providing art classes and workshops in various fields.

Queensland Printmakers Workshop, 34 Station Road, Indooroopilly, Qld 4068.

ALTERNATIVE ART SPACES QUEENSLAND

Access Arts Inc., GPO Box 24, Brisbane, Qld 4000.

Brisbane Womens Club, 105–107 Albert Street, Bribane, Qld 4000. Tel (07) 229 3969.

Half Dozen Group of Artists, 101 Outlook Crescent, Bardon, Qld 4065. Tel. (07) 369 0590.

Womens Creative Art Centre, 651 Stanley, South Brisbane, Qld 4101. Tel. (07) 391 2556.

FINE ART COURSES AND COLLEGES QUEENSLAND

Brisbane College of Advanced Education: The Admissions Officer, 130 Victoria Park Road, Kelvin Grove, Qld 4059. Tel. (07) 352 8153.
The college offer the following courses; an Associate Diploma in art administration: painting, drawing, sculpture, printmaking, photography, ceramics, jewellery, gold and silversmithing, textiles, graphic design and film, television, cinema studies. An Undergraduate (Bachelor's) Degree is offered in painting: drawing, sculpture, dance, printmaking, ceramics, jewellery, gold and silversmithing, textile, dance, drama and music. A Diploma is offered in teaching: art and craft, design. A Graduate Diploma is offered in teaching: art and craft, design.

Capricorna Institute of Advanced Education, The Registrar, MS 76, Rockhampton, Qld 4700. Tel. (079) 36 1177.
The college offers a Diploma in teaching: art and craft, design, printmaking, ceramics, woodcraft. An Undergraduate (Bachelor's) Degree is offered in film, television, cinema studies, professional writing/journalism/radio, dance, drama and music.

Darling Downs Institute of Advanced Education, The Registrar, Post Office, Darling Heights, Toowoomba, Qld 4350. Tel. (076) 30 1300.
The college offers a Diploma in painting, sculpture, printmaking, ceramics, textiles, dance, drama and music.

Queensland College of Art, The Registrar, PO Box 84, Morningside, Qld 4170. Tel. (07) 395 9123.
The college offers an Undergraduate (Bachelor's) Degree in the areas of painting, drawing, sculpture, printmaking, photography, ceramics, jewellery, graphic design illustration, film, television and cinema studies.

Queensland Institute of Technology, The Registrar, GPO Box 2434, Brisbane, Qld 4001. Tel. (07) 223 2371.
The institute offers and Undergraduate (Bachelor's) Degree in industrial design: environmental/landscape design. A Graduate Diploma is offered in industrial design.

Griffith University, Student Secretary, Griffith University, Nathan, Qld 4111. Tel. (07) 275 7111.
Undergraduate (Bachelor's) Degree in film, television and cinema studies.

University of Queensland, The Registrar, University of Queensland, St Lucia, Qld 4067. Tel. (07) 377 1111.
Undergraduate (Bachelor's Degree in art history and theory.

ART SUPPLIES AND MATERIALS QUEENSLAND

Allcrafts Arts and Crafts Materials Centre, Greenslopes Mall, Logan Road, Greenslopes, Qld 4120.
Extensive range of high quality materials for art and craft. Tel. (07) 394 4313.

Art Essentials, The Princess Theatre, 8 Annerley Road, Woolloongabba, Qld 4102. Tel. (07) 891 5354.
Imported art materials and papers.

Art Land, 823 Gympie Road, Chermside, Qld 4032. Tel. (07) 350 1313.
Comprehensive range.

Art Materials (Qld) Pty Ltd, 164 Ipswich Road, Woolloongabba, Qld 4102. Tel. (07) 391 2859.
Wide selection of imported and Australian materials.

Art Requirements, 1 Dickson Street, Wooloowin, Qld 4030. Tel. (07) 857 2732.
One of the best suppliers on the north side of Brisbane. Art classes available in all mediums.

Artistcare (Australia) Pty Ltd, 66 Charlotte Street, Brisbane, Qld 4000. Tel. (07) 229 4811, also at 52 Baxter Street, Fortitude Valley, Qld 4006. Tel. (07) 52 8099.
Leading supplier for the professional artist and student.

Discount Art Materials, 2421 Sandgate Road, Boondall, Qld 4034. Tel. (07) 265 2915.
Selection of artist materials and art books.

Moorooka Arts and Crafts Centre, 136 Beaudesert Road, Moorooka, Qld 4105. Tel. (07) 892 2814.
Full range of art and craft materials and professional framing service.

Southbank Graphics, 128–130 Merivale Street, South Brisbane, Qld 4101. Tel. (07) 844 7144.
Extensive range of graphic art materials and stationary.

The Artist Touch, Shop 51–53a, Stafford City Shopping Centre, Stafford, Qld 4053. Tel. (07) 352 6449.
Comprehensive range of art materials.

2 Art Pty Ltd, 161 Elizabeth Street, Brisbane, Qld 4000. Tel. (07) 221 4866.
Fine and graphic art supplies also school equipment. Professional advise available.

PHOTOGRAPHY, FILM AND VIDEO QUEENSLAND

Australian Photographic Society, PO Box 10, Brisbane Base Hospital, Qld 4029. Tel. (07) 848 5366.

Brisbane Camera Group, PO Box 205, North Quay, Qld 4000. Tel. (07) 277 2792.

Brisbane Cinema Group, PO Box 1655, Brisbane, Qld 4001. Tel. (07) 369 4045.

Brisbane Film Festival, GPO Box 1655, Brisbane, Qld 4001.

Brisbane Film and Television School, Duffield Street, Kingaroy, Qld 4610. Tel. (07) 204 4279.

Brisbane Independent Filmmakers, 4th Floor, People's Palace, 308 Edward Street, Brisbane, Qld 4000. Tel. (07) 229 1410.

Brisbane Railway Film Society, 5/45 Real Street, Annerley, Qld 4103. Tel. (07) 892 3504.

Photographic Society of Queensland, GPO Box 1673, Brisbane, Qld 4001.

Queensland Council for Children's Films and Television, PO Box 151, Corinda, Qld 4075. Tel. (07) 375 5423.

Queensland Film Academy, 97 Elizabeth Street, Brisbane, Qld 4000. Tel. (07) 229 9422.

Queensland Film Corporation, State Law Building, 50 Ann Street, Brisbane, Qld 4000. Tel. (07) 229 1233.

Queensland Film and Drama Centre, c/o Griffith University, Nathan, Qld 4111.

Queensland Film and Television Workshop, 43 Cordeia Street, South Brisbane, Qld 4101. Tel. (07) 275 7414.
Check listings under Fine Art Courses and Colleges—Brisbane, for available courses.

PHOTOGRAPHIC SUPPLIES QUEENSLAND

Bentley's Camera House, Indooroopilly Shoppingtown, Indooroopilly, Qld 4068. Tel. (07) 378 7133.
One hour print service, and all other photographic requirements.

Camera Tech, 270 Adelaide Street, Brisbane, Qld 4000. Tel. (07) 229 5406.
Professional service on developing and printing and camera sales.

Cinecolor Film Laboratories, 55 McDougall Street, Milton, Qld 4064. Tel. (07) 369 3846.
Professional slide processing and duplicating, 16mm & 35mm cinema processing.

Fletchers Fotographics, 562 South Pine Road, Everton Park, Qld 4053. Tel. (07) 354 2454.
New and secondhand photographic equipment, accessories a speciality.

KLIKK, Mountainview Shopping Centre, Mt Gravatt, Qld 4122. Tel. (07) 343 9465.
There are 4 other stores in Brisbane. Developing, repairs, trade-ins and accessories.

The Gap Photographic Centre, Waterworks Road, The Gap, Qld 4061. Tel. (07) 300 4942.

Photo Continental Pty Ltd, 26 Wellington Road, East Brisbane, Qld 4169. Tel. (07) 391 7222.
Also at 440 Queen Street, Brisbane, Qld 4000.

Prolab Laboratories Pty Ltd, 88 Ernest Street, South Brisbane, Qld 4101. Tel. (07) 844 9621.
The professionals' laboratory for all developing, printing and all photofinishing work colour and black & white.

ARTS BOOKSHOPS QUEENSLAND

Art Information, A Bookstore, PO Box 108 Paddington, Qld 4064. Tel. (07) 369 4610.
A specialist service for those interested in the arts.

American Book Store, 197 Elizabeth Street, Brisbane, Qld 4000. Tel. (07) 229 4821.
Wide range of art, music, educational, literature, special overseas imports and a small order service available.

B.C.F. Book Shop, 107 Elizabeth Street, Brisbane, Qld 4000. Tel. (07) 229 5393.
Specialists in technical, hobby and handcraft books.

Folio Books, 81 Elizabeth Street, Brisbane, Qld 4000. Tel. (07) 221 1368.
Specialising in fine books on art, photography and the performing arts.

Institute Bookshop, George Street, Brisbane, Qld 4000. Tel. (07) 223 2433.
Tertiary texts and reference books.

Mary Ryan Bookshop, 179 Latrobe Terrace, Paddington, Qld 4064. Tel. (07) 368 1694.
Australiana, fine arts, hobbies and crafts. A selection of technical books. Open Monday–Friday 9–5, Saturday 9–1, Sunday 11–4.

S.T.A. Bookshop, 26 Roseleigh Street, Wooloowin, Qld 4030. Tel. (07) 857 3411.

The Art Gallery Bookshop, Queensland Art Gallery, Queensland Cultural Centre, South Brisbane, Qld 4101. Tel. (07) 240 7333. Interesting arts bookshop covering visual and performing arts internationally and nationally. The shop is within the main gallery complex.

The Book Nook, Brisbane Community Arts Centre, 109 Edward Street, Brisbane, Qld 4000. Tel. (07) 221 8537.
Concentration on theatre, speech, drama and literature.

The Tamborine Mountain Bookshop, Main Street, North Tamborine, Qld 4272. Tel. (075) 45 2222.
Selected overseas and Australian books on art, literature, travel, the garden, food and wine.

University Bookshop, Staff House Road, St Lucia, Qld 4067. Tel. (07) 377 2657.
Open to the general public. Mail orders welcome. Tel (07) 377 2438.

University Co-operative Bookshop Ltd, Kessels Road, Nathan, Qld 4111. Tel. (07) 275 2475.
Orders welcome from the public. Comprehensive arts section.

FINE ART FRAMING QUEENSLAND

Art Restoration, 112 Lambert Street, Kangaroo Point, Qld 4169. Tel. (07) 4169.
Expert restoration on oils, watercolours, etchings and graphics.

Dee Gee Framers, 1063 Ipswich Road, Moorooka, Qld 4105. Tel. (07) 848 4028.
Specialising in custom framing, timber and aluminium, special concessions to artists and students.

Dimensions Art Galleries, 101 Adelaide Street, Brisbane, Qld 4000. Tel. (07) 229 9701.
Professional picture framing and laminating.

Gallery Two Paddington, 98 Latrobe Terrace, Paddington, Qld 4064. Tel. (07) 369 7156.

Hoisser and Associates, 800 Zillmere Road, Aspley, Qld 4034. Tel. (07) 263 1800.
All types of framing done on the premises, same location as Geoffrey Hoisser Galleries.

Ipswich Framing Centre, 11 Lawrence Street, North Ipswich, Qld 4305. Tel. (07) 202 2525.

Little Dutch Picture Framing, 10 Makerston Street, Brisbane, Qld 4000. Tel. (07) 221 0006.
Wholesale and retail service, also restoration done.

Matisse Picture Frames, 14 Samford Road, Alderley, Qld 4051. Tel. (07) 356 9689.
Custom wood and aluminium frames, dry mounting and laminating.

THEATRICAL ORGANISATIONS QUEENSLAND

Australian Dance Foundation Ltd, GPO Box 1858, Brisbane, Qld 4001. Tel. (07) 300 1610.

Ballet Theatre of Queensland, PO Box 20, North Quay, Qld 4000. Tel. (07) 378 1051.

New Directions Creative Dance Theatre, PO Box 445, Lutwyche, Qld 4030. Tel. (07) 371 6642.

Queensland Ballet Company, 129 Margaret Street, Brisbane, Qld 4000. Tel. (07) 229 3355.

Queensland Experimental Ballet, 44 Newcombe Street, Sunnybank Hills, Qld 4109. Tel. (07) 345 8645.

The Ambrossians (drama group), PO Box 227, Alderley, Qld 4051.

Australian Community Theatre, PO Box 271, Hamilton Central, Qld 4007. Tel. (07) 377 0509.

Brisbane Dramatic Arts Company, 17 Crown Street, Petrie Terrace, Qld 4000.

Brisbane Theatre Company, 10 Glanmire Road, Paddington, Qld 4064. Tel. (07) 399 8242.

Queensland Childrens Theatre and Creative Workshop Association, Playhouse, Cnr Bonney Avenue and Norman Parade, Clayfield, Qld 4011. Tel. (07) 262 7983.

Royal Queensland Theatre Company, GPO Box 21, Brisbane, Qld 4000. Tel. (07) 221 3861.

Speech and Drama Association of Queensland, 21 Elimatta Drive, Ashgrove 4060. Tel. (07) 38 3056.

The N.T. Theatre Company (Twelfth Night), PO Box 124, Woolloongabba, Qld 4102. Tel. (07) 352 5133.

Warana Drama Festival, Organiser, Warana Festival Office, PO Box 1232, North Quay, Qld 4000. Tel. (07) 221 0011.

THEATRICAL VENUES QUEENSLAND

Brisbane Arts Theatre, 210 Petrie Terrace, Qld 4000. Tel. (07) 369 2344.

Brisbane Entertainment Centre, Stanworth Road, Boondall, Qld 4034. Tel. (07) 265 8111.
Events information service Tel. (07) 11 611.

Concert Hall, Melbourne Street, Brisbane, Qld 4000. Tel. (07) 844 0201.

Crystal Theatre Windsor, LeGeyt Street, Windsor, Qld 4030. Tel. (07) 375 7811.

Expressions—The Queensland Dance Theatre Ltd, 39 Leyton Street, Grange, Qld 4051. Tel. (07) 352 6738.

Festival Hall, 65 Charlotte Street, Brisbane, Qld 4000. Tel. (07) 221 5433, bookings Tel. 229 4250.

Her Majesty's Theatre (Brisbane) Ltd, 197 Queen Street, Brisbane, Qld 4000. Tel. (07) 221 2777.

Lyric Theatre, South Bank, South Brisbane, Qld. 4101. Tel. (07) 844 0201.
cc **Playhouse**, 221 Bonney Avenue, Clayfield, Qld 4011. Tel. (07) 262 7333.

Princess Theatre T.N., 8 Annerley Road, Woolloongabba, Qld 4102. Tel. (07) 891 5155.

Queensland Performing Arts Complex, at the Queensland Cultural Centre, South Bank, South Brisbane, Qld 4101. Tel. 844 0201.
For performance details (24 hrs) Tel. (07) 11 632.

Schonell Theatre, The University of Queensland, St Lucia, Qld 4067. Tel. (07) 371 1879.

Twelfth Night Theatre, 4 Cintra Road, Bowen Hills, Qld 4006. Tel. (07) 52 7622.

MUSICAL ORGANISATIONS QUEENSLAND

Australian Society for Music Education (Qld), c/o Music Dept, BCAE, Kelvin Grove Campus, Victoria Park Road, Kelvin Grove, Qld 4059. Tel. (07) 352 8111.

Australian Youth Jazz Big Band, PO Box 153, Spring Hill, Qld 4004. Tel. (07) 831 0283.

Brisbane Chamber Orchestra, PO Box 158, West End, Qld 4101. Tel. (07) 44 5021.

Brisbane Festival Orchestra, PO Box 158, West End, Qld 4101.

Brisbane Light Opera Company, PO Box 193, West End, Qld 4101. Tel. (07) 397 1222.

Brisbane Music Club, 157 Doroch Terrace, Highgate Hill, Qld 4101. Tel. (07) 844 7997.

Council of Music and Drama Queensland, 19 Sixth Avenue, Sandgate, Qld 4017. Tel. (07) 269 2863.

International Society for Contemporary Music (Qld), GPO Box 1570, Brisbane, Qld 4001. Tel. (07) 57 1918.

Metropolitan Opera, c/o Queensland Conservatorium of Music, George Street, Brisbane, Qld 4000. Tel. (07) 229 2650.

Musicians Union of Australia, Brisbane Branch, 5 Prospect Street, Fortitude Valley, Qld 4006. Tl. (07) 52 8867.

Queensland Conservatorium of Music, The Director, George Street, Brisbane, Qld 4000. Tel. (07) 229 2650.

Queensland Symphony Orchestra, General Manager, GPO Box 9994, Brisbane, Qld 4001. Tel. (07) 377 5222.

Queensland University Musical Society, c/o University of Qld Union, University of Queensland, St Lucia, Qld 4067. Tel. (07) 399 4887.

MUSICAL VENUES QUEENSLAND

With outdoor concerts and performances on the increase in Australia you can find band concerts frequently being held in the botanic gardens and King George Square in central Brisbane.

A.B.C. Music Centre, Ferry Road, West End, Qld 4101. Tel. (07) 377 5102 for bookings.

Arts Theatre, 210 Petrie Terrace, Brisbane, Qld 4000. Tel. (07) 369 2344.

Brisbane Entertainment Centre, Stanworth Road, Boondall, Qld 4034. Tel. (07) 265 8111.
Events information service Tel. (07) 11 611.

Bonaparte's Hotel, Cnr Gipps Street and St Paul's Terrace, Fortitude Valley, Qld 4006. Tel. (07) 252 1400.
Excellent live jazz.

La Boîte Theatre, 57 Hale Street, Milton, Qld 4064. Tel. (07) 369 1622.
Live music and theatre.

Lyric Theatre, South Bank, South Brisbane, Qld 4101. Tel. (07) 844 0201.

Metro Arts Theatre, 109 Edward Street, Brisbane, Qld 4000. Tel. (07) 221 527/870 9389.

Old Town Hall, Cnr Racecourse Road and Rossiter Parade, Hamilton, Qld 4007. Tel. (07) 356 4032/356 0525.

Queensland Performing Arts Complex, Concert Hall, (Queensland Cultural Centre), South Bank, South Brisbane, Qld 4101. Tel. (07) 844 0201 for tickets. For 24 hour information service Tel. (07) 11 632.

Redcliffe Entertainment Centre, Downs Street, Redcliffe, Qld 4020. Tel. (07) 283 0308.

The Melbourne Hotel, 2–16 Browning Street, South Brisbane, Qld 4101. Tel. (07) 441 571.
For live jazz and country and western music.

PLACES OF INTEREST BRISBANE

Parks

Brisbane's **Botanic Gardens** are on the foothills of **Mt Coottha**, not far from the centre of Brisbane and are open daily 9.30–4.30. An opportunity to see many of the exotic tropical specimans of flora Queensland has to offer.

Bunya Park, Bunya Park Drive, nr Albany Creek is a sanctuary of natural bushland surrounding a lake, with barbecue and picnic facilities available with plenty of interesting wildlife in the area.

Lone Pine Koala Sanctuary, Fig Tree Pocket, 15 minutes drive west of City Hall in Brisbane. Lunch cruises to the park leave North Quay 2pm daily from Hayles wharf.

New Farm Park, Brunswick Street, Brisbane. Known for its 12,000 rose bushes,jacaranda avenues and poinciana trees. Free band concerts every Sunday.

Lamington National Park, situated in the southeast of Queensland in the mountains covers a large area of magnificent untouched scenery. It has excellent walks, horse riding and hiking. Only one hours drive from Brisbane on the way to the park is **Tamborine Mountain**, regarded as an area of unique natural beauty.

RESTAURANTS BRISBANE

Angies Pizzeria and Trattoria, 10 Dornoch Street, West End, Qld 4101. Tel. (07) 844 9008.

Baguette, 150 Racecourse Road, Ascot, Qld 4007. Tel. (07) 268 6168.
One of Brisbane's best licensed restaurants with tropical setting which features exotic flowers, a selection of fine paintings and sculpture.

Benjamin's, 195 Musgrave Road, Red Hill, Qld 4059. Tel. (07) 369 9297.
Seafood and vegetarian menu.

Cafe on the Bay, Cnr Explanade and Cambridge Parade, Manly, Qld 4179. Tel. (07) 396 9591.

Daniela's Coffee and Tea Lounge, 49 Sherwood Road, Toowong, Qld 4066. Tel. (07) 371 7795.

Houdini's, 55 Elizabeth Street, Brisbane, Qld 4000. Tel. (07) 229 9090 B.Y.O.

Jo Jo's Downstairs, 130 Queen Street, Brisbane, Qld 4000. Tel. (07) 221 1221.

Mocca's, Coffee Shop, 52 Queen Street, Brisbane, Qld 4000. Tel. (07) 312 408.
Good pastries.

Orsino's, 2421 Sandgate Road, Boondall, Qld 4034.
Restaurant near the Boondall entertainment centre. Seafood, steaks and unforgettable pizzas.

Puzzles, 262 Given Terrace, Paddington, Qld 4064. Tel. (07) 369 3291.
Incredible food.

Solutions, Restaurant, 77 Sir Fred Schonell Drive, St Lucia, Qld 4067. Tel. (07) 371 7952.

Solutions, Cafe, 57 Ryans Road, St Lucia, Qld 4067. Tel. (07) 371 7952.
Open 7 days a week. Tropical à la carte menu.

Swiss Cafe, 129 George Street, Brisbane, Qld 4000. Tel. (07) 221 4765.

The Greek Taverna, 167 Elizabeth Street, Brisbane, Qld 4000. Tel. (07) 221 3034.
Licensed Greek traditional style with Greek music and dancing Wednesday–Saturday nights. Lively and fun.

The Little Frog, French Restaurant, 19 Emlyn Street, Coorparoo, Qld 4151. Tel. (07) 397 7114.

The Pippin Took, 86 Macgregor Terrace, Bardon, Qld 4065. Tel. (07) 369 6482.
Dinner Tuesday–Saturday, lunch Thursday & Friday.

Ye Olde Court House Restaurant, 1 Paxton Street, Cleveland, Qld 4163. Tel. (07) 286 1386.
An old Victorian era building dating from 1853, situated near the seashore. Paintings and art objects are on display in this pleasant atmosphere of days gone by. Excellent food as well.

CONTENTS
WESTERN AUSTRALIA

PERTH AND WESTERN AUSTRALIA

Western Australia has a population of some 1.2 million and
most people live in and around the city of **Perth**. Other small
towns are **Bunbury, Albany**, the state's oldest town
Kalgoorlie, once the centre of the 1990's gold rush and again
in the 1970's when iron ore was discovered in the **Pilbara**
(known to the art world through Fred Williams series of
watercolours and paintings). **Broome** is known for its unusu-
ally shaped and coloured pearls. **Fremantle** has now been
almost absorbed into Perth and since the America's Cup in
1986/87 has spruced up its colonial style buildings and
become a smart artistic lively town rather than an old port and
restaurants in the area are worth visiting. The America's Cup
gave the whole state of Western Australia a boost internationally, increasing the number of visitors, as people discovered what a spectacularly unspoilt part of the country it is,
with some of the finest long white beaches, good surf and an
excellent dry and warm climate all year round.

202

The University campus, Perth, West Australia (Heather Waddell)

Perth city is dynamic and youthful and new city buildings are growing up at a fast rate as mining-related industries and tourism provide a need for greater space. **Alan Bond**, **Robert Holmes à Court** and **Lang Hancock** are three of the local tycoons who have helped bring wealth to this area. Robert Holmes à Court has also a major collection of paintings by Western Australian artists and Alan Bond is a well known investor in international art.

The **Perth City Festival** in February and March brings overseas and interstate music, dance, visual arts, literature, film, theatre and television to the city and a spectacular fireworks display ends the festival. Venues range from the **Octagon theatre** inside the stately mock-Spanish university grounds to the **Art Gallery of Western Australia** in a central city arts complex to **Fremantle galleries** and open air settings. Although the citizens of Perth centre their lives very heavily on the open air lifestyle with its many and varying sports they have an amazing capacity for interest in the arts and eating out. Perth is reputed to have more restaurants per (capita) than any other city in Australia.

Places of interest in and around Perth

Rottnest Island. Boats leave from Perth, Fremantle and the new Sorrento Quay (40 minutes by catamaran). The Perth boat goes down the **Swan River** past **Peppermint Grove** and the **Royal Perth Yacht Club**, and although the longer journey, is very enjoyable. Rottnest Island is a must even for a

203

Windsurfing on a Perth beach (Heather Waddell)

day visit although I'd recommend staying. Quokkas (marsupials) wander freely on this paradise island (car free but bicycles are available for hire). The crystal clear turquoise waters make every day breathtaking.

Vineyard Cruises. Either by boat along the Swan River or by car a visit to the local vineyard is memorable. **Houghton's** and **Sandalford's** vineyards are two of the best and the **Margaret River Valley** is worth visiting.

Buckland. A fine example of an Australian colonial homestead in attractive surrounding countryside (at Irishtown near Northam).

204

New Norcia Monastery. A spectacular Spanish style monastery in the outback with a collection of paintings including a Murillo, although these were temporarily stolen by thieves not realising the value of the paintings!

Fremantle still has the atmosphere of an old penal colony port and it is worthwhile just wandering around the market area and enjoying the architecture. At the front the **Esplanade Hotel** interior is modern, but based on the old Australian colonial style. Various art centres, studios and galleries have congregated in this area providing a wide range of arts and crafts for sale.

University of Western Australia. Situated in Nedlands the buildings are very Californian Spanish in style and the grounds are relaxing with palm trees, shady late 19th century buildings with attractive arches and fountains.

The Art Gallery of Western Australia is a modern building with attractive gallery space and within the gallery is pleasant open air sculpture courtyard.

Western Australia Tourist Bureau, 772 Hay Street, Perth. WA 6000. Tel. (09) 322 2999.
Open Monday–Friday 8.30–5, Saturday 9-11.45a.m.

STATE ARTS ORGANISATIONS WESTERN AUSTRALIA

Art Gallery of Western Australia, 47 James Street, Perth, WA 6000. Tel. (09) 328 7233.
Now part of the complex known as the "**Perth Cultural Centre**".

Festival of Perth, c/o University of Western Australia, Mounts Bay Road, Crawley, WA 6009. Tel. (09) 386 7977.

Fremantle Arts Centre, 1 Finnerty Street, Fremantle, WA 6160. Tel. (09) 335 8244.

Film and Television Institute of Western Australia Inc., 92 Adelaide Street, Fremantle, WA 6160. Tel. (09) 335 1055.

Film Council of Western Australia, 336 Churchill Avenue, Subiaco, WA 6008. Tel. (09) 382 2500.

Perth Society of Artists, c/o The Art Gallery of WA, 47 James Street, Perth, WA 6000. Tel. (09) 328 7233.

The National Theatre Inc., 3 Pier Street, Perth, WA 6000.
Tel. (09) 325 3344.

Western Australia Arts Council, 6 Outram Street, West
Perth, WA 6005. Tel. (09) 322 6766.

Western Australia Womens Society of Fine Arts and
Crafts, c/o Boans, Murray Street, Perth, WA 6000.

Western Australia Opera Company Inc., 825 Hay Street,
Perth, WA 6000. Tel. (09) 321 5869.

Western Australian Academy of Performing Arts, 2 Bradford Street, Mt Lawley, WA 6050. Tel. (09) 370 6443.

STATE CRAFT
ORGANISATIONS
WESTERN AUSTRALIA

Batik Association of Western Australia, 69 Ensign Street,
Narrogin, WA 6312.

Ceramic Study Group of Western Australia, 37 Congdon
Street, Swanbourne, WA 6010.

Crafts Council of Western Australia, 1st Floor, Perth City
Railway Station, Wellington Stret, Perth, WA 6000. Tel. (09)
325 2799.

Embroiderers Guild of Western Australia, c/o 3D Design,
Western Australia Institute of Technology, Haymen Road,
Bently, WA 6102.

STATE REGIONAL
MUSEUMS AND
GALLERIES
WESTERN AUSTRALIA

The Art Gallery of Western Australia, 47 James Street,
Perth, WA 6000. Tel. (09) 328 7233.
Specialist Aboriginal collection, historical and contemporary
collection. Major visiting exhibitions and changing shows of
Australia's leading artists. Gallery hours, daily 10–5, free
guided tours Wednesday 12noon & Friday 1.15.

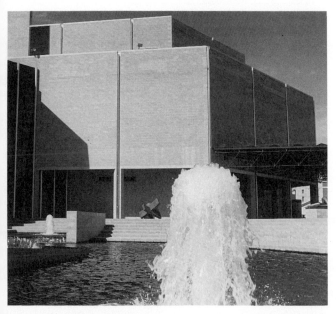

Art Gallery of Western Australia, Perth Cultural Centre

The Bunbury Art Gallery, PO Box 119, Bunbury, WA 6230.
Housing the established city collection.

Fremantle Art Gallery, 43 High Street, Fremantle, WA
6160. Tel. (09) 335 5855.
Changing exhibitions by Western Australian artists and the
gallery collection permanently on exhibition. Open Wednesday–Sunday noon–5.

Fremantle Museum, Ord Street, Fremantle, WA 6101.
Open Monday–Thursday 10.30–5, Friday–Sunday 1–5.

Hills Creative Arts Centre, Cnr Railway and Stirk Road,
Kalamunda, WA 6076. Tel. (09) 293 2579.
Changing exhibitions by local artist. Open Friday 10–4, Satur-
day 10–1, Sunday 1–4.

Undercroft Galleries, University of Western Australia, Nedlands, WA 6009. Tel. (09) 443 3482/380 2006.
Exhibitions of the galleries collection, touring exhibitions, and
works by local artist. Open Monday–Friday 9–5.

Museum of Western Australia, Francis Street, Perth, WA
6000. Tel. (09) 328 4411.

COMMERCIAL AND NON-PROFIT GALLERIES PERTH AND FREMANTLE

Perth and Fremantle art scene

Perth has the excellent spacious **Art Gallery of Western Australia** which was opened in 1979 and holds major art exhibitions especially during the **Perth Arts Festival** such as the Phillips Collection which was visited by some 30,000 Perth citizens. The historical collection includes paintings by Arthur Streeton, Tom Roberts, Frederick McCubbin and the **Heidelberg painters**, Aboriginal art both contemporary and historical. Contemporary artists in the collection include Arthur Boyd, Brett Whiteley, Sidney Nolan and Western Australian artists.

There are many small commercial art galleries in Perth and Fremantle, also several non-profit lively art spaces such as the dynamic gallery space run by **Praxis** in Fremantle and the Beach Gallery space where many of the Curtin University art teachers have shown their work. The "**Where to Go**" of the **West Australian** newspaper lists current exhibitions and arts events and appears on Thursdays.

Local Perth galleries such as **Gallery 52**, **Galerie Dusseldorf**, the **Lister Gallery** and the **Greenhill Galleries** all show quality contemporary professional art by Australian and international artists. Local tycoons such as **Alan Bond**, **Robert Holmes à Court** and **Lang Hancock** have built up both local West Australian art and national art collections adding a local interest in professional art. Perth is one of the world's most isolated cities and West Australia's Californian climate, spectacular scenery and mineral resources have helped develop interest in the arts in a unique way, unlike Sydney, Melbourne and Adelaide. Gold and diamond finds in the **Kimberleys** and **Pilbara** have helped make the city wealthy, dynamic and refreshing in it's approach to life and the one million inhabitants young, active and open-minded.

Fremantle has over 300 artists living in the town and there are numerous art and craft galleries and also studios. **Praxis** as an art organisation has made quite a name for itself both nationally and internationally. They run **Praxis M** art magazine, an art space, art classes and studio space. In late 1988, **PRAXIS** merged with **PICA** (Perth Institute of Contemporary Art) in Central Perth.

Bortignons, Gallery of Man, 67 Snowball Road, Kalamunda, WA 6076. Tel. (09) 293 4033.
Australian contemporary art and Aboriginal art, also interesting tribal art.

Christies Contemporary Art (Art Co-ordinates), 236 St George Terrace, Perth, WA 6000. Tel. (09) 481 0306.

Art Gallery of Western Australia courtyard with sculpture (Heather Waddell)

Open Monday–Thursday 9.30–3, or by appointment. Specialists on Western Australian art, contact Peter Garside.

Cliff Street Gallery, 36 Cliff Street, Fremantle, WA 6160. The gallery deals mainly in international and Australian prints.

Darklight Photo Gallery and Workshop, 33–35 Pakenham Street, Fremantle, WA 6160. Tel. (09) 335 1077. Special photographic exhibitions on a regular basis. Open Wednesday–Sunday 11–5.

Sculpture in the Cultural Centre courtyard, Perth (Heather Waddell)

Prism Gallery, 23 Pakenham Street, Fremantle, WA 6160. Tel. (09) 335 8483.

Eric Car Gallery, 28 Mouatt Street, Fremantle, WA 6160. Tel. (09) 335 3316.
Open Monday–Friday 10–4, Sunday 2–5.

Galerie Dusseldorf, 890 Hay Street, Perth, WA 6000. Tel. (09) 325 2596.
Open Tuesday–Friday 10–4.30, Sundays 2–5. Worth visiting for exhibitions of leading Australian and overseas contemporary artists. Artists include: Su Baker, Jane Barwell,

John Beard, Philip Burns, Michael Carlin, Richard Gunning, Marie Haas, Andrew Hayim, Lidjia Dombrarska Larsen, Brian McKay, John Peart, Howard Taylor, Sean Wake-Mazey.

Gallery 52, 74 Beaufort Street, Perth, WA 6000. Tel. (09) 227 8996.
Open Tuesday–Friday 10–5, Saturdays 10–1, Sundays 2–5. One of Perth's more important commercial art galleries with exhibitions of work by leading Australian artists.

Gallery 350, 360 Hay Street, Subiaco, WA 6008. Tel. (09) 381 6577.
Dealing in original prints and graphics and also provides a framing service.

Graphics Gallery, 357 Rokeby Road, Subiaco, WA 6008. Specialist in all types of graphic art.

Greenhill Galleries, 20 Howard Street, Perth, WA 6000. Tel. (09) 321 2369.
In association with Greenhill Galleries in Adelaide this gallery shows work by prominent Australian artists. Open Tuesday–Friday 10–6, Saturday 10–5, Sunday 2–5.

Glyde Gallery, 32 Glyde Street, Mosman Park, WA 6012. Tel. (09) 383 3929.
Exhibitions of contemporary Australian art.

Goodbridge Galleries, 239 Beaufort Street, Perth, WA 6000. Tel. (09) 328 4817.
Open Tuesday–Friday 10–5, Saturdays 10–12, Sundays 2–4. Australian art and craft works.

Feather Press Print Studio and Gallery, 37 Learoyd Street, Mount Lawley, WA 6050. Tel. (09) 272 2273.
Run by Leon Pericles a Western Australian artist. A commercial print studio.

Hawks Hill Gallery, Goollelal Drive, Kingsley, WA 6026. Tel. (09) 409 9063.

Kalamunda Gallery, 1a Haynes Road, Kalamunda, WA 6076. Tel. (09) 293 2774.
Open Monday–Friday 11–5.30, Saturday & Sunday 2–5.30 or by appointment. Art materials also available.

Lister Gallery, 248 St Georges Terrace, Perth, WA 6000. Tel. (09) 321 5764.
Mixed exhibitions by top Australian artists. Open Monday–Friday 10–5, Saturday & Sunday 2–5.

Miller Gallery, 243 Stirling Highway, Claremont, WA 6010. Tel. (09) 384 6035.
Regular exhibitions of contemporary Australian art. Open Tuesday–Friday 10–5, Saturday 10–1.

Nexus Gallery, 33–35 Pakenham Street, Fremantle, WA 6160. Tel. (09) 335 1077.
Open Tuesday–Sunday 10–5. Dynamic exhibitions by local Fremantle artists.

Praxis Gallery, 33 Pakenham Street, Fremantle, WA 6160. Tel. (09) 335 9770.
Praxis is run by an extremely active group of artists and not only has exhibition space but runs an arts magazine called **Praxis M**, published quarterly and supported by the Visual Arts Board, annual subscription is $15 and is very cosmopolitan in its coverage with reviews both nationally and internationally on contemporary issues.

Quentin Gallery, 20 St Quentin Avenue, Claremont, WA 6010. Tel. (09) 384 8463.
Regular exhibitions by leading contemporary Australian and overseas artists. Open Tuesday–Friday 10–5, Sundays 2–5.

Rics Gallery, 89 Waratah Avenue, Dalkeith, WA 6009. Tel. (09) 386 4726.
Exhibitions featuring Western Australian artists.

Settlers Art Gallery and Settlers Antiques, Avon Terrace, York, WA 6302. Tel. (09) 325 9430.
Open Wednesday–Sunday 10–4.

The House That Jack Built, 10 Camberwell Road, Balga, WA 6061. Tel. (09) 349 7117.
Local contemporary art. Open Monday–Friday 12–5.30, Saturday & Sunday 10–5.30, or by appointment.

Van Hall Gallery, 23 Hovia Terrace, South Perth, WA 6151. Tel. (09) 367 7020.
Original prints by leading European artists. Open Monday–Friday 9–5, Saturday 10–1, or by appointment.

New Collectables Gallery, 643 Albany Highway, Victoria Park, WA 6100. Tel. (09) 362 6960.
Dealers in fine art with regular exhibitions.

CRAFT GALLERIES
WESTERN AUSTRALIA

Bannister Street Workshop, 8–12 Bannister Street, Fremantle, WA 6160. Tel. (09) 335 9165.
Crafts people working in studios on the premises, open to the public for sales, phone and check for opening times.

Clayforms, 46A Angove Street, North Perth, WA 6006. Tel. (09) 227 7206.
Open Tuesday–Saturday 10–5, Sunday 1–5.

Heritage Crafts, Shop 50, Carillon Centre, Perth, WA 6000. Tel. (09) 322 3162.
Specialising in Australian crafts.

Indigo 119, 119 Broadway, Nedlands, WA 6009. Tel. (09) 386 2959.
Specialising in handcrafted textiles.

Kalangadoo Krafts, Narrikup, WA 6326. Tel. (09) 53 2007.
Selected exhibitions of high quality crafts, phone first and check opening times.

Moondyne Arts and Crafts, 79a Russell Highway, Margaret River, WA 6286.
Selected exhibitions of Australian crafts. Open Tuesday 10.30–3, Wednesday 1–4, Saturday 10–12 noon.

The Cheese Factory Craft Centre and Gallery, Nannup Road, Balingup, WA 6253. Tel. (09) 64 1018.
Open Tuesday–Sunday with exhibitions of high quality hand-crafted goods.

The Cliff Street Gallery, 36 Cliff Street, Fremantle, WA 6160. Tel. (09) 335 8897.
Selected exhibitions of fine art and crafts. Open Monday–Friday 11–5, Saturday & Sunday 2–4.

ABORIGINAL ART GALLERIES WESTERN AUSTRALIA

Aboriginal Art Gallery, 224 St George Terrace, Perth, WA 6000. Tel. (09) 321 4440.
Good selection of original paintings and craftworks.

Birukmarri Gallery, 47 High Street, Fremantle, WA 6160. Tel. (09) 335 4741.
Open Tuesday–Saturday 9.30–5.30, Sundays 11–5. Variety of Aboriginal art exhibitions.

Bortigons Kalamunda Gallery of Man, 67 Snowball Road, Kalamunda, WA 6076. Tel. (09) 293 4033.

Dreamtime Gallery, Shop 32, Merlin Centre, Perth, WA 6000. Tel. (09) 325 9274.
A wide selection of Aboriginal bark paintings and artifacts.

Gallery Australia, 96 Fitzgerald Street, Perth, WA 6000. Tel. (09) 328 2568.
Specialists in Aboriginal art, bark paintings and artifacts of varying regions.

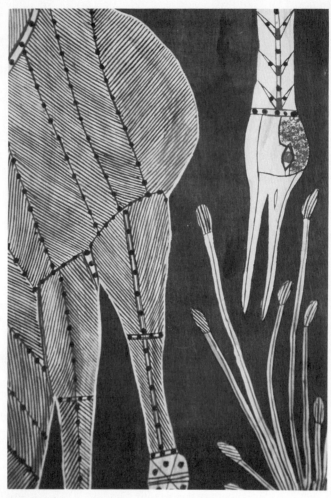

Detail from an Aboriginal bark painting

The Gallery of Original Arts and Artifacts, 45 Cliff Street, Fremantle, WA 6160. Tel. (09) 336 1281.
Collection of original Australian Aboriginal bark paintings, artifacts, etc.

Ridji Dij, 101 South Terrace, Fremantle, WA 6160. Tel. (09) 335 5990.
Wide selection of Australian Aboriginal arts and crafts.

GALLERIES DEALING IN PRE-1900 EXHIBITS WESTERN AUSTRALIA

Art Cellars, 27 Railway Road, Subiaco, WA 6008. Tel. (09) 382 2828 AH 386 1394.
Specialists in Australian antiquarian prints, maps and rare books.

Stirling Galleries Pty Ltd, 163 Stirling Highway, Nedlands, WA 6009. Tel. (09) 386 5161.
Fine antiques and works of art, one of Perth's oldest businesses.

The Treasure Trove, 162 High Street, Fremantle, WA 6160. Tel. (09) 336 1405.
Specialising in ancient arts of Asia, antiques and works of art.

Veasy Irene, 19 Swansea Street, Swanbourne, WA 6010. Tel. (09) 384 5403.
Antiquarian maps and prints, fine old books. Subiaco car park market, Saturday & Sunday 9–5 or by appointment.

WORKSHOPS, STUDIOS AND ART CENTRES WESTERN AUSTRALIA

Lesmundie Art and Craft Group, 7 Ford Road, Lesmurdie, WA 6076. Tel. (09).

Potters Workshop, Mews Road, Fremantle, WA 6160. Tel. (09) 335 1999.

The Bannister Street Workshop, 8 Bannister Street, Fremantle, WA 6160. Tel. (09) 335 9165.
Crafts people working in glass, pottery, wood, iron, leather, fabrics, stained glass, furniture, weaving, silver and cane. Located in one of Fremantles oldest warehouses. Open Monday–Friday 10–4.30, Saturday 10–2, Sunday 1–5.

The Western Australia Arts Council office should have further detail about access workshops and studio space when it becomes available and the same applies with the Crafts Council of Western Australia.

FINE ART COURSES AND COLLEGES WESTERN AUSTRALIA

Claremont School of Art, 7 Princess Road, Claremont, WA 6010. Tel. (09) 384 9099.
The school offers a Diploma in Fine Art: painting, sculpture, art studies). Certificate in Fine art and non-certificate courses in: ceramics, sculpture, weaving and other crafts.

Curtin University of Technology (WAIT), Kent Street, Bentley, WA 6102. Tel. (09) 351 2281/2317.
The university offers the following courses: Undergraduate and Graduate Diplomas in Teaching: art & craft, design, painting, sculpture, printmaking, ceramics, jewellery, gold & silversmithing, woodcraft, industrial design, textiles, graphic design, film, television & cinema studies, dance, drama & music. Master's Degree by either courswork or by research in film, television & cinema, dance, drama & music. Professional writing, journalism & radio is only available as an Undergraduate Course at this point in time.

Western Australian College of Advanced Education PO Box 217, Doubleview, WA 6018. Tel. (09) 387 9455.
The college offers the following courses in Undergraduate studies Arts Administration: teaching, art & craft, design, dance, drama & music. Both Undergraduate Studies and Graduate Diploma studies in painting, sculpture, printmaking, professional writing, journalism & radio. A Graduate Diploma is offered in film, television & radio.

Murdoch University, South Street,Murdoc, WA 6150. Tel. (09) 332 2211.
Contact the university for information on its arts related courses.

Perth Technical College Art School (TAFE), Aberdeen Street, Perth, WA 6000. Tel. (09) 427 2444.
The school offers a Diploma in advanced ceramics, art studies, graphic design, printmaking. Art Certificate in advanced ceramics, art studies, design (theatrical arts), merchandising display.

ART SUPPLIES AND MATERIALS
PERTH AND FREMANTLE

Aba Graffics, 7 High Street, Fremantle, WA 6160. Tel. (09) 430 4256.
General art materials.

Alscraft, 9 Keans Crescent, Applecross, WA 6153. Tel. (09) 364 7764.
Large variety of art and craft materials, art and craft books and framing service.

Art Papers and Supplies, rear 243 Stirling Highway, Claremont, WA 6010. Tel. (09) 384 6035.
Arches, rives paper from France, Japanese hand made papers etc. General variety of high quality fine art supplies.

Creative Hot Shop, 12 Aberdeen Street, Perth, WA 6000. Tel. (09) 328 5437.
Fine art and graphic supplies, papers, boards and accessories.

Greenwood Craft Centre, Shop 6, Greenwood Village Shopping Centre, Greenwood. Tel. (09) 448 6996.
Quality art and craft materials.

Jackson Drawing Supplies Pty Ltd, 148 William Street, Perth, WA 6000. Tel. (09) 321 8707.
There are ten branches of Jacksons materials in Perth.

The Potter's Market, 56 Peel Street, O'Conner, WA 6163. Tel. (09) 337 6888.
Suppliers of raw materials, books, kilns, clay and glazes. Equipment can be hired.

PHOTOGRAPHY, FILM AND VIDEO ORGANISATIONS
PERTH AND FREMANTLE

Fanny Samson's Cottage Theatre, 33 Cliff Street, Fremantle, WA 6160.
The ground floor of this historic building serves as a film and lecture theatre while upstairs is a museum.

Australia Council of Film Societies, PO Box 238, Subiaco, WA 6008. Tel. (09) 277 4682.

Film Centre Australia, 42 Harcourt Street, Bassendean, WA 6054. Tel. (09) 297 4544.
Producers and consultants.

Film Corporation of Western Australia Ltd, 282 Newcastle Street, Perth, WA 6000. Tel. (09) 328 2278.

Film Council of Western Australia, 336 Churchill Avenue, Subiaco, WA 6008. Tel. (09) 382 2500.

Film and T.V. Institute (WA) Inc., 92 Adelaide Street, Fremantle, WA 6160. Tel. (09) 335 1055.

The Filmmakers, 6 Welshpool Road, Victoria Park, WA 6100. Tel. (09) 470 2620.

Photography Resource Centre, 99 Goodwood Parade, Rivervale, WA 6103. Tel. (09) 470 2833.

PHOTOGRAPHIC SUPPLIES PERTH AND FREMANTLE

Carousel Camera House, Shop 12, Carousel Shopping Centre, 1352 Albany Highway, Cannington, WA 6107. Tel. (09) 451 8833.
There are 8 branches in the Perth area.

City Arcade Photographics, Shop H22, City Arcade, Hay Street, Perth, WA 6000. Tel. (09) 321 6129.
Trade-ins, repairs and excellent selection of equipment for the professional and the amateur.

Frank Evans, University Cameras, Shop 23, Broadway Fair, Nedlands, WA 6009. Tel. (09) 386 8095.
Competent and practical advice on all photographic matters, trade-ins, hire, advice on duty-free buying and a wide range of new equipment.

Perth Photographics, 268 Lord Street, East Perth, WA 6000. Tel. (09) 328 3377.
Professionals.

Klikk, 540 Hay Street, Perth, WA 6000. Tel. (09) 321 2230.
Large range of new equipment, and photographic accessories. 22 branches throughout Perth.

Plaza Camera Centre, 28 Plaza Arcade, Perth, WA 6000. Tel. (09) 325 4040.
Rentals, repairs, buy and sell all equipment.

FINE ART FRAMING
PERTH AND FREMANTLE

Accent Frames, 32 Railway Road, Subiaco, WA 6008. Tel. (09) 381 6177.
All types of framing.

Art Framers, 1 Leura Avenue, Claremont, WA 6010. Tel. (09) 384 2203.
Framer and art supplies.

Art Heritage, 316 Rokeby Road, Subiaco, WA 6008. Tel. (09) 381 1285.
Large selection of mouldings, conservation materials.

Aywon Framers, 6a King William Street, Perth, WA 6000. Tel. (09) 272 1218.
Art supplies, photo service and full framing service.

Gallery 350, 360 Hay Street, Subiaco, WA 6008. Tel. (09) 381 6577.
Restorations retail and wholesale framing, kit framing and photographic framing.

Glyde Gallery, 32 Glyde Street, Mossy Point, WA 2537. Tel. (09) 383 3929.
General framer.

Modern Art, 28 Market Street, Fremantle, WA 6160. Tel. (09) 336 2233.
Large selection of custom framing.

Prestige Arts and Crafts, 555 Wellington Street, Perth, WA 6000. Tel. (09) 321 4453.
7 day service, wholesale and retail.

ART BOOKSHOPS
PERTH AND FREMANTLE

Angus and Robertson Bookshops, 196 Murray Street, Perth, WA 6000. Tel (09) 325 5622, also at 625 Hay Street, Perth.
Excellent selection of books on all the arts.

Assembly Book Shop, 2 Hyde Street, Mt Lawley, WA 6050. Tel. (09) 328 4764.

City Arcade Bookshop, Shop M20 City Arcade, Perth, WA 6000. Tel. (09) 322 2362.

Market Street Book Arcade, 50 Market Street, Fremantle, WA 6160. Tel. (09) 335 4095.
Wide selection of books and materials.

Midlands Book and Art Shop, 308 Great Eastern Highway, Midland, WA 6056. Tel. (09) 274 3860.
Specialising in art books and art materials.

Sailing on the Swanriver, Perth (Heather Waddell)

New Edition Bookshop and Tea Room, 50 South Terrace, Fremantle, WA 6160. Tel. (09) 335 2386, (tea room 335 3277).
Specialising in literature, the arts, architecture and design. Open 7 days a week till late.

Ramsay's Discount Books, 113 Rokeby Road, Subiaico, WA 6008. Tel. (09) 382 1945.
Large variety of arts related books all discounted.

Rellim Booksellers, 834 Hay Street, Perth, WA 6000. Tel. (09) 321 5684.

Subiaco Bookshop, Shop 4, Barker Road, Subiaco, WA 6008. Tel. (09) 381 6637.
Specialising in the arts, Australia and children's books.

Terrace Bookshop, 208 Trinity Arcade, Hay Street, Perth, WA 6000. Tel. (09) 321 6009.
Large selection of quality art books.

The Academic Bookshop, 34 Pier Street, Perth, WA 6000. Tel. (09) 325 7600.

The University Bookshop, Mounts Bay Road, Crawley, WA 6009. Tel. (09) 386 5578.
Located within the university at Nedlands.

THEATRICAL ORGANISATIONS PERTH

Australian Elizabeth Theatre Trust, at His Majesty's Theatre, 825 Hay Street, Perth, WA 6000. Tel. (09) 321 4953.

Patch Theatre Company, 161 Burswood Road, Victoria Park, WA 6100. Tel. (09) 361 8364.

Theatre Workshop, 144a William Street, Perth, WA 6000. Tel. (09) 321 5410.

The Hole in the Wall Theatre Inc., 180 Hamersley Road, Subiaco, WA 6008. Tel. (09) 381 3694, and for bookings 381 2733.

The Western Australian Academy of Performing Arts, 2 Bradford Street, Mt Lawley, WA 6050. Tel. (09) 370 6443.

The Western Australian Opera Co. Inc., 825 Hay Street, Perth, WA 6000. Tel. (09) 321 5869.

W. A. Academy of Dance and Drama, 9 Corbusier Place, Balcatta, WA 6021. Tel. (09) 344 8767.

W. A. Mime Theatre, 229 Walcott Street, Mt Lawley, WA 6050. Tel. (09) 328 4386.

West Australian Ballet Co. Inc., 825 Hay Street, Perth, WA 6000. Tel. (09) 481 0707.

Western Australian Theatre Co. Inc., 2 Pier Street, Perth, WA 6000. Tel. (09) 325 3344.

THEATRICAL VENUES PERTH AND FREMANTLE

Astor Theatre, 659 Beaufort Street, Mt Lawley, WA 6050. Tel. (09) 370 1777.

Garrick Theatre, 8 Sutherland Street, Guildford, WA 6055. Tel. (09) 279 9003.

Harbour Theatre, 278 South Terrace, Perth, WA 6000. Tel. (09) 335 8079.

His Majesty's Theatre, 825 Hay Street, Perth, WA 6000. Tel. (09) 322 2929.

Hole in the Wall Theatre, 180 Hamersley Road, Subiaco, WA 6008. Tel. (09) 381 3684.

National Film Theatre of Australia, 92 Adelaide Street, Fremantle, WA 6010. Tel. (09) 335 7597.

Perth Concert Hall, 5 St George Terrace, Perth, WA 6000. Tel. (09) 325 3399.

Perth Entertainment Centre, Wellington Street, Perth, WA 6000. Tel. (09) 322 4766.

Playhouse Theatre, 3 Pier Street,Perth, WA 6000. Tel. (09) 325 3500.

Princess May Theatre, Cantonment Street, (Cnr Edward Street), Perth, WA 6000. Tel. (09) 430 4259.

Regal Theatre, 474 Hay Street, Subiaco, WA 6008. Tel. (09) 381 1557.

Spare Parts Puppet Arts Theatre, 1 Short Street, Fremantle, WA 6160. Tel. (09) 335 5044.

Stirling Theatre, Cedrick Street, Osborne Park, WA 6017. Tel. 349 6044.

The Quarry Amphitheatre, Reabold Hill, Oceanic Drive, City Beach.
Open air theatre.

Windsor Theatre, 98 Stirling Highway, Nedlands, WA 6009. Tel. (09) 386 3554.

MUSICAL ORGANISATIONS PERTH AND FREMANTLE

Australian Guild of Music and Speech, 235 Main Street, Osborne Park, WA 6017. Tel. (09) 344 6022.

Musicians Union, 200 Hay Street, East Perth, WA 6000. Tel. (09) 325 3817.

W. A. Music Teachers Assoc. Inc., 70 Churchill Avenue, Subiaco, WA 6008. Tel. (09) 381 6953.

West Australian Irish Pipe Band, 95 Jean Street, Hamlyn Heights, WA 3215. Tel. (09) 337 1585.

West Australian Mandolin Orchestra, 21 Parry Street, Fremantle, WA 6160. Tel. (09) 335 4182.

West Australian Pipe Band Assoc., 8 Muswell Street, Balga 6061. Tel. (09) 342 8153.

MUSICAL VENUES PERTH

Celtic Music Club, Hayloft Folk Centre, Malcolm Street, West Perth, WA 6005.

Hannibal's, 69 Lake Street, Perth, WA 6000. Tel. (09) 328 1065.
Discotheque created out of a church with a glass dance floor.

Octagon Theatre, The University of WA, Mt Bay Road, Crawley, WA 6009. Tel. (09) 380 2440.
Musicians in residence at the university, free lunchtime concerts 1pm.

Perth Concert Hall, 5 St George Terrace, Perth, WA 6000. Tel. (09) 325 3399.

Sorrento Quay, Hillary's Harbour, North Perth.
Venue for open air jazz concerts in summer, in an outdoor setting.

PLACES OF INTEREST
PERTH

Parks

The **Supreme Court Gardens**, Cnr of Riverside Drive and Barrack Street, Perth.

Colonial House Gardens, Cnr of Barrack Street and St George Terrace, Perth.

Wellington Square Gardens, Hill Street and Wellington Street, Perth.

Russell Square, James Street and Shenton Street, Perth.

Langley Park, along Riverside Drive, Perth.

Queen's Gardens, Hay Street and Plain Street, Perth.

Victoria Square, on Victoria Avenue, Perth.

King's Park. This is Perth's pride seen from all sides of the city it has a variety of wildflowers everywhere. The Botanic Gardens are in the park and there is an excellent lookout tower to enjoy views of surrounding Perth.

Wireless Hill Park, close to King's Park, has large picnic grounds and bicycles can be hired from here to explore King's Park. For information Tel. (09) 321 3203.

Markets

The original ornate market buildings were opened in 1897 on the corner of South Terrace and Henderson Streets, Fremantle. Today there are 140 stalls offering fresh local seafood, spices, jewellery, antiques, bric-à-brac and crafts. The market opens Friday 9—9 and Saturday 9—1.

Markets are also held weekly on Saturday and Sunday from 9—5 at Subiaco.

The Bannister Street Workshop opens its doors to the public on a regular basis, check for opening times Tel. (09) 335 9165.

Perth city looking across the Swan river from South Perth (Heather Waddell)

RESTAURANTS
PERTH AND FREMANTLE

In order to cope with the onslaught of thousands of visitors for the America's Cup, Fremantle became a town with many cosmopolitan restaurants, bars and hotels. The stylish **Lombardo's** at Fishing Boat Harbour was built at a cost of $13 million and houses two seafood restaurants. **Papa Luigi's** is a very popular Italian restaurant for young people

225

with seafood and pasta served al fresco Italian style. The **Oyster Beds** has more typical Australian seafood and you can enjoy views across the Swan River.

In Perth the city centre is so crowded with hundreds of restaurants of every nationality that it is hard to choose where to go. Perth citizens like eating out in cool attractive surroundings. Fish restaurants serve barramundi, dhufish, crayfish, prawns, whitebait, oysters and lobster. Wine is excellent from the local vineyards at **Swan Valley** and **Margaret River** and I'd also recommend Houghton's Chablis.

Saigon Vietnamese restaurant, Northbridge area, Perth (Heather Waddell)

Anna Vietnamese Restaurant, 175 Oxford Street, Leederville. Tel. (09) 444 3122.

Bretts, 44 Parliment Place, West Perth. Tel. (09) 322 2533. A top city restaurant.

Cicero' Italian Restaurant, 105 Francis Street, Northbridge. Tel. (09) 328 5361.
Good seafood.

Churchill's, 5 St George Terrace, Perth. Tel. (09) 325 4033. On the riverside at Perth concert hall.

Corzino's, 483 Beaufort Street, Mt Lawley. Tel. (09) 328 1770.
One of the best Italian restaurants in Perth.

The Emperor's Court, 66 Lake Street, Perth. Tel. (09) 328 8860.
Cantonese and Szechuan dishes.

The Esplanade Plaza Hotel, 45 Marine Terrace, Fremantle. Tel. (09) 430 4000.
Well worth having a drink or a meal here to sit in the peaceful spectacular old colonial style, but newly decorated, interior, with sails overhead, remnants of the America's Cup heady days.

The Establishment, 35a Hampden Road, Nedlands. Tel. (09) 386 5508.
Modern French cuisine.

Felix's Restaurant, 88 Rokeby Road, Subiaco. Tel. (09) 381 5242.
A beautiful garden restaurant open for lunch.

Greenjeans, 566 Hay Street, Perth. Tel. (09) 325 8132.
Excellent vegetarian restaurant.

India Restaurant, 10 Lake Street, Perth. Tel. (09) 328 4171.

Janica and Me, 376 Fitzgerald Street, North Perth. Tel. (09) 328 6220.
Charming terrace house setting.

The Little Corner, 66 Thomas Street, West Perth. Tel. (09) 321 9954.

Ludwig II von Bayern Bavarian Gasthof, 33 West Coast Highway, North Beach. Tel. (09) 447 1638.
Jolly German restaurant opposite the beach, just north of Perth.

Luis', 6 The Esplanade. Tel. (09) 325 2476.
Smart French restaurant.

Lombardo's, Fishing Boat Harbour, Mews Road, Fremantle. Tel. (09) 430 4343.
On the harbour front at Fremantle, and was built especially to cope with hungry America's Cup visitors. Two seafood restaurants, one smart and the other a bistro.

The Mediterranean, 414 Rokeby Road, Subiaco. Tel. (09) 381 2188.
Relaxed garden setting. Meeting place for successful Perth entrepreneurs. Alan Bond lunches here occasionally.

Papa Luigi's, 33 South Terrace, Fremantle. Tel. (09) 430 4522.
Lively young stylish restaurant. Recommended. Eating al fresco and indoors. Excellent Italian seafood.

Prideau's, 176 Stirling Highway, Nedlands. Tel. (09) 386 8933.

The Ord Street Cafe, 27 Ord Street, Perth. Tel. (09) 321 6021.
It previously won the best food in Perth award.

The Orchard, 707 Wellington Street, Perth. Tel. (09) 327 7000.

The Shalimar, 115 Francis Street, Northbridge. Tel. (09) 328 7558.
Kashmir and Mogul dishes. One of Perth's top Indian restaurants.

Seabird, 1 Scarborough Beach Road, Scarborough. Tel. (09) 341 1109.

The Tamarisk Tree, 134 West Coast Highway, Sorrento. Tel. (09) 448 0220.
Local friendly atmosphere in one of the pretty beach suburbs north of Perth. Sorrento Quay newly built in 1987 has several restaurants and is an ideal place for family visits, with safe protected swimming for young children as the coastal surf is often too strong.

CONTENTS
TASMANIA

TASMANIA

Tasmania, known affectionately as "Tassie" is an island state with a relatively small population of 450,000. The state can easily be divided into the northern region, the north west and west coast and the southern region with **Hobart** the capital city in the southern region. Hobart is the centre for most artistic and cultural activity and is Australia's second oldest city established in 1804. It grew up initially as a penal colony. Standing astride the lovely **Derwent River** and nestling in the shadow of **Mt Wellington**, Hobart can justifiably claim to be one of the most beautiful harbour cities anywhere.

The scenery in Tasmania varies from rich agricultural country near **Wynyard** to **Cradle Mountain** and **Lake St Clair National Park** to mining moonscapes near **Queenstown** and attractive deep water lakes at **Lake Pedder**. Other well established large cities include **Burnie**, **Devonport** and **Launceston** and all have good regional galleries. Throughout Tasmania there are very active communities involved in the various arts and crafts with a high standard of craft work now being attributed to Tasmania.

STATE ARTS ORGANISATIONS TASMANIA

Abstract and Contemporary Artists, 23 Crescent Street, Penguin, Tas. 7316. Tel. (004) 37 1125.
Statewide organisations promoting the concerns of contemporary artists in all media through workshops and exhibitions. Membership nominations to the secretary.

Arts Council of Australia, Tasmanian Division, Room 8, Days Building, Best Street, Devonport, Tas. 7310. Tel. (09) 24 5497.
Conducts a programme including touring artists to schools, community arts and regional theatre. Services 15 branches throughout the state, each of which conducts its own community arts programme.

Australian Society For Education Through The Arts (ASEA), 73 Brisbane Street, Hobart, Tas. 7000. Tel. (002) 30 3875.

Community Arts Network, Tasmania, 77 Salamanca Place, Hobart, Tas. 7000. Tel. (002) 23 3828.

Festival of Tasmania, 32a Clarke Avenue, Battery Point, Tas. 7000.

Tasmanian Arts Advisory Board, 161 Davey Street, Hobart, Tas. 7000. Tel. (002) 30 8022.
Advises government on policy and financial assistance to the arts.

Tasmania Museum and Art Gallery, 5 Argyle Street, Hobart, Tas. 7000. Tel. (002) 231 422.

Tasmanian Centre for Contemporary Arts, "Chameleon", 46 Campbell Street, Hobart, Tas. 7000. Tel. (002) 34 2744.

Bellerive Community Art Centre, 17 Cambridge Road, Bellerive, Tas. 7018. Tel. (002) 44 2592.

Salamanca Arts Festival, 77 Salamanca Place, Hobart, Tas. 7000. Tel. (002) 23 7300.

STATE CRAFT ORGANISATIONS TASMANIA

Crafts Council of Tasmania Inc., 65 Salamanca Place, Hobart, Tas. 7000. Tel. (002) 23 5622.

The Embroiders Guild of Northern Tasmania, 4 Adelaide Street, Launceston, Tas. 7250.

Hand Weavers, Spinners and Dyers Guild of Tasmania, 26 Mawhera Avenue, Sandy Bay, Tas. 7005. Tel. (002) 25 1868.

Potters Supply Co-operative Society Ltd, 47a Wellington Street, Hobart, Tas. 7000. Tel. (002) 34 8744.

STATE REGIONAL GALLERIES AND MUSEUMS TASMANIA

Burnie Art Gallery, Civic Centre, Wilmont Street, Burnie, Tas. 7320. Tel. (004) 31 5918.
Open Tuesday–Friday 10.30–5, Saturday & Sunday 2.30–4.30. The gallery specialises in contemporary works on paper and changing exhibitions.

Devonport Gallery and Art Centre, 45–47 Stewart Street, Devonport, Tas. 7310. Tel. (004) 24 0561.
Open Tuesday–Friday 10–4.30, Saturday 9.30–12 noon, Sunday 2.30–4.30.

National Trust Information Centre, 25 Kingsway Place, Hobart, Tas. 7000.

Queen Victoria Museum and Art Gallery, Wellington Street, Launceston, Tas. 7250. Tel. (003) 31 6777.
Open Monday–Saturday 10–5, Sunday 2–5. Gallery collection and visiting exhibitions both national and international.

Tasmanian Museum and Art Gallery, 40 Macquarie Street, Hobart, Tas. 7000. Tel. (002) 23 1422.
Gallery collection, special exhibitions held regularly and touring exhibitions from overseas and Australia. Open daily 10–5.

Tasmanian School of Art Gallery, Engineering Building, 3rd Floor, Tasmanian College of Advanced Education, Mt Nelson, Tas. 7007.
Open Monday–Friday 10–4, Saturday 10–12 noon.
The Allport Library and Museum of Fine Art, State Library, Murray Street, Hobart, Tas. 7000.
Interesting collection of Australian prints. Open Monday–Friday 9–5.
Van Diemen's Land Memorial Folk Museum, 103 Hampden Road, Battery Point, Tas. 7000. Tel. (002) 34 2791.
University of Tasmania Fine Arts Gallery, University Centre, Churchill Avenue, Sandy Bay, Tas. 7005. Tel. (002) 20 2101 ext 2233.
Open Monday–Friday 10–4, Saturday 11–2, Sunday 2–4.
University of Tasmania Centre for the Arts Gallery, Hunter Street, Hobart, Tas. 7000. Tel. (002) 38 4305.
Open Monday–Sunday 12 noon–5. An arts forum-programme is held at the gallery.

COMMERCIAL AND NON-PROFIT GALLERIES TASMANIA

Hobart art scene

Hobart, the capital city of the state of Tasmania has the greatest number of commercial galleries and is the major port of call for anyone visiting the state. The galleries show a high level of local art and craft with many national and international exhibitions reaching Hobart. Many of Australia's leading crafts people now live in Tasmania, enjoying the quieter life and closeness to nature. The **Chameleon Artists Co-operative** in Hobart, established by artist **Ray Arnold**, is a very active centre for contemporary artists incorporating a gallery and studio spaces. The **Tasmanian University** has a very active art school and within the school its own paper mill run by **Penny Carey-Wells**, providing a unique opportunity for students interested in the art of paper making. The old portside in Hobart is a focal point for fine art galleries and craft galleries, similar to that in Fremantle, WA.

Southern region

Chameleon Gallery, 46 Campbell Street, Hobart, Tas. 7000. Tel. (002) 34 2744.
Open Tuesday–Saturday 10–4, Thursday 10–7. Artist-run gallery showing the work of contemporary Australian and international artists.

Derek Smith's Oakwood Gallery, "Oakwood", Midland Highway, Mangalore, Tas. 7030. Tel. (002) 68 1273.
Open Monday–Sunday 9–6. Exhibits of both fine art paintings, prints and crafts.

Despard Street Gallery, Despard Street, Hobart, Tas. 7000. Tel. (002) 23 1236.
Open Tuesday–Friday 11.30–5.30, Saturday 11–3, Sunday 12–4. Exhibitions of both craft and fine art.

Freeman Gallery, Ellerslie House, 119 Sandy Bay Road, Hobart, Tas. 7000. Tel. (002) 23 3379.
Exhibitions by Tasmanian, interstate and overseas artists. Open Monday, Wednesday, Friday & Saturday 11–5.30, Tuesday, Thursday & Sunday 2–5.30.

Granary Gallery, 36 Bridge Street, Richmond, Tas. 7025. Tel. (002) 62 2264.
Open Monday–Sunday 9–5. Regular changing exhibitions with an ongoing display of the work of Tasmanian artists.

Handmark Gallery, 77 Salamanca Place, Hobart, Tas. 7000. Tel. (002) 23 7895.
Open Monday–Sunday 10–6. Exhibitions of both fine art and crafts.

Lady Franklin Gallery, Lenah Valley Road, Lenah Valley, Tas. 7008 (just beyond the bus terminal). Tel. (002) 28 0076.
Open Saturday & Sunday 1–5. Local and interstate artists.

Long Gallery, 77 Salamanca Place, Hobart, Tas. 7000. Tel. (002) 34 8749.
Open Monday–Sunday 10–5. Exhibitions by contemporary Tasmanian artists.

Masterpiece Fine Arts Gallery, 63 Sandy Bay Road, Hobart, Tas. 7000. Tel. (002) 23 2020.
Open Monday–Saturday 10–5.30. Leading fine art gallery in Hobart with both traditional and contemporary exhibitions.

Saddlers Court Gallery, 48 Bridge Street, Richmond, Tas. 7025. Tel. (002) 62 2132.
Open Monday–Sunday 10–5. Continuing exhibition of paintings and crafts by Tasmanian artists.

Strickland Galleries, 190a Strickland Avenue, South Hobart, Tas. 7000.
Open Monday–Sunday 10–5. Exhibits of local and interstate artists.

Northern region

Cockatoo Gallery, 11 Tamar Street, Launceston, Tas. 7250. Tel. (003) 31 7017.
Open Tuesday–Saturday 11–5. Interesting venue for contemporary artists, installations, exhibitions and events by Cockatoo members.

Colonial houses

Colonial Gallery, 6 Russell Street, Evandale, Tas. 7217. Tel. (003) 91 8480.
Monday–Sunday 11–4. Continuous changing exhibitions of fine art and Tasmanian painting from colonial times to the present day.

Connelly–French Galleries, Village Antique Building, Village Centre, Evandale, Tas. 7212. Tel. (003) 91 8160 AH (003) 44 2905.
Open Monday–Sunday 10–5. Early Australian, colonial and fine European works of art, objets d'art and fine antique furniture.

Cottage Gallery, 50 Abbott Street, Launceston, Tas. 7250. Tel. (003) 31 3025.
Open Wednesday–Sunday 11–5. Tasmanian artists and other exhibitions.

Design Centre of Tasmania, Tamar Street, Launceston, Tas. 7250. Tel. (003) 31 5506.
Open Monday–Friday 10–6, Saturday 10–1, Sunday 2–5. Exhibitions connected with quality design from overseas and nationally.

The Institute Gallery TSIT, Newham Drive, Launceston, Tas. 7250. Tel. (003) 26 0562.
Open Monday–Friday 9–5. Touring exhibitions, works on show from the collection and forums on Thursday at 12 noon in A 153, of the gallery.

Gallery Two, Ritchies Mill Arts Centre, 2 Bridge Road, Launceston, Tas. 7250. Tel. (003) 31 2339.
Open Monday–Sunday 10–5. Selected works by Tasmanian artists both fine arts and crafts.

Longford Gallery, 3 Marlborough Street, (Main Street), Longford, Tas. 7301. Tel. (003) 91 2299.
Open Tuesday–Saturday 10–5.30, Sunday 12–5 and by appointment.

North west & west coast

Coastal Art Gallery, 211 Mount Street, Upper Burnie, Tas. 7320. Tel. (004) 31 7731/45 1487.
Open Wednesday–Sunday 1–4. Exhibitions by young contemporary artists, crafts people and interstate artists.

Joyce's Gallery, 40 Wilson Street, (1st level), Burnie, Tas. 7320. Tel. (004) 31 2477.
Open Monday–Friday 9.30–5.30, Saturday 9.30–12 noon. Contemporary Australian artists.

Gallery Z, Main Street, Zeeham, Tas. 7469. Tel. (004) 71 6243.
Exhibitions by local and other Tasmanian artists.

CRAFT GALLERIES TASMANIA

Many of the above mentioned galleries deal in crafts and fine arts. The following list mentions some of the galleries specialising in the crafts.

Southern region

Aspect Design, 79 Salamanca Place, Hobart, Tas. 7000. Tel. (002) 23 2642.
Open Monday–Friday 10–5.30, Saturday 10–2. Established in a warehouse on Hobart's historic waterfront. Wide range of well-designed products by leading Tasmanian craftspeople.

Crafts Council of Tasmania, 11/65 Salamanca Place, Hobart, Tas. 7000. Tel. (002) 23 5622.
Open Monday–Friday 9–5, Saturday 10–12 noon. Regular changing exhibitions of local and interstate work.

Derek Smith's Oakwood Gallery and Pottery, "Oakwood", Midland Highway, Mangalore, Tas. 7030. Tel. (002) 68 1273.
Open Monday–Sunday 9–6. Work by local and mainland artists and craftspeople.

Handmark Gallery, 77 Salamanca Place, Hobart, Tas. 7000. Tel. (002) 23 7895.
Open Monday–Sunday 10–6. One of Tasmanias leading craft galleries, of excellent standard.

Hythe Gallery, "Hythe", Summerleas Road, Kingston, Tas. 7150. Tel. (002) 29 2588.
Open Monday–Sunday 9–5.30. Changing exhibitions of highest quality crafts.

Jon de Jonge Jewellery, 79 Salamanca Place, Hobart, Tas. 7000. Tel. (002) 23 3522.
Open Monday–Friday 10–5.30, Saturday 10–2. Handcrafted jewellery of original design in gold and silver.

Saddler's Court Gallery, 48 Bridge Street, Richmond, Tas. 7025. Tel. (002) 62 2132.
Open Tuesday–Sunday 10.15–5 and public holidays. Selected craft exhibitions.

Sullivan's Cove, 47 Salamanca Place, Hobart, Tas. 7000. Tel. (002) 23 7262.
Open Monday–Friday 10–6, Saturday 10–4, Sunday 2–4. Exhibitions of Tasmanian designers and craftspeople.

GALLERIES DEALING IN PRE-1900 EXHIBITS TASMANIA

Foscan Fine Art, 354 Davey Street, Hobart, Tas. 7000. Tel. (002) 23 6472.

Launceston Gallery, Dicky White's Lane, The Quadrant, Launceston, Tas. 7350.
19th century Australian colonial prints and antiquarian European prints.

National Trust of Australia (Tasmanian branch), "Runnymede", 61 Bay Road, New Town, Tas. 7008. Tel. (002) 28 1269.

Norfolk Galleries, Arthur Highway, Tarana (Port Arthur), Tas. 7180.
Specialising in Australian prints, maps and old drawings.

The Gilt Edge, Shop 30, Mayfair in the Bay, 236 Sandy Bay Road, Tas. 7005. Tel. (002) 23 8108.
The gallery specialises in early Australian paintings.

WORKSHOPS, STUDIOS AND ART CENTRES TASMANIA

P.I.P. Foundation, PO Box 374 Sandy Bay Road, Hobart, Tas. 7000.
Exhibition space is available through the foundation.

Pilot Art Foundry, TCAE School of Art, PO Box 1214, Launceston, Tas. 7250. Tel. (003) 260 560.
Complete reliable casting service for sculptures in bronze, brass and aluminium. Specialists areas include sandcasting, lost wax, full patination, polishing and finishing services.

Ritchies Mill Arts Centre, Bridge Road, Launceston, Tas. 7250. Tel. (003) 312 422.

Russell Street Workshop. For information contact Ritchies Mill Arts Centre.

Cameleon, 46 Campbell Street, Hobart, Tas. 7000. Tel. (002) 34 2744.
Artist-run studio spaces with a gallery in the complex.

FINE ART COURSES AND COLLEGES TASMANIA

The University of Tasmania, The Registrar, GPO Box 252c, Tas. 7001. Tel. (002) 20 3220.
The university offers the following: Undergraduate Degree in teaching: art & craft and design, painting, sculpture, printmaking, photography, ceramics, graphic design. A Master's Degree by coursework in painting, sculpture, printmaking, photography and ceramics. These are full time programmes, check with the university for the availability of part time courses.

Tasmanian College of Advanced Education (Tas CAE), The Student Administration Officer, Tas. CAE, PO Box 1214, Launceston, Tas. 7250. Tel. (003) 26 0201.
The college offers the following: Diploma in art history, textiles, dance, drama and music, painting, drawing, sculpture, printmaking, ceramics, jewellery, gold and silversmithing. Graduate Diploma in painting, drawing, sculpture, printmak-

ing, ceramics and jewellery, gold and silversmithing. Associate Diploma in woodcraft. BA Degree offered in teaching, art & craft and design. Master's Degree by coursework and an Undergraduate Degree are offered in environmental/landscape design. Check with the college for part time availability on the courses offered.

ART SUPPLIES AND MATERIALS HOBART

Artery, 31 Davey Street, Hobart, Tas. 7000. Tel. (002) 23 2130.
Specialist in fine art and graphic art materials, also good framing service.

Birchalls, 93 Harrington Street, Hobart, Tas. 7000. Tel. (002) 34 2122.
General art materials.

Salamanca Place Gallery, Salamanca Art Shop, 65 Salamanca Place Gallery, Hobart, Tas. 7000.
Wide range of artist materials, calligraphy specialists. Mail and telephone orders welcome.

Walsh J & Sons Pty Ltd, 130 Macquarie Street, Hobart, Tas. 7000. Tel. (002) 23 3444.

Willems Frames, 12 Davey Street, Hobart, Tas. 7000. Tel. (002) 34 7024.

The University of Tasmania and **The Tasmanian College of Advanced Education** both have student stores and wide selection of materials for the artist.

PHOTOGRAPHY, FILM AND VIDEO ORGANISATIONS TASMANIA

Australian Film Institute, 375 Elizabeth Street, North Hobart, Tas. 7000. Tel. (002) 34 6318.

Hobart Film Society, 65 Murray Street, Hobart, Tas. 7000. Tel. (002) 34 5998.

Film Combiners, 77 Salamanca Place, Hobart, Tas. 7000. (002) 23 7743.

Tasmanian Film Corporation, 1 Bowen Road, Moonah, Tas. 7000. Tel. (002) 308 033 or 28 6263.

PHOTOGRAPHIC SUPPLIES HOBART

Ash Bester & Co, 102 Elizabeth Street, Hobart, Tas. 7000. Tel. (002) 34 4166.
Specialising in all photographic equipment, hiring and repairs.

Graphic Arts Pty Ltd, 13 Centreway Arcade, Launceston, Tas. 7250. Tel. (003) 31 8482.
Processing, photographic equipment and hiring.

Goulburn Street Cameras, 14 Goulburn Street, Hobart, Tas. 7000. Tel. (002) 23 8325.
Open 6 days a week for camera repairs, and sales of all photographic equipment.

Photoforce, 1st Floor, 164 Macquarie Street, Hobart, Tas. 7000. Tel. (002) 23 4097.
Professional processing and enlarging.

Sheppards Camera Shop, 45 Cat & Fiddle Arcade, Hobart, Tas. 7000. Tel. (002) 34 1502.

Stallard's Camera House, 101 Liverpool Street, Hobart, Tas. 7000. Tel. (002) 34 5034.
Professional and amateur equipment, quality processing and camera repairs. Also shops in Launceston, Devonport and Ulverstone.

W.E.P.P., 14 Goulburn Street, Hobart, Tas. 7000. Tel. (002) 23 8325.
Buy and sell photographic equipment, custom processing black & white and colour.

ART BOOKSHOPS HOBART

Angus and Robertsons Bookshops, OBM Arcade, 36 Elizabeth Street, Hobart, Tas. 7000. Tel. (002) 34 4288, also at 96 Collins Street, Hobart. Tel. 344 288.
Excellent arts section with special order service available.

Fullers Bookshop Pty Ltd, 27 Murray Street, Hobart, Tas. 7000. Tel. (002) 34 4770.
New and secondhand art books.

Greensleeves Bookshop, 247 Sandy Bay Road, Sandy Bay, Tas. 7005. Tel. (002) 23 8839.
Open seven days a week, arts, literature, etc.

International Bookshop, Mary Welsh, 63 Burnett Street, North Hobart, Tas. 7000. Tel. (002) 34 8423.
Specialising in languages, travel and overseas publications.

The Institute Bookshop, Newham Drive, Launceston, Tas. 7250. Tel. (003) 26 3100.

Twelvetrees Bookshop, 247 Sandy Bay Road, Sandy Bay, Tas. 7005. Tel. (002) 34 1951.

University Bookshop, 301 Churchill Avenue, Sandy Bay, Tas. 7005. Tel. (002) 23 2066.
Open to the general public Monday–Friday 8.30–5.30. Academic and research books.

FINE ART FRAMERS HOBART

Artery, 31 Davey Street, Hobart, Tas. 7000. Tel. (002) 23 2130.
Fine art framing.

Beattie's Studio, 33 Cat & Fiddle Arcade, Hobart, Tas. 7000. Tel. (002) 34 2267.
Over 100 years of service, wide selection of mouldings.

Nigel Houston, 221 Macquarie Street, Hobart, Tas. 7000. Tel. (002) 23 5536.

Tudor Studios, Shop 11, 15 Bank Arcade, Hobart, Tas. 7000. Tel. (002) 34 3780.
Complete service of custom framing for all works.

Willems Frames, 12 Davey Street, Hobart, Tas. 7000. Tel. (002) 34 7024.
Professional advice on all aspects of framing, conservation framing and restoration of work.

THEATRICAL ORGANISATIONS HOBART

Breadline Theatre Co. Inc., 75 Salamanca Place, Hobart, Tas. 7000 (002) 23 1617.

Northern Theatre Pty Ltd, 86 Murray Street, Hobart, Tas. 7000. Tel. (002) 32 5600.

Performing Arts Club, 29 Campbell Street, Hobart, Tas. 7000. Tel. (002) 31 0155.

Salamanca Theatre Company, 77 Salamanca Place, Hobart, Tas. 7000. Tel. (002) 23 1617.

Tasmanian Dance Company, 197 Wellington Street, Launceston, Tas. 7250. Tel. (003) 31 6644.

Tasmanian Theatre Company, 68 Collins Street, Hobart, Tas. 7000. Tel. (002) 34 6992.

Tasmanian Theatre in Education, 77 Salamanca Place, Hobart, Tas. 7000. Tel. (002) 23 5259.

Terrapin Puppet Theatre Ltd, 77 Salamanca Place, Hobart, Tas. 7000. Tel. (002) 34 6086.

THEATRE VENUES HOBART

Salamanca Theatre Co., 77 Salamanca Place, Hobart, Tas. 7000. Tel. (002) 23 5259.

Theatre Royal, 29 Campbell Street, Hobart, Tas. 7000. Tel. (002) 34 6266.

The Playhouse, 106 Bathurst Street, Hobart, Tas. 7000. Tel. (002) 34 1536.

The State Theatre, 357 Elizabeth Street, Hobart, Tas. 7000. Tel. (002) 34 6318.
Also the **Australian Film Institute Cinema.**

MUSICAL ORGANISATIONS HOBART

Hobart College of Music, 1st Floor, McCann Building, 141 Elizabeth Street, Hobart, Tas. 7000. Tel. (002) 34 4285. Private tuition available.

Musicians Union of Australia, 141 Elizabeth Street, Hobart, Tas. 7000. Tel. (002) 34 1340.

Tasmanian Folk Festival Inc., 196 Brisbane Street, Hobart, Tas. 7000. Tel. (002) 34 9250.

Tasmanian Pipe Band Association, 1 Calder Crescent, Blackmans Bay, Tas. 7152. Tel. (002) 29 4491.

Tasmanian Symphony Orchestra, ABC Odeon, 167 Liverpool Street, Hobart, Tas. 7000. Tel. (002) 35 3632.

Tasmanian Youth Orchestra Council, 23 Commercial Road, North Hobart, Tas. 7000. Tel. (002) 34 6198.

MUSICAL VENUES HOBART

Performing Arts Club, 29 Campbell Street, Hobart, Tas. 7000. Tel. (002) 31 0155.

The Playhouse, 106 Bathurst Street, Hobart, Tas. 7000. Tel. (002) 34 1536.

Salamanca Theatre, 77 Salamanca Place, Hobart, Tas. 7000. Tel. (002) 23 5259.

Theatre Royal, 29 Campbell Street, Hobart, Tas. 7000. Tel. (002) 34 6266 for bookings.

It is advisable to check the daily papers for current performances and venues. There are many venues in Hobart where you can enjoy live music from both local artists and interstate. Some important overseas performers even find their way down to the most southern state of Australia. Check the local papers for performances and times.

PLACES OF INTEREST HOBART

Parks

The city of **Hobart** has a beautiful setting as it nestles in the shadow of Mt Wellington on the shores of the lovely **Derwent River**. The inner city has several small parks including **Franklin Square**, **St Davids Park**, **Princess Park** and **Parliament Square**. The **Royal Tasmanian Botanical Gardens** are magnificent and have much to offer the visitor with the new "Japanese Gardens", a large variety of cold climate trees and very colourful displays in the conservatory.

Mt Wellington's pinnacle is 20kms by road from Hobart and is 1,27m above sea level. The mountain offers one of the finest panoramic views in the world and the mountain park is traversed by many walking tracks, the most popular being the 3km walk from **The Springs** to the pinnacle.

Hobart's waterfront is only a few minutes from the city centre at the lower end of Elizabeth Street. Here you will find the main port of Hobart and the famous **Constitution Dock**, the home for finishing yachts of the famous "Sydney to Hobart Yacht Race" held late December. From here Trans Derwent ferries provide regular service across the harbour. They can be booked from **Franklin Wharf**. The Cruise Company offers a choice of cruises along the beautiful River Derwent its estuary and The D'Entrecasteaux Channel, all a most

Light and shade (Heather Waddell)

delightful experience. Departures from Franklin Wharf Tel. (002) 34 9294.

You can visit the historic area of **Port Arthur** on the Tasman peninsula, evocative of convict colonial Australia. The peninsula has rugged coastlines and is isolated by **Eagle Hawk Neck**, only 410 metres across making ideal conditions for the location of a penal colony on the peninsula. On route is the lovely quiet town of **Richmond** equally as elegant today as it was in the 1820's when it served as a military post and convict station, linking **Port Arthur** and Hobart. Leafy trees shade the village green and provide an attractive place for wandering about amongst many historic landmarks.

RESTAURANTS HOBART

Ball and Chain Grill, 87 Salamanca Place, Hobart. Tel. (002) 23 2925.
Delicious à la carte menu.

Botanical Gardens Restaurant, Domain Road, Hobart. Tel. (002) 34 4849.
Attractive setting.

Chaplin's Lamplight Bar and Restaurant, 1 Murray Street, Hobart. Tel. (002) 34 6645.

Cock and Bull Bistro, 394 Sandy Bay Road, Sandy Bay, Hobart. Tel. (002) 25 3879.
Open daily, serving local seafood and steaks.

J.C.'s Seafood Restaurant, 160 Sandy Bay Road, Sandy Bay, Hobart. Tel. (002) 23 6220.
Local seafood.

Medallion Seafood Restaurant, 91 Elizabeth Street, Hobart. Tel. (002) 34 6018.
One of Hobart's best loved seafood restaurants.

Mondo Piccolo Ristorante, 196 Macquarie Street, Hobart. Tel. (002) 23 2362.
Fine Italian cuisine.

Pirate and Parrot Restaurant, 128 Elizabeth Street, Hobart. Tel. (02) 34 5690.
Tasty local fare and excellent seafood.

Sweeny's Vegetarian Restaurant, 353 Elizabeth Street, North Hobart. Tel. (002) 34 9307.

Salamanca Terrace Restaurant and Coffee Shop, 31 Salamanca Place, Hobart. Tel. (002) 23 8450.
Dine on the lovely open terrace or in the old world charm of the restaurant indoors.

The Nose Bag, 3 Beach Road, Sandy Bay, Hobart. Tel. (002) 25 1071.
Tasty light meals and snacks.

Prosses on the Beach, Beach Road, Longpoint, Sandy Bay, Hobart. Tel. (002) 25 2276.

The Paris Restaurant, 356 Macquarie Street, Hobart. Tel. (002) 23 5028.
Classic French cuisine.

CONTENTS
AUSTRALIAN CAPITAL TERRITORY

AUSTRALIAN CAPITAL TERRITORY (ACT)

Canberra the capital city of Australia was created as a planned city and the small region designated to surround the capital was called the ACT, a region that was not acclaimed as very good pasture land and so, lying mid way between Melbourne and Sydney, a suitable site on which to develop a capital city. **Walter Burley Griffin**, an American landscape architect won a competition to design the city in 1911 and the man-made lake bears his name as do several statues in the city. In 1988, 200 years after the first settlement from England, the city has opened its new **Parliament House**, at great expense and amidst great controversy. The House is well worth a visit to see some of the numerous works of art commissioned for the interior.

The **Australian National Gallery** has major collections of contemporary Australian and European art, tribal art and artefacts to traditional painting and sculpture. The gallery has

246

Opening of the new houses of Parliament, Canberra, ACT

been fostering its collection of works on paper and greatly enhanced by the efforts of **Pat Gilmour**. The gallery holds top touring exhibitions both of painting and photography as well as craft and sculpture. If visiting in summer try and sit in the garden restaurant as the interior sometimes has trouble catering for all the crowds.

A short walk across from the entrance of the ANG stands the monumental building which houses Australia's High Courts. The foyer is open to the public and worth the extra 15 minutes to wander inside.

A visit to Canberra is not complete without a drive to the viewing platforms on top of **Black Mountain** and if you like heights take the lift up to the restaurant inside Telecom Tower.

STATE ARTS ORGANISATIONS ACT

ACT Arts Bureau—ACT Administration, GPO Box 158, Canberra City, ACT 2601 North Building London Circuit, Canberra. Tel. (062) 46 2715/46 2470.

ACT Arts Development Board, GPO Box 158, Canberra City, ACT 2601.

ACT Council of Cultural Societies Inc., Bunda Street, Canberra City, ACT 2601. Tel. (062) 49 6542.

Artists Society of Canberra (ASOC), PO Box 89, Mawson, ACT 2607. All enquiries Tel. (062) 86 2351.
ASOC is an old Canberra community body founded in 1927.

Arts Centre—ANU, Australian National University, GPO Box 4, Canberra City, ACT 2601. Tel. (062) 49 4787.

Arts Council of the ACT, Gorman House, Ainslie Avenue, Braddon, ACT 2601. PO Box 181, Civic Square, ACT 2608. Tel. (062) 48 9813.
Administrators of Tuggeranong Community Arts and **MUSE** magazine a monthly news release of arts events, information and interesting articles for the community.

Cultural Industries Council of the ACT, PO Box 127, Civic Square, ACT 2608. Tel. (062) 48 5057.
Aimed at promoting the arts industry in Canberra.

Australian National Gallery Association, c/o Australian National Gallery, GPO Box 1150, Canberra City, ACT 2601. Tel. (062) 71 2411.

Canberra Australia Day Council, Gorman House, Ainslie Avenue, Braddon, ACT 2601. Tel. (062) 49 7780.

Canberra Community Arts Front, PO Box 442, Civic Square, ACT 2608. Tel. (062) 498 092.
Situated within Gorman House.

Canberra Contemporary Art Space, PO Box 885, Civic Square, ACT 2608.
Situated within Gorman House. Membership and monthly newsletter with an update on information and events.

Canberra Cultural Centre, 21 Altree Court, Phillip, ACT 2606. Tel. (062) 85 1003.

Canberra Festival Inc., PO Box 173, Civic Square, ACT 2608. Tel. (062) 49 1277.
Situated in Gorman House.

Canberra Film Festival Inc., PO Box 405, Civic Square, ACT 2608. Tel. (062) 813 725.

Canberra Stereo Public Radio, Curtin Place, Curtin, ACT 2605. Tel. (062) 81 6286.

Capital Arts Patrons Organisations, c/o Gorman House, Ainslie Avenue, Braddon, ACT 2601. Tel. (062) 49 7780.

Gorman House Community Arts Centre, PO Box 561, Civic Square, ACT 2608. Tel. (062) 497 780.
Established in 1981 as a community arts centre to provide accommodation and facilities to a variety of individual artists, writers and craftspeople as well as many arts organisations with an ever-growing participation over a broad range of arts activities.

CRAFT ORGANISATIONS ACT

Batik Association, 62 The Pines, 12 Oliver Street, Lyneham, ACT 2602. Tel. (062) 51 3356.

Belconnen Machine Knitting Club, PO Box 150, Belconnen, ACT 2616. Tel. (062) 58 2256.

Canberra Gem Society, Griffin Centre, Bunda Street, Canberra City, ACT 2601. Tel. (062) 58 3989.

Canberra Potters' Society Inc., 1 Aspinall Street, Watson, Act 2602. Tel. (062) 82 2062.

Canberra Quilters Inc., PO Box 29, Jamison, ACT 2614. Tel. (062) 54 1180.

Canberra Spinners and Weavers Inc., PO Box, Rivett, ACT 2611. Tel. (062) 31 2575.

Craft Bookbinders' Guild Inc., PO Box 322, Kingston, ACT 2604. Tel. (062) 95 3619.

Crafts Council of the ACT, 1 Aspinall Street, Watson, ACT 2602. Tel. (062) 41 2373.
The Crafts Council provides an information centre for craft retailers, galleries and craftspeople, grants available, a members library, workshops, seminars and other related information. Most smaller craft organisations in the ACT are members of the Crafts Council.

Australian National Gallery, Canberra

Embroiderers Guild, GPO Box 146, Canberra City, ACT 2601. Tel. (062) 48 9691.

Woodcraft Guild of the ACT, PO Box 1411, Woden, ACT 2606. Tel. (062) 31 9443.

STATE REGIONAL GALLERIES AND MUSEUMS ACT

Arts Council Gallery, Gorman House, Ainslie Avenue, Braddon, ACT 2601. Tel. (062) 48 9813.
Open Wednesday–Sunday 11–5.

Australian National Gallery, King Edward Terrace, Canberra, ACT 2600. Tel. (062) 71 2501.
The gallery is open daily from 10–5. Admission is £3 for adults. The gallery is also open to the public from 5–8 on the last Thursday of every month with special lectures and films offered. The **University Drill Hall Gallery** on the campus of the ANU is an annexe to the National Gallery, check separate listing. The gallery displays an extensive collection of Austra-

lian traditional and contemporary art with a permanent collection of European art, Australian Aboriginal art, a sculpture gallery and sculpture garden adjoining the lake, photography galleries and galleries with continuously changing displays. The gallery has a magnificent collection of works on paper thanks to the efforts of Pat Gilmour. The gallery offers a restaurant, outdoor garden restaurant in summer, members lounge, theatre, gallery shop and regular guided tours. Membership scheme $40 family, $25 individual, $12 concessionary.

Australian National Library, Parkes Place, Parkes, ACT 2600.
Housing over three million volumes, maps, pictures, prints, photographs and cine films. Special exhibitions held in the foyer gallery regularly. Exhibition areas are open Monday–Thursday 9–5, Friday–Sunday and public holidays 9–4.45. Guided tours available and film screenings.

Australian War Memorial, Top end of Anzac Parade, Campbell. GPO Box 345, Canberra City, ACT 2601. Tel. (062) 43 4211.
Information is available on current exhibitions, film screenings and special events. The memorial is a museum and art gallery of international renown, housing a magnificent art collection, relics of wars in which Australians were involved and rich holdings of documentary and audio visual material. Open 9–4.45 daily except Christmas day, admission free.

Aboriginal rights protest at the opening of the new houses of Parliament, Canberra 1988

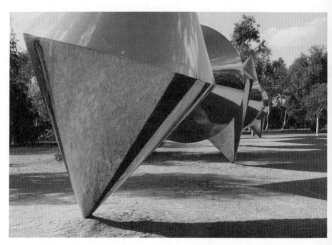

Australian National Gallery sculpture garden with sculpture by Bert Flugaman

Calthorpes' House. A 1920s house and garden open as a domestic museum. Admission by bookings only Tel. (062) 95 1945.

Canberra Bicycle Museum, 2 Badham Street, Dickson, ACT 2602. Tel. (062) 48 0999.
Housed within the Canberra Trade Union Club. Open 9.30–midnight for adults and 9.30–8 for children.

Canberra Institute of the Arts, School of Art Gallery, Baldessin Crescent, Acton, ACT. Tel. (062) 46 7942.
Open Monday–Friday 10–5. Regular changing exhibitions of leading Australian and overseas artists and craftspeople.

Contemporary Art Space, Galleries I & II, Gorman House, Ainslie Avenue, Braddon, ACT 2601. Tel. (062) 48 9813/49 1464.
Open Tuesday–Saturday 11–5. Gallery III, Bougainville & Furneaux Streets, Manuka, ACT 2603. Open Tuesday–Saturday 11–5.

Melville Hall, ANU. Large exhibition hall at the Australian National University with a diversity of events and exhibitions taking place. Tel. (062) 49 4787 for information.

National Film and Sound Archives, McCoy Circuit, Acton, ACT 2601.
Open 9.30–4 daily. Screening takes place on a regular basis. Check for details.

National Museum of Australia, Vicitor Centre, Lady Denman Drive, Yarramundi, ACT 2753.
A look at environmental issues, Aboriginal Australia and Australia since 1788, plans and models of the major museum project, films and videos in the theatre. Open daily 1–4.

Nolan Gallery and Lanyon House, Lanyon Via Tharwa, ACT 2620. Tel. (062) 37 5192.
Open Tuesday–Sunday 10–4 and public holidays. The gallery houses a permanent collection of the famous Ned Kelly series of paintings by Nolan. A beautiful, gracious old colonial homestead built in 1859 and sitting in pleasant gardens on the banks of the Murrumbidgee River adjoins the recently built gallery. Both gallery and homestead open Tuesday–Sunday and public holidays 10–4. Country style lunch and afternoon teas available.

The New Houses of Parliament, Capital Hill, Canberra, ACT.
The recently opened new Parliament House May 1988, houses an enormous collection of artworks commissioned for the building by the Australian Government and undertaken by artists and craftspeople from all over Australia. The building itself is an architectural wonder now attracting crowds equal to those visiting the famous Sydney Opera House. The main entrance forecourt has an Aboriginal mural of tribal significance. A visit to the House is a **must** if in Canberra.

University Drill Hall Gallery (National Gallery annexe) Canberra

The Old Parliament House. Plans are still undecided for the continuing use of this magnificent old building but it is hoped that the proposal for it to become a National Portrait Gallery will be accepted.

Photospace Gallery, Canberra Institute of the Arts, School of Art, Baldessin Crescent, Acton, ACT 2601.
Open Monday–Friday 9–4. For details of exhibitions Tel. (062) 46 7974.

University Drill Hall Gallery, Kingsley Street, Acton, ACT 2601. Tel. (062) 71 2502.
The Australian National Gallery's contemporary art venue. Regular changing exhibitions. Open Wednesday–Sunday 10–5.

COMMERCIAL AND NON-PROFIT GALLERIES CANBERRA

Canberra art scene

There are few established galleries in the capital city of Canberra, which still has a population of less than 300 thousand people. There is no particular centre for the variety of galleries; they are evenly scattered throughout the suburban

Art school student performance, Canberra Institute of the arts

254

areas and at times can be found in private homes such as **Gallery Huntly** and **Chapman Gallery**. The lively **Ben Grady Gallery** is found on the top floor of a multi-purpose complex, housing artists studios and workshops. At the other side of Canberra you can find the architect-designed **Solander Gallery** with its interior courtyard coffee shop and adjoining bookshop. At perhaps the other end of the scale is the unique **Contemporary Art Space Gallery III**, which is the converted local conveniences standing in the middle of a car park at Manuka! Private transport is essential if you are attempting to visit several galleries in one or two days, and many galleries deal in both areas of fine arts and crafts.

Beaver Galleries, 81 Denison Street, Deaken, ACT. Tel. (062) 82 5249.
New exhibitions mounted monthly. Open Wednesday—Sunday 10.30—5 and public holidays.

Ben Grady Gallery, Top Floor, Kingston Art Space, 71 Leichhardt Street, Kingston, ACT 2604. Tel. (062) 95 0447. Open Wednesday—Sunday 11.30—5. A lively gallery specialising in leading contemporary Australian art.

Canberra Contemporary Art Space, Galleries I & II, Gorman House, Ainslie Avenue, Braddon, ACT 2601. Tel. (062) 47 0188. Gallery III, Cnr Bougainville and Furneaux Streets, Manuka, ACT 2603. Tel. (062) 95 7319.
Exhibitions by Australian and overseas artists. Open Wednesday—Saturday 11—5, Sunday 1—5.

Henry Moore sculpture in the National Gallery sculpture garden

255

Chapman Gallery, 31 Captain Cook Crescent, Manuka, ACT 2603. Tel. (062) 95 2550.
Exhibits of Australian and overseas sculpture, prints and paintings. Aboriginal paintings on canvas from central Australian desert regions. Artefacts in stock. Open Wednesday–Sunday 11–6.

Gallery Huntly, 11 Savige Street, Campbell, ACT 2601. Tel. (062) 47 7019.
Paintings, original graphics and sculpture from Australian and overseas artists. Open Saturday–Tuesday 12.30–5.30 or by appointment.

Giles Street Gallery, 31 Giles Street, Kingston, ACT 2604. Tel. (062) 95 0489.
Showing contemporary Australian painting, sculpture, prints, ceramics and jewellery. Open Wednesday–Sunday 11–5.

Hugo Galleries, Shop 9, Thetis Court, Manuka, ACT 2603. Tel. (062) 95 1008.
Specialising in contemporary graphics and works on paper. Open Monday–Thursday 9–5, Friday 9–9, Saturday 9–12.30pm.

Solander Gallery, 36 Grey Street, Deakin, ACT 2600. Tel. (062) 73 1780.
New exhibitions twice monthly representing major Australian artists and professional crafts. Open daily 10–5. The gallery includes a coffee shop with open air courtyard and bookshop.

Canberra Theatre Centre Gallery, Foyer, Canberra Theatre, Civic Square. Tel. (062) 43 5711.

Southlands Gallery, Shops 4 & 5, Southlands Centre, Mawson, ACT 2607. Tel. (062) 86 5330.

CRAFT GALLERIES ACT

Beaver Galleries, 81 Denison Street, Deakin, ACT 2600. Tel. (062) 82 5294.
Open Wednesday–Sunday and public holidays 10.30–5. Three spacious galleries exhibiting fine arts and decorative arts and crafts. Changing exhibitions and stock displays.

Bungendore Wood Works, Coast Road, Bungendore, NSW 2621. Tel. (062) 38 1596.
40 minutes drive from Canberra to historic Bungendore, the gallery offers a place for woodworkers to display diverse work and fine craftsmanship in wood. Open 8–8 weekdays.

Canberra School of Art Gallery, Baldessin Crescent, Acton, ACT 2601. Tel. (062) 46 7946.
Open Wednesday–Friday 11–5, Saturday & Sunday 2–5. Regular changing exhibitions of fine arts and a high standard of crafts from Australia and overseas.

Crafts Council Gallery, 1 Aspinall Street, Watson, ACT 2602. Tel. (062) 41 2373.
Open Wednesday–Sunday 10–4. New exhibitions mounted monthly. Check for details, occasional closure between shows.

Earth-N-Wares Pottery, The Bridge Arts and Crafts Cente, Woden Plaza, Woden, ACT 2606. Tel. (062) 81 1937.
Open Monday–Thursday 9–5.30, Friday 9–9, Saturday 9–4. Australian handcrafted pottery.

Ginninderra Country Crafts, Barton Highway, Ginninderra, ACT 2617. Tel. (062) 30 2679.
Open 7 days a week 9.30–5. A variety of Australian hand-crafted goods. The Elms Coffee Pot serves excellent coffee with home-made tasty cakes.

Giles Street Gallery, 31 Giles Street, Kingston, ACT 2640. Tel. (062) 95 0447.
The gallery deals in both fine art and crafts, local and inter-state artists.

Narek Galleries, Cuppacumbalong Art and Craft Centre, Naas Road, Rharwa, ACT 2620. Tel. (062) 37 5116.
Open Wednesday–Sunday 11–5 and public holidays. Wide selection of works by local craftspeople. Resident craftsmen in furniture, ceramics and wood. A worthwhile drive to the area near the Murrumbidgee River not far past historic Lanyon House and the Nolan Gallery.

One Tree Woodturning Studio and Gallery, Ginninderra Village, Barton Highway, Gungahlin, ACT 2617. Tel. (062) 30 2430.
Open daily 10–5. Selection of fine Australian craftworks.

Potters Place Gallery, 32 Giles Street, Kingston, ACT 2604. Tel. (062) 95 0063.
Open Monday–Thursday 10–5, Friday 10–7, Saturday 9.30–1.30. The gallery exhibits ceramics, glass, jewellery and woodwork/furniture.

Southlands Gallery, Shops 4 & 5, Southlands Centre, Mawson, ACT 2607. Tel. (062) 86 5330.
Open Monday–Friday 10–5.30, Saturday 10–5, Sunday 2–5. A wide selection of Australian crafts with new exhibitions featured every three weeks.

Studio Altenberg, 104 Wallace Street, Braidwood, NSW 2622. Tel. (048) 42 2384.
Open 7 days a week 10–5. A main stopping point in historic Braidwood for anyone interested in the arts and crafts. The

complex includes a gallery, pottery, crafts shop and delightful cafe. About one hour and fifteen minutes drive from Canberra towards the coast.

The Coast Road Gallery, 200 Wallace Street, Braidwood, NSW 2622. Tel. (048) 42 2666.
Fine handcrafts.

University Drill Hall Gallery, Kingsley Street, Acton, ACT 2601. Tel. (062) 71 2501, GPO Box 1150, Canberra City, ACT 2601.
Open Wednesday–Sunday noon–5. Exhibitions of both fine arts and high quality crafts.

ABORIGINAL ART GALLERIES CANBERRA

Chapman Gallery, 31 Captain Cook Crescent, Manuka, ACT 2603. Tel. (062) 95 2550.
Permanent stock of Aboriginal Papunya and Yuendumu paintings on canvas, other artifacts from the area, carvings, also Utopia Batiks. Open Wednesday–Sunday 11–6.

The Australian National Gallery, Parkes Place, Parkes, ACT 2600.
Has a permanent exhibition of Australian Aboriginal paintings in one of its smaller exhibition areas. The gallery shop often has works or artifacts on display and for sale.

The Crafts Council Gallery, 1 Aspinall Street, Watson, ACT 2602.
From time to time has exhibitions of Australian Aboriginal paintings and artefacts and works, the result of encouragement amongst the outback communities.

ART SUPPLIES
CANBERRA

Artistcare, 9 Lonsdale Street, Braddon, ACT 2601. Tel. (062) 47 4877.
Specialising in graphic art materials, imported paints and papers and drawing materials.

Arttec Warehouse Pty Ltd, 23 Lonsdale Street, Braddon, ACT 2606. Tel. (062) 57 1711.
Art, graphic and drafting materials.

Buvelot Enterprises, 45 Colbee Court, Phillip, ACT 2606.
Comprehensive range of imported artists materials.

Canberra Institute of the Arts, School of Art Shop, Baldessin Crescent, Acton, ACT 2601. Tel. (062) 46 7896.
A wide selection of European and Japanese papers, pigments, canvas, sketch books, drawing and painting materials etc. etc.

Collie Cooke Consolidated, Graphic Arts Division, 64 Wollongong Street, Fyshwick, ACT 2609. Tel. (062) 80 6843.
Suppliers of high quality printing inks and photographic emulsions for screenprinting.

Swains Pty Ltd, Garema Place, Canberra City, ACT 2601. Tel. (062) 47 8515.
An extensive department of art materials within the store, a leading stationery and office supplier.

Phillip Craft Supplies, 53 Colbee Court, Phillip, ACT 2606. Tel. (062) 82 2919.
A variety of fine art and craft supplies. Open all day Monday–Saturday.

Black Sheep Gallery, 19 Kennedy Street, Kingston, ACT 2604. Tel. (062) 95 2485.
Supplier of fibre and yarns.

FINE ART COURSES AND
COLLEGES
CANBERRA

Australian National University, GPO Box 4, Canberra, ACT 2601. Tel. (062) 49 5111.
The university offers an Undergraduate Degree (BA) in art history and theory.

259

Studio One printmaking workshop, Canberra

Canberra College of Advanced Education, PO Box 1, Belconnen, ACT 2616. Tel. (062) 52 2225.
The college offers an Undergraduate Degree (BA) in cultural materials conservation, teaching, art & craft, design, industrial design, environmental/landscape design and film, television, cinema studies. An Associate Diploma is offered in film, television, cinema studies and a Master's by coursework is offered in cultural materials conservation.

Canberra Institute of the Arts, School of Art, GPO Box 804, Canberra, ACT 2601, Baldessin Crescent, Acton. Tel. (062) 46 7811.
The school of art offers both an Undergraduate Degree (BA) and Associate Diploma and a Graduate Diploma (Post Grad.) in all of the eleven workshops, painting, drawing, sculpture, printmaking, photography, ceramics, jewellery, gold & silversmithing, glass, woodcraft, leather, textiles. Some non-award courses are offered on a semester basis and the school is considering offering a Master's Degree programme.

WORKSHOPS, STUDIOS AND ART CENTRES CANBERRA

Gorman House Community Arts Centre, Ainslie Avenue, Braddon, ACT 2601. Tel. (062) 49 7780.
The facilities available at Gorman House include a 100 seat theatre, a cabaret space, large meeting room complete with open fire, individual studios for hire, coffee shop and pleasant courtyard gardens. There are 32 tenants at present using the variety of facilities at Gorman House ranging from groups to individuals, visitors welcomed. It is only a ten minute walk from the civic bus interchange, or bus routes 303 and 385 stop outside the centre.

Kingston Art Space, PO Box 164, Kingston, ACT 2604, 71 Leichardt Street, Kingston, ACT 2604. Tel. (062) 95 9438.
The centre provides studio space available for rent on a regular basis. Within the complex is the **Ben Grady Gallery** and **Studio One.**

Megalo Screenprint, PO Box 940, Civic Square, ACT 2608. Located at the rear of Ainslie Village, at the top of Quick and Hayley Streets, Ainslie, ACT 2602. Tel. (062) 49 6086.
Megalo is a non-profit community access screenprint facility

Basil Hall at Studio One printmaking workshop

offering assistance to individuals and groups wishing to use the silkscreen process to create their own fabric or paper item. Check for possible new location.

Photo Access, GPO Box 939, Canberra City, ACT 2601, Kingsley Street, Acton, ACT 2601. Tel. (062) 49 7878.
Photographic workshops and facilities available, graphic darkroom work.

Studio One, PO Box 164, Kingston, ACT 2604, 71 Leichhardt Street, Kingston, ACT 2604. Tel. (062) 95 2781.
The studio offers regular etching classes day and evening, drawing classes, school extension programmes, weekend workshops in printmaking and related areas, facilities for artists to rent a regular work space and editioning services available.

The Crafts Council of the ACT, 1 Aspinall Street, Watson, ACT 2601. Tel. (062) 41 2373.
Workshops and classes are run at regular intervals for people at various levels and skills.

PHOTOGRAPHY, FILM AND VIDEO CANBERRA

ANU Film Group, c/o ANU Arts Centre, PO Box 4, Canberra City, ACT 2601. Tel. (062) 49 4787.

Canberra Film Festival Inc., PO Box 405, Civic Square, ACT 2608. Tel. (062) 81 3725.
The annual film festival held in Canberra.

Goëthe Institute, German Cultural Centre, Nat West House, 40 Allara Street, Canberra City, ACT 2601.
Regular film screenings available to the public.

Independent Video, Gorman House, Ainslie Avenue, Braddon, ACT 2601. Tel. (062) 47 5026.
Individual VHS CV's for actors, directors, dancers and choreographers. Artists portfolios for cataloguing purposes. Telephone for an appointment and discuss any type of work.

National Film and Sound Archives, McCoy Circuit, Acton, ACT 2601. Tel. (062) 67 1742.
Regular screenings from the collections.

National Library of Australia, Parkes Place, Parkes, ACT 2600. Tel. (062) 62 1279.
From time to time interesting films being screened. Check for details.

The Canberra School of Art has a very active **Photomedia Dept** with a permanent gallery space "Photospace" on the second floor, open to the public weekdays 9–4.

The Electric Shaddows an independent cinema in Civic Square is always worth a look in, with the programme changing daily and always of interest. Tel. (062) 45 5060/48 8352.

Film Australia, Stuart Street, Griffith, ACT 2603. Tel. (062) 95 3209.

PHOTOGRAPHIC SUPPLIES CANBERRA

Atlantic Film Laboratories Pty Ltd, 55 Townsville Street, Fyshwick, ACT 2609. Tel. (062) 80 4559.
High quality machine and custom printing, colour and black & white.

City Camera House, Garema Arcade, Bunda Street, Canberra City, ACT 2601. Tel. (062) 48 5864.
1 hour colour processing, agents for most new brands of camera equipment.

Fletcher's Fotographics, Shop 3, Custom Credit House, 38 Akuna Street, Canberra City, ACT 2601. Tel. (062) 47 8460/ 47 8471.
Retail and industrial sales, camera repairs and all darkroom equipment available, professional film available.

KLIKK, 43 Northbourne Avenue, Canberra City, ACT 2601. Tel. (062) 47 4030.
1 hour photo service, new equipment, colour and black & white processing.

Pro-Foto Sales, 63 Wollongong Street, Fyshwick, ACT 2609. Tel. (062) 80 4009.
Major stockist for film and paper and chemicals, computor graphics products, lab equipment.

Ted's Camera Store, 9 Petrie Place, Canberra City, ACT 2601. Tel. (062) 47 8711.
Secondhand and new equipment, colour and black & white processing.

The Black and White Lab, Unit 2, Kemble Court, Mitchell, ACT 2911. Tel. (062) 41 6129.
Urgent work welcomed, black & white processing specialists.

ART BOOKSHOPS
CANBERRA

Angus and Robertson Bookshops, 23Garema Place, Canberra City, ACT 2601. Tel. (062) 49 1652.
Interesting selection covering the visual and performing arts.

Chenka Pty Ltd, Centre Court, Cnr Barrier & Pirie Streets, Fyshwick, ACT 2609. Tel. (062) 80 6853.
General bookseller with an interesting selection of craft books.

Collins Booksellers, Monaro Mall, Canberra City, ACT 2601. Tel. (062) 47 5430.

Dalton's Bookshop, Capital Centre, 54 Marcus Clark Street, Canberra City, ACT 2601. Tel. (062) 49 1844.
Speciality bookshop, limited editions, travel and the arts.

Mary Martin Bookshop Pty Ltd, Alinga Street, Canberra City, ACT 2601. Tel. (062) 47 9930.
Visual and performing arts, crafts and often a large selection of remainder books.

Solander Gallery Bookshop, 36 Grey Street, Deakin, ACT 2600. Tel. (062) 82 5294.
Within the gallery complex there is the bookshop and coffee shop. Arts, crafts, Australian publications and alternative books.

The Co-op Bookshop, University Co-op Bookshop Ltd, Australian National University, Canberra City, ACT 2601. Tel. (062) 49 6244/57 2673.
Open 7 days a week 9–5 in the centre of the university. Wide selection of arts related books.

The National Gallery of Australia Bookshop, Parkes Place, Parkes, ACT 2600. Tel. (062) 71 2420.
The gallery shop stocks a wide range of speciality visual and performing arts books with an extensive range of Australian art books, magazines and journals. Open during regular gallery hours.

FINE ART FRAMING
CANBERRA

Art and Archival Paper Conservation, 41 Crawford Street, Queanbeyan, NSW 2620. Tel. (062) 97 7670.

Canberra Art Framing Co., 13 Lonsdale Street, Braddon, ACT 2601. Tel. (062) 49 7733.

Frame Factory, 1 Kembla Street, Fyshwick, ACT 2609. Tel. 062) 80 6395.
Conservation framing.

Framing Corner, Cooleman Court, Weston (upper level), ACT 2611. Tel. (062) 88 0777.
Timber or aluminium frames with conservation work.

Green Door Picture Framing Co., 47 Lorn Road, Queanbeyan, NSW 2620. Tel. (062) 97 2501.
Fine art prints, paintings and graphic work, all conservation framing, discount for artists.

THEATRICAL ORGANISATIONS CANBERRA

Australian Association for Dance Education, PO Box 287, Jamison, ACT 2614, Gorman House, Ainslie Avenue, Braddon, ACT 2601. Tel. (062) 48 8992.

Canberra Dance Ensemble, 31 Weston Street, Yaralumla, ACT 2600. Tel. (062) 81 5528.

Canberra Youth Ballet Company, 43 Brierly Street, Weston, ACT 2611. Tel. (062) 88 7316.

Canberra Youth Theatre Co., Gorman House, Batman Street, Braddon, ACT 2601. Tel. (062) 48 5057.

Eureka Theatre Company, 75 Wybalena Grove, Cook, ACT 2614. Tel. (062) 51 5534.

Human Veins Dance Theatre, Gorman House, Ainslie Avenue, Braddon, ACT 2601. Tel. (062) 47 3103.

Interact Theatre, English Dept at the ANU and Gorman House, Ainslie Avenue, Braddon, ACT 2601. Tel. (062) 49 3314.

Jigsaw Theatre Company, PO Box 617, Civic Square, ACT 2608, Gorman House, Ainslie Avenue, Braddon, ACT 2601. Tel. (062) 47 2133.

Skylark Puppet and Mast Theatre, PO Box 186, Dickson, ACT 2602. Tel. (062) 41 4442.

Stagecoach Theatre School, PO Box 4, Garran, ACT 2605. Tel. (062) 85 1134.

Storytellers Guild, The guild meets at the Griffin Centre monthly and storytellers are available for bookings. Tel. (0620 81 4059.

TAU Community Association, PO Box 201, Dickson, ACT 2602 or Mort Street, Braddon, ACT 2601. Tel. (062) 48 0911.

Tempo Theatre Inc., 16 Badgery Street, Macquarie, ACT 2614. Tel. (062) 51 1877.

Tuggeranong Community Youth Theatre, Tuggeranong Community Art Project, for information call (062) 92 2033 or the Director 95 9539.

Black Inc. Theatre Inc, Gorman House, Ainslie Avenue, Braddon, ACT 2601. Tel. (062) 49 7780.

THEATRICAL VENUES CANBERRA

Canberra Theatre Centre, Civic Square, Canberra City, ACT 2601. Tel. (062) 43 5711.
The theatre complex also includes the playhouse.

Gorman House Community Arts Centre, Ainslie Avenue, Braddon, ACT. Tel. (062) 49 7780.
Housing the Bogong Theatre Cafe, Theatre E, Fireplace Room.

Reid House Theatre Workshop, also at Gorman House. Tel. (062) 47 2133.

Rehearsal Room, Canberra Theatre Centre, Civic Square, Canberra City, ACT 2601.
Theatre 3, Ellery Crescent, Act, ACT 25{601. Tel. (062) 47 4222.

School of Arts Cafe, 108 Monaro Street, Queanbeyan, NSW 2620. Tel. (062) 97 6877.

The Bedrock Cafe, 139 Newcastle Street, Fyshwick, ACT 2609. Tel. (062) 80 7637.
Providing theatre, film, music and wholesome food with jazz on Fridays.

MUSICAL ORGANISA- TIONS AND VENUES CANBERRA

Canberra Philharmonic Society, PO Box E253, Queen Victoria Terrace, ACT 2600. Tel. (062) 47 0860.

Canberra Repertory Society, Theatre 3, Ellery Crescent, Acton, ACT 2601. Tel. (062) 47 4222.

Canberra Stereo Public Radio, Curtin Place, Curtin, ACT 2605. Tel. (062) 81 6286.

Canberra Symphony Orchestra, PO Box 1919, Canberra City, ACT 2601. Tel. (062) 47 9191.

Canberra Youth Orchestra Society Inc., Griffen Centre, Bunda Street, Canberra City, ACT 2601. Tel. (062) 47 4714.

Theatre Organ Society of Australia, ACT Branch, Magrath Crescent, Spence, ACT 2615. Tel. (062) 58 2157.

Monaro Folk Music Society, 12 Hovea Street, O'Conner, ACT 2601. Tel. (062) 57 2696.

Musical venues are similar to the list of **theatrical venues** with the increasing trend for coffee shops to provide musical entertainment.

The concert hall within The Canberra School of Music (Canberra Institute of the Arts), Baldessin Crescent, Acton, ACT 2601. Tel. (062) 46 7811. Provides an important venue for concert performances and soloists visiting Canberra. Regular concerts held and open to the public. Check for programme details in the **Canberra Times.**

Friends of the Canberra School of Music. A group of people enjoying music from jazz to classical and who support the staff and students of the Canberra School of Music. Membership enquiries to the Secretary, GPO Box 804, Canberra, ACT 2601 or Tel. (062) 95 1683.

PLACES OF INTEREST CANBERRA

Canberra, the capital city of Australia has all the qualities of a newly planned dynamic city. It has many landmarks worth visiting when touring around the city but one cannot ignore the newly opened Parliament House, a most impressive building and the focal point of the city. Within 20 minutes by car you can be out in the wide open spaces of the surrounding plains and sheep grazing country or heading for foothills of the **Snowy Mountain Range** and places such as the **Brindabella Mountain Range** where the film "My Brilliant Career" was filmed.

Parks

Canberra Wildlife Gardens, Mugga Lane across from Red Hill. Natural bushland and parkland with picnic areas and barbecue facilities.

Canberra Botanic Gardens, situated on the lower slopes of Black Mountain behind the Australian National University. The gardens are open daily 9–5. Of particular interest to visitors from overseas is the native Australian section, well worth a visit. The Botanic Gardens kiosk is open daily serving

Tidbinbilla Nature Reserve, ACT

breakfasts from 9, lunches from 11.30 and afternoon teas from 2.30. Tel. (062) 48 9680.

Lanyon House and **Nolan Gallery** are a pleasant hour's drive from central Canberra along Tharwa Drive. Occassionally outdoor concerts are held in the gardens of Lanyon House, check for details Tel. (062) 37 5136. Also listed in detail under "Museums".

Tidbinbilla Nature Reserve is worth a visit as the animals run free on the reserve in their natural environment. The drive from Canberra is scenic and well worth the trip, and if you have the time, continue on to **Narek Galleries**, **Cuppacumbalong Art and Craft Centre** (062) 37 5116.

In central Canberra there is access to almost all of the lakeside and on the north west side of Kings Avenue Bridge there is a small cafeteria and bicycle hire is available with extensive cycle paths around the lake and through areas of Canberra.

268

Near **Yarralumla** there are enormous picnic grounds with barbecue facilities and access to the lake for windsurfing and boating. Swimming in the lake is not recommended by the locals!

If approaching Canberra from the Federal Highway along Northbourne Avenue the **Tourist Information Centre** is a suggested stop as it will have up to date information on what's on in Canberra and appropriate maps.

Markets

Belconnen Market is held in the vicinity of Belconnen Shopping Mall every weekend with produce bargains late Sunday afternoon. Great selection of fresh fruit and vegetables.

Fyshwick Market held in the area of Dalby Street, Fyshwick. Produce market both Saturday and Sunday every week with various stalls with secondhand goods. Just near the fire station.

Gorman House Markets, Ainslie Avenue, Braddon, ACT 2601. Stallholder inquiries Tel. (062) 497 780.
The market is a very lively atmosphere every Saturday 10–4 with stalls selling crafts, fabrics, antique toys, pottery, books, records, jewellery and clothes. The Zig Zag Cafe is open for light snacks in the centre.

Home Produce Market, country market to support the ACT Society for the Physically Handicapped Inc. First Sunday of the month from 11 at Hall Showground. Inquiries Tel. (062) 82 4411.

RESTAURANTS CANBERRA

Dorette's, 17 Garema Place, Canberra City, ACT 2601. Tel. (062) 47 4946.
In the civic plaza open Monday–Saturday 5 till late. Live jazz and classical music, exhibitions by local artists.

Gus' Coffee Lounge, Bunda Street, Canberra City, ACT 2601. Tel. (062) 48 8118.
One of the best coffee lounges in Canberra and popular with the art community. Outdoor setting for cool summer evenings and cosy indoors with papers and journals available.

Mama's Trattoria, 7 Garema Place, Canberra City, ACT 2601. Tel. (062) 48 0936.
Delicious Italian food and reasonable prices. Open for lunch Monday–Friday from 12 noon, dinner Monday–Saturday from 6

Mopokes, 173 City Walk, Canberra City, ACT 2601. Tel. (062) 48 8709.
New York style deli and family restaurant. Open 7 days.

Pipi's Seafood, Keltie Street, Woden Plaza, Phillip, ACT 2606. Tel. (062) 82 1560.
Excellent seafood. Open for lunch and dinner.

School of Arts Cafe, 108 Monaro Street, Queanbeyan, NSW 2620. Tel. (062) 97 6857.
Interesting old school of arts atmosphere with nightly musical entertainment. Inexpensive and good coffee. Open for lunches, afternoon teas and dinners.

Solander Coffee Room, 36 Grey Street, Deakin, ACT. Tel. (062) 73 2420.
Situated within the Solander Gallery complex, an excellent place for lunch and morning or afternoon tea.

Sinbads, 25 East Row, Canberra City, ACT. Tel. (062) 47 4068.
Traditional Lebanese cuisine.

Sophie's Restaurant, Wales Centre, Boulevard, Canberra City, ACT. Tel. (062) 48 7701.
Open 11–3.

The Bedrock Cafe, 139 Newcastle Street, Fyshwick, ACT. Tel. (062) 80 7637.
Open 7 days 10–4. Shows on Thursdays, Friday & Saturday nights. Theatre, music, film and innovative wholesome food.

The Gambat Coffee Shop, 7 Deakin Court, Deakin, ACT. Tel. (062) 82 4362.
Great spot for weekend morning coffee with seating outside on a sunny day. Good coffe and cakes.

The Gallery Brasserie and The Mirrabook, The National Gallery, Parkes, ACT. Tel. (062) 73 2836.
If your lunching at the gallery, entrance is free. The Mirrabook is the outdoor restaurant near the lake, set amongst the sculpture gardens. Best on a sunny day.

The Hermitage, Woden Plaza, Phillip, ACT. Tel. (062) 81 5649. (Kelly Street).
Excellent à la carte cuisine, blackboard menu. Open for lunch 12–2, dinner 6–10.

Tivoli Italian Restaurant, 70 Kent Street, Deakin, ACT. Tel. (062) 82 4964.
Genuine Italian cuisine.

Zig Zag Coffee Shop, Gorman House, Community Arts Centre, Ainslie Avenue, Braddon, ACT. Tel. (062) 49 632.
Open Monday–Saturday 9.30–5, for morning and afternoon teas, snacks and delicious lunches in a garden courtyard.

The Left Bank Bookshop and Cafe, 55 Stuart Street, Griffith.
Enjoy coffee and snacks and support progressive politics in Canberra.

TAU Cafe, 31 Mort Street, Braddon, ACT. Tel. (062) 48 5654.
Interesting coffee shop with entertainment.

CONTENTS
NORTHERN TERRITORY

NORTHERN TERRITORY

Northern Territory is a state with breathaking variety in land-scape from the tropical regions to the rugged stark mountains and classical ghost gums set against sheer blue sky and ochre red earth. Distances are vast with a small state popula-tion of only 137,000, of whom half live in or around **Darwin** on the far north coast. **Alice Springs** is a key tourist centre situated almost in the geographical centre of Australia, giving easy access to the world famous landmark **Ayers Rock** (Aboriginal name **Uluru**) one of the most spiritually sacred places in Australia for the Aboriginal people. The **Olga Mountains**, **Arnhem Land** and **Kakadu National Park** are rich in Aboriginal art and have become favoured visiting regions for those seeking out the untamed spirit of this enor-mous continent. Many Aboriginal communities have owner-ship of large areas of the land (reserves) with an increasing awareness by the white Australian community of what should belong to the Aborigines through 40,000 years of inhabiting the area. Native wildlife is protected in the Northern Territory including saltwater crocodiles, kangaroos, buffalo and wild pigs not to mention the lush variety of bird life.

The arts community is small in both **Darwin** and **Alice Springs** compared with other capital centres but interest is strong and the growing awareness of the richness of Aborigi-nal arts and crafts make these cities unique for there proxim-ity to contact with the Aboriginal artists of northern and central Australia.

The Olgas, Central Australia

STATE ARTS ORGANISATION NORTHERN TERRITORY

Arts Council of Australia, Northern Territory Division, Shop 2, Harry Chan Arcade, 60 Smith Street, Darwin, NT 5794. Tel. (089) 81 5181/81 5280.

Brown's Mart Community Arts Project, Cnr Smith Street and Harry Chan Drive, Darwin, NT 5794. Tel. (089) 81 5522.

Community Access Centre, 44 Mitchell Street, Darwin, NT 5974. Tel. (089) 81 5015.

Dreamtime Dance Group, Schaber Road, Alice Springs, NT 5750. Tel. (089) 52 4610.

STATE CRAFT ORGANISATIONS NORTHERN TERRITORY

Crafts Council of Northern Territory Inc., Bullocky Point, Fannie Bay, Darwin, NT 5974. Tel. (089) 81 6615.

Potters Place, 2 Parap Place, Parap, NT 5790. Tel. (089) 81 7071.

Weavers Workshop Pty Ltd, Parap Shopping Village, Darwin, NT 5974. Tel. (089) 81 6986.

STATE REGIONAL GALLERIES AND MUSEUMS NORTHERN TERRITORY

Northern Territory Museum of Art And Sciences, Conacher Street, Bullocky Point, Fannie Bay, Darwin, NT 5794. Tel. (089) 82 4211.
The museum has a permanent collection of Australian fine art works, touring exhibitions from interstate and overseas, Aboriginal, south east Asian and oceanic art and natural history of the Northern Territory and nearby regions.

COMMERCIAL AND NON-PROFIT GALLERIES DARWIN AND ALICE SPRINGS

Art Mart, 54 Todd Street, Alice Springs, NT 5750. Tel. (089) 52 5552.
Mainly a crafts gallery with paintings from local artists, including South Australia. Some Aboriginal work.

El Cerito Garden Gallery, Undoolya Road, Alice Springs, NT 5750. Tel. (089) 52 7188.

Gallery Blom, Polana Centre, Smith Street, Alice Springs, NT 5750. Tel. (089) 52 3396.
Local scenes in oils by resident artists.

Gaproad Gallery, 40 Gap Road, Alice Springs, NT 5750. Tel. (089) 52 5119.
Oils and watercolours by local artists and limited edition prints.

Panorama Guth, Studio and Museum, 65 Hartley Street, Alice Springs, NT 5750. Tel. (089) 52 2013.
Oil paintings and Aboriginal artefacts with museum relics of local history.

Studio Star Art Gallery, Smith Street Mall, Darwin, NT 5794. Tel. (089) 81 6488.
Works by noted Australian artists. Open Monday–Friday 10–5, Saturday 10–1.

The Esplanade Gallery, Cnr Knuckey Street and the Esplanade, Darwin, NT 5974. Tel. (089) 81 5042.
Changing exhibitions every two weeks. Work by mainly Top End artists. Monthly features of ceramics by Darwin potters. Open Monday–Friday 9–5, Saturday & Sunday 10–6. Leading fine art gallery for Darwin.

CRAFT GALLERIES DARWIN AND ALICE SPRINGS

Craftsman Galleries, 38 Cavenagh Street, Darwin, NT 5974. Tel. (089) 81 6335.

Flamingo Gallery, Shop 61, Ford Plaza, Todd Mall, Alice Springs, NT 5750. Tel. (089) 53 0233.
Quality craft works by leading Australian craftspeople. Ceramics, textiles/fibre, glass, jewellery, woodwork, leather, metalwork, sculpture, prints and photography.

Raintree Gallery, 29 Knuckey Street, Darwin, NT 5974. Tel. (089) 81 2732.

Sybil and Maudes, 65 Paterson Street, Tennant Creek, NT 5760. Tel. (089) 62 3114.
Displays of art and crafts by local artists, Aboriginal artifacts and old mining displays.

The Craft Centre, 33 Smith Street, Darwin, NT 5974. Tel. (089) 81 4494.
Works on display by quality craftspeople of Northern Territory.

Yirrkala Arts, Yirrkala, Nhulunbuy, NT 5797. Tel. (089) 87 1701.

ABORIGINAL ART GALLERIES DARWIN AND ALICE SPRINGS

Aboriginal Art Australia Pty Ltd, 88 Todd Street, Alice Springs, NT 5750. Tel. (089) 52 3408.

Aboriginal Heritage Gallery, 44 The Mall, Darwin, NT 5974. Tel. (089) 81 1394.
Wholesale and retail outlet for Aboriginal arts and crafts.

Buku Larrnggay Arts, Yirrkala, Nhulunbuy, NT 5797. Tel. (089) 87 1701.

Katherine Aboriginal Arts and Crafts Centre, Crawford Street, Katherine, NT 5780. Tel. (089) 72 3034.
Works by local Aboriginal groups.

Mbantua, 55 Gap Road, Alice Springs, NT 5750. Tel. (089) 52 1732.
Genuine Aboriginal art and artifacts and weapons.

Outback Arts and Souvenirs, Shop 8, Todd Plaza, 63 Todd Mall, Alice Springs, NT 5750. Tel. (089) 52 3416.
Artifacts by local craftspeople.

Outcrop Gallery, Todd Mall, Alice Springs, NT 5750. Tel. (089) 52 3662.
Aboriginal artifacts.

Detail from an Aboriginal bark painting

FINE ART COURSES AND COLLEGES NORTHERN TERRITORY

Darwin Community College, PO Box 40146, Casuarina, NT 5792. Tel. (089) 20 4211.
The college offers an Undergraduate Degree (BA) in painting, sculpture, printmaking, photography, ceramics and an Associate Diploma in dance, drama and music.

ART MATERIALS
DARWIN AND ALICE
SPRINGS

Art Mart, 54 Todd Street, Alice Springs, NT 5750. Tel. (089) 52 5552.
Watercolours, oils, paper boards etc.

Bloms Picture Framing, Polana Centre, Smith Street, Alice Springs, NT 5750. Tel. (089) 52 3396.

Jacksons, Unit 5, 43 Sadgroves Cnr, Winnellie, Darwin, NT 5789. Tel. (089) 84 3738.
Complete range of art materials for the professional, schools and amateurs.

Palette and Brush Art Gallery, 3 Vaughton Place, Rapid Creek, Darwin, NT 5792. Tel. (089) 85 4860.
Selection of fine art and craft material.

Souvenarta, 23 Cavenagh Street, Darwin, NT 5790. Tel. (089) 81 2758.
Stocks all handcrafted and art supplies and technical and fine art books. Orders are sent to the outback as required.

ART BOOKSHOPS
DARWIN AND ALICE
SPRINGS

Angus and Robertsons Bookshop, Shop 3, Ford Plaza, Todd Mall, Alice Springs, NT 5750. Tel. (089) 52 4057.
General art section with mail order service available.

Book Centre, 27 Cavenagh Street, Darwin, NT 5790. Tel. (089) 81 6268.

Bookworld, 30 Smith Street, Darwin, NT 5790. Tel. (089) 81 5277.
Complete range of books, arts and crafts etc. Also located at the Northern Territory Museum and at Darwin Institute of Technology Bookshop. Tel. (089) 20 4271.
Territory Book Dept Pty Ltd, Casuarina Shopping Square, 247 Trower Road, Casuarina, NT 5792.
General and educational, art selection and paper backs.

THEATRICAL ORGANISATIONS DARWIN AND ALICE SPRINGS

Brown's Mart Community Arts Theatre, 12 Smith Street Darwin, NT 5790. Tel. (089) 81 5522.

Darwin Theatre Group Inc., **Community Theatre**, 12 Smith Street, Darwin, NT 5790. Tel. (089) 81 8424. Workshop (089) 81 9045.

Dreamtime Dance Group, Schaber Road, Alice Springs, NT 5750. Tel. (089) 52 4610.

Totem Theatre, Anzac Oval, Alice Springs, NT 5750. Tel (089) 52 3837.

Territory North Theatre Company Inc., Dripstone Road Casuarina, Darwin, NT 5792. Tel. (089) 20 4257.

Northern Territory Theatre Company, Harry Chan Arcade Darwin, NT 5790. Tel. (089) 41 1568.

RESTAURANTS DARWIN AND ALICE SPRINGS

Clickitys, The Botanical Gardens, "The Gardens", Darwin. Tel. (089) 81 8658.
Licensed à la carte restaurant. Open till very, very, very late.

Gabby's Bistro, Hot Gossip, Entertainment Complex, 21 Cavenagh Street, Darwin. Tel. (089) 41 1811.
Open 11–2. Excellent bistro style meals. Open 7 days serving tropical sea delights, buffalo and crocodile steaks.

Harrison's Coffee Studio, 27 Smith Street, Darwin (Vic Complex Mall). Tel. (089) 81 4120.
Open Monday–Thursday 8.30–5, Friday 8.30–9, Saturday 8.30–1.

Hindquarter Steakhouse Melanka Lodge, 94 Todd Street, Alice Springs. Tel. (089) 52 2233.
Succulent grain-fed beef and buffalo. From Australia's northern waters, Barramundi and a variety of fresh salads.

278

Oasis, The Garden Motel, Gap Road, Alice Springs. Tel. 089) 52 1444.

Olympic Restaurant, 20 Austin Lane, Darwin. Tel. (089) 81 3298.
Specializing in superb Italian prepared seafood, pasta and meat dishes. Open 7 days a week 11.30–2, dinner 6–midnight.

Splendour Restaurant, 2nd Floor, Jade Plaza, 20 Cavenagh Street, Darwin. Tel. (089) 81 9292.
Authentic Chinese cuisine. Live music. Open 7 days.

The Beagle, Museums Complex, Conacher Street, Fannie Bay, Darwin. Tel. (089) 81 7791.
An excellent seafood restaurant on the beach.

The Rock Oyster, 17 Cavenagh Street, Darwin. Tel. (089) 81 3472.
Freshly caught seafood, oysters a speciality. Also incorporating a tropical open air restaurant during the dry season May–October. Open Monday–Saturday 6.30 till late.

The Terrace—Bistro and Safari Bar, The Darwin Travelodge, 122 Esplanade, Darwin. Tel. (089) 81 5388.
Tropical selection of fine foods in the Terrace and a wide selection of quick snacks and a cool drink by the pool at the Safari bar.

The Esplanade Gallery, open-air cafe, cnr Knuckey Street and Esplanade, Darwin. Tel. (089) 81 5042.
A tropical garden setting. Open 7 days 10–5 within the gallery complex.

AUSTRALIAN ARTS PUBLICATIONS

Art Almanac, 5/171 Darlinghurst Road, Darlinghurst, NSW 2010. Tel. (02) 332 3225 also at Rm 8, 3rd Floor, 329 Little Collins Street, Melbourne, Vic. 3000. Tel. (03) 650 4283. Monthly directory of exhibitions and galleries for both Sydney and Melbourne. 10 issues annually. Often available in galleries.

Art in Education, Journal of Arts Education Society of NSW, 49 Cuzco Street, South Coogee, NSW 2034.

Art and Australia. Long established glossy magazine with reviews, news and feature articles. Available quarterly, good quality colour reproductions. Fine Art Press Pty Ltd, 653 Pacific Highway, Killara, NSW 2071. Tel. (02) 498 4933.

Art Bulletin, 2/27 Abercrombie Street, Chippendale, NSW 2008.
Poster size information sheet every 2 months, covering Sydney's major exhibitions plus an interesting "Open File" news column. Available at most galleries.

Art Monthly, 653 Pacific Highway, Killara, NSW 2071. Tel (02) 498 1236.
Australian and international art issues, reviews, interviews and information (black & white).

Art & Text, Prahran College of Advanced Education, 142 High Street, Prahran, Vic. 3181.
Very interesting art criticism and reviews.

Artlink, 363 Esplanade, Henely Beach, South Australia 5022. Tel. (08) 356 8511.
Coverage of contemporary art issues in Australia and overseas with reviews criticism, theory, politics and information available quarterly.

Artemis, Official publication of the Newcastle Gallery Society, PO Box 5206c, Newcastle West, NSW 2302.

Artforce, News digest of the Australia Council, 6 issues annually. Arts information programme, Australia Council 168 Walker Street, North Sydney, NSW 2060. Tel. (02) 922 2122, PO Box 302, North Sydney, NSW 2060.

Artlook, The West Australian Art Magazine, 33 Stuart Street, North Perth, WA 6006. Tel. (09) 328 9188.
Monthly issues with excellent coverage on all the arts.

Artworks, Newspaper of the Woollahra-Waverly Arts Centre Co-op Ltd, 266a Grafton Street, Bondi Junction, NSW 2022.

Australia Architecture and Design, 26–29 Beatty Avenue, Armidale, Vic. 3143. Tel. (03) 20 2989.
6 issues per annum.

Australian Artist, Suite 207, Equity House, 284 Victoria Avenue, Chatswood, NSW 2067. Tel. (02) 419 6333.
A monthly magazine with emphasis on techniques and art suppliers.

Australia Camera Craft, PO Box 143, Mona Vale, NSW 2103. Tel. (02) 938 5277.
Available monthly, reports and technical information.

Australian Photography, PO Box 4689, GPO Sydney, NSW 2000. Tel. (02) 267 7171.
Available monthly, comprehensive reviews and reports. Ed. Terry Swan.

Billy Blue, The Grandstand, Cnr Miller & Ridge Streets, North Sydney, PO Box 728, North Sydney, NSW 2059. Tel. (02) 957 2844.
A free magazine available around Sydney compiled for a graphic arts audience, writers and publishers.

Craft Arts, Craft Australia Pty Ltd, PO Box 363, Neutral Bay, NSW 2089. Tel. (02) 908 4797.
Comprehensive glossy magazine, well-illustrated, events, reviews, exhibitions and interesting articles on national and international craft.

Craft Tasmania, The magazine of the Craft Council of Tasmania, 65 Salamanca Place, Hobart, Tasmania 7000. Tel. (002) 23 5622.

Directory of Australian Printmakers, 172 Roden Street, West Melbourne, Vic. 3003. Tel. (03) 328 2140.
Produced by the Australia Print Council, updated edition now available.

Directory of Australian Festivals, Published by the Arts Information Programme of the Australia Council, PO Box 302, North Sydney, NSW 2060.
A comprehensive guide to festivals throughout Australia.

Film News, Published by the Sydney Filmmakers Co-operative Ltd, PO Box 217 Kings Cross, NSW 2011. Tel. (02) 33 5368.

Guide to Craft Supplies, Produced by the Crafts Council of Australia, 100 George Street, The Rocks, NSW 2000.

Imprint, Produced by the Print Council of Australia, 172 Roden Street, West Melbourne, Vic. 3003. Tel. (03) 328 2140.
A journal about Australian printmaking with reviews and interviews, awards and exhibitions and special features.

Jazz, 74–76 Commonwealth Street, Surry Hills, NSW 2016. Tel. (02) 212 1288.
The Australian contemporary music magazine, twice monthly, with what's on.

Lip, c/o PO Box 139, Parkville, Vic. 3052.
A feminist art journal, articles invited, supported in part by the Visual Arts Board.

Metro, liftout suppliment in Friday's Sydney Morning Herald.
A weekly guide to events in Sydney including galleries, theatre, music, film, excursions and exertions, with special features about Sydney. Essential reading for visitors to Sydney.

Ozarts, Order from Arts Information, Australia Council, PO Box 302, North Sydney, NSW 2060.
A guide to over 200 visual arts, community arts, literature, music, craft, Aboriginal arts, film, radio, TV and theatre organisations. All non-profit organisations with details and contacts.

Photofile, produced by the Australian Centre for Photography, Dobell House, 257 Oxford Street, Paddington, NSW 2021. Tel. (02) 331 6253.
A quarterly journal on photography and contemporary issues.

Pottery in Australia, published by the Potters Society of Australia, 48 Burton Street, Darlinghurst, NSW 2010. Tel (02) 331 3151.
Including technical articles, features and general news.

Queensland Cultural Diary, issued monthly by the Director of Cultural Activities for Queensland, PO Box 155, North Quay, Qld 4000. Tel. (07) 227 6192. Tel. (07) 227 6192.
A comprehensive listing of all cultural activities throughout Queensland.

Tension, Virgin Press Publishing Co. Pty Ltd, 1 Oban Street South Yarra, Vic. 3142. Tel. (03) 240 0654.
A fine arts magazine with a wide variety of interesting articles on the contemporary arts and events, 6 issues annually. Contributions welcomed.

The Melbourne Report, 324–328 Napier Street, Fitzroy Vic. 3065. Tel. (03) 417 3121.
A monthly magazine with information on theatre, dance, cinema photography, exhibitions etc.

Words on Paper, a newsletter produced by the Papermakers of Australia, contact Penny Carey-Wells, GPO Box 252c Hobart, Tas. 7001. Tel. (002) 384 4300.

Visual Arts News Letter, newsletter produced by the National Association for the Visual Arts, 100 George Street Sydney, NSW 2000. Tel. (02) 27 7995.

The Fremantle Arts Review, PO Box 891, Fremantle, WA 6160. Tel. (09) 335 8244.
A monthly digest with focus on arts activities nationally and locally with special focus on Fremantle.

The Victorian Tourism Commission publish directories and informative guides to the arts and crafts of Victoria with concentration on regional areas. For details 230 Collins Street Melbourne, Vic. 3000. Tel. (03) 619 9444. Similar guides are becoming available in other states at tourist information offices.

MUSE, published by the Arts Council of Australia, ACT Division, PO Box 181, Civic Square, ACT 2608.
A monthly magazine which gives a coverage on arts and entertainment in Canberra, available free at Block B, Gorman House, Theatres, Schools of Music & Art ANU, Colleges and other selected outlets. Articles of any kind welcome, payment made to contributors

AUSTRALIAN ART AWARDS AND COMPETITIONS

The Australia Council, Visual Arts Board and many consulates also offer substantial scholarships. Please check with them for details. Listings are often available at the State Art Galleries in each capital city.

ACTA Australian Maritime Art Award. An open acquisitive $10,000 prize. Closing date usually April, details from ACTA Shipping, ACTA House, 447 Kent Street, Sydney, NSW 2000. Exhibition usually held in Blaxland Gallery, Sydney.

Albany Art Competition. Total prize money of $6,150 in any medium, closing date early March. Entry forms from General Manager/Town Clerk Town of Albany, PO Box 484, Albany, WA 6330.

Alice Bale Art Award. Traditional realism and figurative art. $25,000 travelling scholarship 1st prize. Additional awards $6,000 annual award. Contact McClelland Gallery, McClelland Drive, Langwarrin, Vic. 3910. Tel. (03) 789 1671.

Alice Prize. Annual award for outstanding art work in any medium, $7,000 used for acquisitions. Entries close October, apply to Alice Springs Art Foundation Inc., PO Box 1854, Alice Springs, NT 5750.

Alliance Française Fellowship. Australian artist under the age of 30 years, air travel and stay in France, annual award. Contact the Visual Arts Board, 168 Walker Street, North Sydney, NSW 2060. September.

Andrew and Lillian Pederson Memorial Prize. Prize for printmaking held every four years, inaugural year 1976. $500 acquisitive. Prize for small sculpture held every two years, $1,000 prize money. Prize for drawing held every four years, inaugural year 1978, $500 acquisitive. Apply to The Director, Queensland Art Gallery, Queensland Cultural Centre, South Bank, South Brisbane, Qld 4101. Tel. (07) 240 7333.

Ansett R. M. Hamilton Art Award, City of Hamilton Art Gallery, PO Box 9, Hamilton, Vic. 3000. For information contact the director Julian Faigan.

Annual Pioneer Purchase Award. The gallery collect contemporary Australian prints drawings through this award. Apply to Swan Hill Art Gallery, Pioneer Settlement, Swan Hill, Vic. 3586. Tel. (050) 32 1403.

Archibald Prize. Portrait (oil or watercolour) of some man or woman distinguished in the arts, letters, science or politics.

Annual, entries close December. Apply to The Director, Art Gallery of New South Wales, Art Gallery Road, The Doman, Sydney, NSW 2000. Tel. (02) 221 2100.

Ashtons Scholastic Picture Book Awards. Awards offered to those who have not previously written or illustrated a published picture book. Apply to PO Box 579, Gosford, NSW 2250. Writers $2,000, Illustrators $2,500.

Australian Design Award and Prince Phillip Prize. Award for fine design in volume produced items (pottery, printed textiles, etc). Apply to The Industrial Design Council of Australia, National Office, 20 Commercial Road, Melbourne, Vic. 3000. Tel. (03) 820 1100.

Barry Stern Print Award. Open to technical students. Contact the Head Teacher, Printmaking Workshop, East Sydney Technical College Art School, Forbes Street, Darlinghurst, NSW 2010. Tel. (02) 339 8626. $1,000. September.

Basil and Muriel Hooper Scholarship. Awarded to fine art students in recognised art schools who have difficulties in meeting their expenses. Apply to the Art Gallery of New South Wales through your art school.

Bathurst Art Prize. Biennial art prize (1989), open prize $5,000. Sections include ceramics and works on paper, entries close August. Apply to Secretary, Bathurst Art Purchase, c/o Bathurst Regional Art Gallery, Private Mailbag 17, Bathurst, NSW 2795.

Bega Caltex Awards. Open section $1,000, annual award in September. Contact Mrs Jan Bolsius, 8 Little Church Street, Bega, NSW 2550.

Berrima District Art Society Art Award. Two catergories works on paper any medium and print size. Closing date first week before Easter. Apply to Exhibitions Secretary, Berrima District Art Society, PO Box 144, Bowral, NSW 2576.

Blake Prize for Religious Art. Annual award of $10,000 for religious art. September. Secretary, Box 4484, GPO Sydney, NSW 2000.

Brisbane Royal Show. Annual award, entries close in June. Apply to the Secretary, RNA Society, Gregory Terrace, Fortitude Valley, Qld 4006.

Building Bookshop Design Award. Entries invited for the following categories: craft (functional objects in clay, glass, metal or wood) and graphics (screen printed poster or original serigraph). The winner awarded a certificate and $250 (acquisitive). For details apply to The Building Bookshop, Sydney Building Information Centre Ltd, 525 Elizabeth Street, Sydney, NSW 2010. Tel. (02) 699 5435.

Caltex Art Award. Awarded in each state of Australia with the winning entry being acquired and donated back to the local art centre. Contact any local State Art Gallery for details.

Canberra Times National Art Award. Apply to the Promotions Manager, The Canberra Times, Newcastle Street, Fyshwick, ACT 2609. Tel. (062) 80 2122. Landscape, streetscape (acquisitive).

Capital Permanent Award. Information from The Director, Geelong Art Gallery, Little Malop Street, Geelong, Vic. 3220.

Camden Municipal Art Exhibition. Open section for any medium, $3,000 purchase award. Entry forms from The Secretary, Camden Municipal Art Exhibition Committee, John Street, Camden, NSW 2570.

Churchill Scholarship. Apply to Winston Churchill Memorial Trust, Churchill House, 218 Northbourne Avenue, Braddon, ACT 2601. Tel. (062) 47 8333.

City of Toowoomba Art Purchase. Acquisitive prize for prints and drawings totalling over $3,000, annually in August. Contact The Secretary, City of Toowoomba Art Purchase, Carnival of Flowers Office, 293 Ruthven Street, Toowoomba, Qld 4350.

Civic Permanent Art Award. Details, The Secretary, Arts Council of Australia, ACT Division, Gorman House, Ainslie Avenue, Braddon, ACT 2601.

Cromacryl Annual Painting Award. Open to all students in Art and Design within the colleges of Technical and Further Education (TAFE). Prize of $1,000, entries close early November. Details from Head Teachers within TAFE art schools.

Cloncurry Ernest Henry Memoral Art Contest. Annual prize approx. $3,500. Entries close usually October. Details from The Secretary, Cloncurry Art Society, PO Box 326, Cloncurry, Qld 4824.

Concrete Sculpture Exhibition. Apply to the Concrete Institute of Australia, 100 Walker Street, North Sydney, NSW 2060. $1,500 prize money.

Conservation and Curatorial Grants. For purposes such as study visits overseas, general research and preparation of major exhibitions. Apply to the Visual Arts Board, PO Box 302, North Sydney, NSW 2060. Tel. (02) 92 3333.

Cultural Grants Advisory Council, Box R105, Royal Exchange, Sydney, NSW 2000.

Darnell De Gruchy Investment Purchase Award. Details, c/o Fine Arts Dept, University of Queensland, St Lucia, Brisbane, Qld 4067.

Diamond Valley Art Award—Invitation Exhibition. Annual award in the categories of glass, ceramics, works on paper, painting, metal, textiles and sculpture. Total acquisitive prize money $16,000. Closing date June, apply to The Diamond Valley Art Award Committee, PO Box 115, Greensborough, Vic. 3088.

Drummoyne Art Award. Non-acquisitive art competition with sections as follows: modern, traditional, watercolour, graphics. Entries close in August. Details from The Secretary, PO Box 178, Drummoyne, NSW 2047.

Dyason Bequest. Grants for Australian art students who have already won scholarships and are able to afford to study. $2,500. Applications any time to The Art Gallery of New South Wales.

Faber-Castell Award for Drawing. $4,000 for professionals and $1,000 for amateurs. Apply to Faber-Castell, 25 Pavesi Street, Guildford, NSW 2160. Entries in September.

Fremantle Art Centre Print Award. Exhibition and award February annually. For information contact The Exhibitions Officer, Fremantle Art Centre, PO Box 891, Fremantle, WA 6160. Tel. (09) 335 8244.

Fulbright Scholarship. Applications to the American Embassy, Yarralumla, ACT 2600. Tel. (062) 73 1352.

Georges Invitation Art Prize. Annual art prize given by Georges Australia Ltd, Melbourne. The largest prize to be awarded in Melbourne. For details contact The National Gallery of Victoria, 180 St Kilda Road, Melbourne, Vic. 3000. Tel. (03) 62 7411.

Gold Coast City Art Prize. Annual, non-competitive exhibition for the purchase of selected works at catalogue prices to a minimum of $10,000. Entries usually close August. Details from The Secretary, Gold Coast City Art Prize, PO Box 1010, Southport, Qld 4215.

Gosford City Festival of the Waters. Phyl Bennett watercolour prize of $450. Drawing prize of $250. Print prize of $250. Pottery prize $200 for functional and $200 for decorative. Annual competition, entries closing early September. Apply to the Festival Art Director, PO Box 312, Gosford, NSW 2250.

Grand Australia Art Competition. Biennial competition awarded in painting or drawing in any medium and of any subject. Details from The Manager, National Hotel, Queen Street, Brisbane, Qld 4000.

Gruner Prize. Best oil study of landscape painted by a student, resident in NSW (art student). Prize $400. Entries close late October. Apply to The Art Gallery of New South Wales.

Hugh Williamson Prize. Contemporary art, 1st prize $15,000 and two emerging artists $4,000 each. Biennial, September and invitational. Contact City of Ballarat Fine Art Gallery, 40 Lydiard Street, North Ballarat, Vic. 3350. Tel. (053) 31 5622.

Henry Worland Memorial Art Prize. Annual prize open to all printmakers in Australia, entries close in November. Details from Warrnambool, Vic. 3280.

Ian Potter Foundation Sculpture Commission. First awarded 1980, $10,000 acquisitive. Enquiries to The National Gallery of Victoria, 180 St Kilda Road, Melbourne, Vic. 3000.

Kiffy Rubbo Memorial Fellowship. This award is initiated by the Visual Arts Board to provide an opportunity for a young artist, arts administrator or curator who shows promise in the contemporary field to spend a year at a place of their choice, either in Australia or overseas, to widen and extend their experience in the visual arts. A grant of $12,000 is awarded for a 12 months project. Apply to Visual Arts Board, PO Box 302, North Sydney, NSW 2060. Tel. (02) 923 3333. Closing date October.

La Trobe Valley Purchase Award. Details from The Director, La Trobe Vallery Art Centre, PO Box 708, Morewell, Vic. 3840.

L. H. Harvey Memorial Prize for Drawing. Biennial prize held in conjunction with the Trustees Purchase Exhibition, Queensland Art Gallery, Queensland Cultural Centre, South Bank, South Brisbane, Qld 4101. Tel. (07) 240 7333. $500 acquisitive.

Maitland Prize. Annual art competition. For details contact The Secretary, Maitland Prize, PO Box 37, Maitland, NSW 2320.

Marten Bequest. Travelling scholarship of $5,800 awarded for sculpture every three years (1986). Apply to Permanent Trustee Co. Ltd, 25 O'Connell Street, Sydney, NSW 2000. Tel. (02) 232 4400.

Maude-Vizard Whelohan Art Prize. A biennial art prize. Information and entry forms from the Art Gallery of South Australia, North Terrace, Adelaide, SA 5000.

Mayfair Ceramics Award. Information available from The Craft Council of NSW, 100 George Street, The Rocks, Sydney, NSW 2000.

Mobil Fellowship in Arts Administration. Entries close September. Apply to Arts Research Training and Support Ltd, 9 Rush Street, Woollahra, NSW 2025. Tel. (02) 32 0832.

Moët and Chandon Australian Art Fellowship. Air travel to and from France, housing and studio accommodation, allowance for 12 months. Annual. Apply to 1 Eastgate Avenue, Killara, NSW 22071. $50,000, artist must be under 36 years old.

Mona McCaughey Prize. Annual prize for the best picture of the year painted by an Australian artists, which has hung in the Art Gallery of New South Wales during the previous year. Awarded in December.

Moya Dyring Memorial Scholarship. Paris studio for 3 months, applications at any time from established artists. Contact the Visual Arts Board, PO Box 302, North Sydney, NSW 2060. Tel. (02) 923 3333.

National Art Award. Open to secondary school students, annual in June. Contact, National Art Award, GPO Box 4162, Sydney, NSW 2001.

New South Wales Travelling Art Scholarship. Annual award, currently $15,000 for two or three years to enable a student of art or artist to study abroad. July/August and under 30 years. Details from The Secretary, Travelling Art Scholarship Committee, GPO Box 2626, Sydney, NSW 2001 or the Art Gallery of NSW.

Portia Geach Memorial Award. Annual prize for the best portrait by a female artist of a man or woman distinguished in the arts, letters or the sciences. $4,000. The Trustees, Portia Geach Memorial Award, c/o Permanent Trustees, 1st Floor, 56 Kellett Street, Potts Point, NSW 2011.

Pring Prize. For the best watercolour landscape by a woman artist $200. Details from the Art Gallery of NSW.

Robin Hood Committee Art Competition. Annual, four sections, best in Section 1, any medium $600. Contact The President, PO Box 592, Potts Point, NSW 2011.

Royal Melbourne Show. Annual arts and crafts competitions, entries close July. Apply to The Director, Rroyal Show Grounds, Epsom Road, Ascot Vale, Vic. 3032. Tel. (03) 376 0471.

Robert LeGay Brereton Prize. Drawing studies by an art student $500. Entries close late June. Apply to the Art Gallery of NSW, Art Gallery Road, Sydney, NSW 2000.

Sydney Morning Herald Art Scholarship. "To Capture the Spirit of Sydney", amateurs and students only, annually in January.

Sydney Morning Herald Art Prize. Annual prize of $7,500, open. "To Capture the Spirit of Sydney", past or present and have a feeling for the importance of its manmade or natural environment. John Fairfax, GPO Box 506, Sydney, NSW 2001.

Sydney Royal Easter Show. Annual arts and crafts competition, $4,000 prize money. Entries close around November of previous year. Apply to The Director, Royal Agricultural Society, GPO Box 4317, Sydney, NSW 2000. Tel. (02) 31 7781.

Stuart Devlin Award. English speaking union. A non-acquisitive cash award of $3,500 presented to a workshop to enable further development. Entries close in March, work received August. Contact The National Gallery of Victoria for details.

SABEMO—TLC Sculpture Award. Annual award of $2,500 prize money, restricted to works in WA industry. Entries close end of October. Apply to WA Trades & Labour Council, Trades Hall, Perth, WA 6000. Tel. (09) 28 1882.

Sulman Prize. Awarded for figure composition, genre, mural projects or subjects as specified by the trustees. $5,000. Exhibition held at the Art Gallery of NSW, for details contact the gallery in October.

Trustees' Watercolour Prize. At the same time as the Archibald, Sulman and Wynne Prizes at the Art Gallery of

NSW, awarded if the winning entry in the Wynne Prize is not watercolour, $2,000. Contact the Art Gallery of NSW in October.

University of New South Wales Art Prize & Scholarship. Awarded annually, for entry details contact the University of NSW, PO Box 1, Kensington, NSW 2033.

University of Sydney Art Award. Annual award, use of the universities studio in the Cite Internationale des Arts, Paris. Entries close August. Apply to The Register, University of Sydney, Sydney, NSW 2006.

Wynne Prize. Landscape (oil or watercolour) or figure sculpture (any medium), $10,000. Exhibition held at the Art Gallery of NSW. Contact the gallery in October for details.

Waverly Art Prize. Annual prize held in September, open section—painting $2,500, watercolour $1,250, print $500. Acquisitive. Apply to Waverly—Woollahra Arts Centre, 138 Bondi Road, Bondi, NSW 2026. Tel. (02) 387 2461.

Woollongong Art Purchase. For details contact The Secretary, Woollongong Art Purchase, PO Box 186, Woollongong East, NSW 2500.

AUSTRALIAN CRAFT AWARDS AND COMPETITIONS

Some awards have already been listed under "Art Awards and Competitions" such as **The Diamond Valley Art Award**, the following list includes more specific craft orientated awards throughout Australia. The division of the Crafts Council of Australia in each capital city will have more extensive regional listings.

Ascraft Award. An annual award of $1,000 for consistent critical writing on the crafts. For details contact Crafts Council of Australia, 100 George Street, The Rocks, Sydney, NSW 2000. Tel. (02) 241 1701.

Batman Festival Craft Purchase Exhibition. Annual exhibition with $2,000–$3,000 prize money, usually held March/April, entry by invitation. Apply to The Queen Victoria Museum and Art Gallery, Wellington Street, Launceston, Tasmania 7250. Tel. (002) 31 6777.

Creative Copper Award. Annual award with $3,000 prize money student section and $1,500 open section. Sponsored by Austral Bronze Copper Crane Co. Apply to Sydney Teachers College, PO Box 63, Camperdown, NSW 2050. Tel. (02) 660 2855.

Excellence in Aluminium Award. Biennial (1988), $9,000 in total prize money, 3 categories. Sponsored by the Aluminium Development Council and Industrial Design Council of Australia. Apply to Industrial Design Council of Australia, 50 Margaret Street, Sydney, NSW 2000. Tel. (02) 29 4273.

Festival of Perth Invitation Ceramic Award. $500 prize money. Apply to Fremantle Arts Centre, Finnerty Street Perth, WA 6000. Hunters Hill Art Exhibition, annual exhibition $1,000 craft prize, $100 local craft award, $100 best young local crafts person, entries close March. Apply to the Exhibition Secretary, PO Box 21, Hunters Hill, NSW 2110. Tel. (02) 816 1555.

Institute of Industrial Arts Craft Award. Annual award for the best piece of craftwork by a NSW high school student chosen from regional award winners selected during the year across the state. Apply to The President, Institute of Industrial Arts, 2 Thomond Street, Hurstville, NSW 2220.

Jewellery Design Award—Australia, Tri-annual award, six sections, entries close August (prize money). Apply to Australian Jewellers Association, 21 Burwood Road, Hawthorn, Vic. 3122. Tel. (03) 819 1311.

Moora Woolcraft Awards. Four major awards of $1,000 and $100 in each of 10 categories. Apply to Mrs Julie Kearny, "Cardo", Watheroo, WA 6513.

Northside Creative Artist Association. $1,500 prize money, art and craft competition. Entries close November. Apply to Northside Creative Artist Association, c/o 1–26 Norman Street, Wooloowin, Qld 4030. Tel. (07) 57 6461.

Tamworth National Fibre Exhibition. Acquisitive biennial exhibition held in August. Award of $2,500. Contact James Gidy (067) 663 641 or the NSW Crafts Council Office.

Tennant Creek Art/Craft Award. Annual award of $1,000, acquisitive. Sponsored by Peko Wallsend, entries close September. Apply to CWA Tennant Creek Branch, PO Box 212, Tennant Creek, NT 5670.

Territorian Craft Acquisition Award. Annual award with $1,000 prize money. Sponsored by the Museum and Art Galleries, NT. Entries close August. Apply to the Crafts Council of Northern Territory, PO Box 1479, Darwin, NT 5794.

The Makers Mark Award. Annual competition in jewellery, $500 acquisition prize, different subjects with a jewellery form will be nominated yearly. Entries close July, apply to The Makers Mark Gallery, Shop 1, 205 Flinders Street, Melbourne, Vic. 3000. Tel. (03) 63 3254.

Town of Cockburn Art Purchase Award. $2,000 for the purchase of works. Entries close October, apply to Mr

McLeod, Town of Cockburn, South Australia 5440. Tel. 418 3311 (dial operator 080911).

Wales Bank City of Brisbane Craft Award. Annual award $2,500 total prize money, ceramics, fibre and mixed media. Entries close late October. Apply to Wales Bank City of Brisbane Craft Award, c/o Activities Centre, City Hall, King George Square, Brisbane Qld 4000.

Warringah Art Prize. Acquisitive annual award for contemporary and traditional work. Entries close July. Apply to Arts Officer, Civic Centre, Dee Why, NSW 2099.
For information on grants and scholarships available the following publications are very useful. Both are revised regularly, so be sure to ask for the latest available edition at your libraries.

Grants Register, London, Macmillan.

Study Abroad, International Scholarships, International Courses. Paris, Unesco Press.

Art Guide Publications Books, London Art and Artist Guide, Paris Art Guide, New York Art Guide, Amsterdam Art Guide, Berlin Arts Guide and the **Artist Directory** all list more detailed information about awards, scholarships and competitions in Europe and North America, also Madrid Arts Guide and Glasgow Arts Guide in Spring 1989. Distributed in Australia by **Hodder and Stoughton**, Sydney (Tel. 638 3299) and should be available at most bookshops, galleries and art centres.

AUSTRALIAN FESTIVAL CALENDAR

Listed in the calendar that follows are just some of the festivals taking place throughout Australia, in most cases annually. For a complete coverage of all Australian festivals the Arts Council of Australia are able to provide all the necessary information.

The **Sydney Biennale** is one of the major visual art exhibitions held in Australia and occurs every two years, next will be in 1990. The Biennale alternates with the Australian Perspecta exhibition which sets out to make available to a wide audience the broad concern evident in contemporary Australian art.

Other unique Australian festivals and of somewhat lighter note are events such as the **Henley-on-Todd Regatta** and **The Camel Cup** both held in Alice Springs. If you can imagine a regatta in the middle of the desert and camels at a checkec flag you begin to get the picture. Lots of fun if you're in the area.

Canowindra County show, New South Wales

National

March	National Folk Festival
April	Australian Theatre Week and Arts Festival
September	Australian Library Week

Australian Capital Territory

| March | Canberra Week Festival |
| Sept/Oct | Italian Arts Festival |

New South Wales

January	Festival of Sydney
March	Orange City Festival of Arts
April	Royal Easter Show, Sydney
	Mittagong Easter Festival Biennale Chamber Music
May/June	Dubbo Art & Craft Purchase
	Newcastle Arts Council Drama Festival
May/Aug	NSW High Schools Drama Festival
June	The Art Show, Sydney
	Hills District Eistedford
	Newcastle Folk Festival

July	Ashfield Art Exhibition
	Stroud International Brick and Rolling Pin
	Throwing Contest
August	NSW Drama Festival
	Wagga Wagga School of Arts Festival of
	Plays
September	Spring Fair Sydney
	Orange Blossom Festival, Sydney
	Addison Road Community Festival, Sydney
October	Armidale Arts Festival
	Cooma Beer Fest Crafty Bunyip Festival
	Parkes Country Music Jamboree
	South Sydney Festival, Sydney
November	Paddington Festival, Sydney
December	Australian Folk Life Festival, Sydney
	The Ella Festival, Sydney
June/July	Sydney Biennale (every two years)

Northern Territory

May	The Camel Cup, Alice Springs
	Bangtail Muster
June	Katherine Karnival
August	Darwin Youth Festival
	Henley-on-Todd Regatta, Alice Springs
	Tennant Creek Goldrush Folk Festival
November	Alice Springs, Acquisitive Exhibition
	Alice Springs, Festival Week
	Folklorico

Queensland

	Gatton and Bribie Island Australian Theatre Week and Arts Festival
April	
	Arts Festival
	Queensland Eistedford, Brisbane
May	Children's Film Festival, Brisbane
	Ipswich Little Theatre Drama Festival and
June	Playwrighters Competition, Brisbane
	Brisbane Royal National Show
	Caloundra Arts and Crafts Festival
	Festival of Arts, Brisbane
September	Boony Festival of Arts, Brisbane
	Corinda Festival of Arts, Brisbane
October	Goondiwindi Festival of Sport and Culture
	Mackay Festival of Performing Arts
November	Home Hill Harvest Festival
	Innisfail North Queensland Conservation
December	of Music Festival
	Nerang Festival of Art

South Australia

January	Australia Day Fair
	Adelaide Festival of Arts, Adelaide (every
February	two years)
	Adelaide Open Air Arts Exhibition, Adelaide
	International Film Festival for Children,
April	Adelaide
June	Adelaide Folkloric Festival
September	Royal Adelaide Show
	Adelaide Carols by Candelight Christmas
December	Earth Fair, Adelaide

Tasmania

January	String Summer School, Hobart
March	Festival of Tasmania, Hobart
June	Arts Festival Competition, Hobart
	Council for Children's Film and Television, Hobart
	Scottsdale North Eastern Arts and Crafts Association Display
July	Burnie Youth Drama Festival
	Deloraine Dramatic Society Youth Drama Festival
August	Circular Head Arts Festival
	Devonport Eistedford
	Hobart Film Festival
October	Market Week, Hobart
	Rosebery Arts and Crafts Festival
December	Tasmania Fiesta, Hobart

Victoria

March	Melbourne Moomba Festival
April	Bendigo Easter Fair
May	Greek Festival, Melbourne
	Victorian Council for Children's Film and Television, Melbourne
June	Melbourne Film Festival
	Ballarat Grand National Eistedford of Australia
August	
September	Melbourne Bach Festival
October	Waverly Festival of Arts, Melbourne

Western Australia

	Children's Council for Film and Television, Perth
January	
March	Cranbrook Crowea Drama Festival
May	Dampier Drama Festival

June	**Busselton Festival of Arts and Crafts**
	Northam Festival of Arts
July	**Country Women's Associaton State Drama and Choir Festival**
August	**Fremantle Week, Perth**
September	**Perth Royal Show**
October	**Bunbury Festival of Arts and Crafts**
December	**Wongan Festival of Dance**
	Sun City Show, Perth
February	**Festival of Perth**

After Venice, Bill Pengelly and Garth Welsh, Sydney Dance Company (Branco Gaica)

LIBRARIES

Canberra Institute of the Arts, Art School Library, Baldessin Crescent, Acton, ACT 2601. Tel. (062) 46 7811.

Craft Resources Productions, Crafts Council of Australia, 100 George Street, The Rocks, Sydney, NSW 2000. Tel. (02) 241 1701.
Slide library and reference library.

City Art Institute Library, Cnr Albion Avenue & Selwyn Street, Paddington, NSW 2021. Tel. (020 339 9555.
Open institute hours.

East Sydney Technical College, National School Library, Forbes Street, Darlinghurst, NSW 2010. Tel. (020) 339 8666.
Open college hours.

Fisher Library, University of Sydney, Parramatta Road, Sydney, NSW 2006. Tel. (02) 689 2222.
Open 9–5.

Grainger Museum Library, University of Melbourne, Gate 8, Royal Parade, Parkville, Vic. 3052. Tel. (03) 341 5270.
The library is attached to the gallery and available to approved research workers.

Melbourne State Library, 304–328 Swanston Street, Melbourne, Vic. 3000. Tel. (03) 699 9888.
Comprises of over one million volumes with a special collection of Australians in the La Trobe Library.

Mitchell Library, State Library of NSW, Macquarie Street, Sydney, NSW 2000. Tel. (02) 230 1414.

National Film and South Archives, McCoy Circuit, Acton, ACT 2601. Tel. (062) 67 1711.

National Library of Australia, Parkes Place, Parkes, ACT 2600. Tel. (062) 62 1111.

Queensland Cultural Centre Library, South Bank, South Brisbane, Qld 4101. Tel. (07) 840 7666.

State Library of Queensland, William Street, Brisbane, Qld 4000. Tel. (07) 221 8400.

State Library of Tasmania, 91 Murray Street, Hobart, Tas. 7000. Tel. (002) 30 7011.

The Australia Council Library, Australia Council, 168 Walker Street, North Sydney, NSW 2060. Tel. (02) 923 3333.
Extensive coverage on all areas of the arts including crafts. Lists of publications national and international, reports and journals in the collection are available on request and inter-library loans.

The John Oxley Library, William Street, Brisbane, Qld 4000.
Tel. (07) 221 8400.

TOURIST AND TRAVEL INFORMATION

Tourist information centres in each capital city

Australian Tourist Commission, William Street, Sydney, NSW 2000.

NSW Tourist Information (The Travel Centre) Cnr Spring & Pitt Streets, Sydney, NSW 2000. Tel. (02) 231 4444.

NSW Government Travel Centre, 16 Spring Street, Sydney, NSW 2000. Tel. (02) 231 4444/231 7100.

South Australian Government Tourist Bureau, 18 King William Street, Adelaide, SA 5000. Tel. (08) 212 1644.
Open Monday–Friday 8.45–5, Saturday 9–11, Sunday 10–2.

Tasmanian Government Tourist Bureau, 80 Elizabeth Street, Hobart, Tas. 7000. Tel. (002) 30 0211.
Open Monday–Friday 8.45–5.30, Saturday, Sunday & holidays 9–11.

Western Australian Government Tourist Bureau, 772 Hay Street, Perth, WA 6000. Tel. (09) 321 2471.

Victorian Government Tourist Bureau, Collins Street, Melbourne, Vic. 3000.Tel. (03) 602 94444.

Queensland Government Tourist Bureau, Brisbane City Hall, King George Square, Brisbane, Qld 4000. Tel. (07) 221 8411.

Northern Territory Government Tourist Bureau, 31 Smith Street, Darwin, NT 5794. Tel. (089) 81 6611.

Australian Capital Territory Government Tourist Bureau, Jolimont Centre, Northbourne Avenue, Canberra City, ACT 2601. Tel. (062) 45 6464.

Travel in Australia

Air travel

Three main airline companies operate domestic flights within Australia—**Ansett Airlines of Australia, Australian Airlines** (once TAA) and **East West Airlines**. All offer a range of attractive package holidays and concession fares on route around Australia. It is advisable to visit the airlines and choose the "Pass" which suits your travel plans and budget best. Other smaller airlines also operate within each state and often reduced internal flights are offered to overseas visitors.

Ansett Airlines of Australia, Cnr of Oxford Street & Riley Street, East Sydney, NSW 2010. Tel. (02) 268 1111 for flight information and reservation.
Check for available passes.

Australian Airlines, Hunter Street, Sydney, NSW 2000. Tel. (02) 693 3333.
Enquiries and reservations all hours. Currently offered is a "Go Australia Pass" with varying maximum distance kilometres. It is essential to stay a minumum of 4 nights in a non-capital city or town, unlimited number of stops and always in one direction.

East West Airlines—Head Office, 19th Level, 323 Castlereagh Street, Sydney, NSW 2000. Tel. (02) 219 5111 Fax (02) 219 5215.
The company offers a variety of Australian airpasses including East side air pass and coastal air pass and overseas visitors receive a 30% discount on presenting their passport. Check for new available passes.

Train travel

Australia has a network of inter-capital, country and urban trains of high standard. There are two classes of travel over long distances, economy and 1st class (with little difference). An "Australia pass" issued by Railways of Australia is available giving unlimited travel and can be purchased by overseas visitors in Australia on presentation of your passport or purchased overseas before arrival in Australia. Starts 1st day of travel. Excursion and day trips are available from within capital cities and major country centres. **New South Wales Rail Travel Centre**, Ground Floor, Transport House, 11–31 York Street, Wynyard, Sydney, NSW 2000 (nr Wynyard Station). Tel. (02) 29 7614.

Ferries in Sydney

Sydney Harbour has a very reliable network of ferries operating daily, providing an excellent opportunity to enjoy the harbour views, especially at sunset and the famous Manly Ferry connecting **Circular Quay** to **Manly** the closest northern beach. The ferry service to **Taronga Park Zoo** makes an interesting and convenient day's outing also the inner harbour small bays such as **Mosman** are close with lovely shady walks along the water's edge.

Ferries, trains and bus information around Sydney call **Sydney Metro Trips** Tel. (02) 29 2622.

Bus travel

Express coach services operate throughout Australia connecting capital cities and country towns. Three of the major long distance coachlines are: **Ansett Pioneer**, Cnr Oxford Street & Riley Street, East Sydney, NSW 2010. Tel. (02) 268

1881. The company offers the 'Aussie pass" with the 21 days pass available in Australia but the 7 days and 15 days passes only available outside Australia. Pass starts on first day of travel and your journey can be interchangeable with Greyhound Coaches.

Greyhound Australia, Cnr Oxford Street & Riley Street, Oxford Square, East Sydney. Tel. (02) 268 1414.
The company offers the "**Bus pass**" with unlimited kilometre travel. The 15 days pass is only available for purchase overseas with the 21 days, 30 days and 60 days available in Australia.

Delux Coach Lines, Sydney Coach Terminal, Cnr Castlereagh Street & Hay Street, Sydney, NSW 2000. Tel. (02) 212 4888.
The company offers the "**Koala pass**" with a 10 day pass only available to overseas visitors and 15 days, 22 days, 32 days, 62 days and 90 days all available in Australia. Offices throughout Australia and overseas in New Zealand, USA, London, Japan, Singapore.
Buses operate in all capital cities, providing a cheap and reliable means of transport around the inner city and to the outstretched suburbs. Look for the correct bus "No." as many buses end their journey at the same terminal as indicated on the front of the bus. **The Sydney Explorer** is a cheap and convenient way to see the sights of Sydney, departing every 15 minutes. For details Tel. (02) 231 4444. Similar services are available in the other capital cities.

Useful information

Airport Departure Tax. A tax of $25 is paid all at once, $20 for departure and $5 for re-entry, only accepted in Australian dollars at the airport.

Banking hours. Most banks Monday–Thursday open 9–4 some 9.30–4, Fridays 9–5. In the capital city centres some banks have special extended hours.

Cab hire in Sydney. ABC Cabs Tel. (02) 922 2233, Cumberland Cabs Tel. (02) 682 0155 and Legion Cabs Tel. (02) 2 0918.

Car rental in Sydney. Avis Tel. (02) 922 8161, Budget Rent-a-Car Tel. (02) 339 8811.

Currency. The decimal system is used throughout Australia for both measures and currency. ie. 100 cents = $1. Coins include 1c, 2c, 5c, 10c, 20c, 50c, $1 & $2.

Post office. Opening hours Monday–Friday 9–5. Australia Post, Martin Place, Sydney, NSW 2000. Tel. (02) 230 7013.

Shopping. Monday–Friday 9–5.30 with each capital city having one late night till 9, Saturday generally 9–4 with some smaller shops closing at 12 noon. In central Sydney now many shops are also open on Sundays especially in and around Darling Harbour.

Sydney Harbour Bridge from Circular Quay (Heather Waddell)

Emergency services. Call 000 for Police, Fire and Ambulance.

Sydney entertainment tickets. Monday–Friday 9–9. Tel. (02) 266 4800. All credit cards welcome.

Licensing hours in Australia. Hotels and pubs are open 10.30 a.m.–11 p.m. Within the inner city there are plenty of hotels with extended hours and wine bars and clubs with licensing till 3am and later.

Student Travel Australia, Head Office, 1a Lee Street, Sydney, NSW 2000. Tel. (02) 212 1255.

International travel from Australia—The Travel Specialists, Ground Floor, 62 Clarence Street, Sydney, NSW 2000. (behind Wynyard Station over York Street). Tel. (02) 262 3555.
A very professional young team of travel experts offering excellent discount fares—travel anywhere in the world anytime—very friendly helpful service for all types of travel. Visa service available and all insurance needs.

Public transport information in Sydney. For buses, trains and ferries Monday—Friday 7–7 Tel. (02) 290 2988.

Public transport information centre in Melbourne. For buses, trains and trams Monday—Friday Tel. (03) 602 9011.

Interstate Express Coach Lines. Delux Tel. (02) 212 4888, McCaffertys Tel. (02) 33 5125 and Sunliner Express Tel. (02) 498 7166 are just a few of the many services available, as well as those previously mentioned under "bus travel".

Walcha, New South Wales, grazing country

AUSTRALIA'S GREAT OUTDOORS—SPORT

Australia is one of the greatest sporting nations in the world and with its mild winters and beautiful hot summers it's not

Sailing, Sydney Harbour

surprising that most Australians participate in some kind of sport. Outdoor sports such as tennis, golf, sailing, horseriding, rowing, bush walking, surfing, football, soccer, athletics, hockey, etc., etc., can be enjoyed all the year round with the summer season being November–April and the winter season May–October.

With so many sporting clubs and recreation areas available to the public in each capital city it is suggested that you contact the appropriate Department of Sport and Recreation. They will be able to give a very comprehensive listing of all the registered associations and clubs for anyone wishing to use the membership facilities.

New South Wales Dept of Sport and Recreation, 140 Phillip Street, Sydney, NSW 2000. Tel. (02) 231 7100 also 105 Miller Street, North Sydney, NSW 2060. Tel. (02) 923 4234.

Victorian Dept of Youth, Sport and Recreation, 570 Bourke Street, Melbourne, Vic. 3000. Tel. (03) 602 1566.

South Australian Division of Sport and Recreation, 25 Grenfell Street, Adelaide, SA 5000. Tel. (08) 213 0555.

Queensland Dept of Culture, National Parks and Sport, State Law Building, George Street, Brisbane, Qld 4000. Tel. (07) 227 4111/Sport 227 4839.

Western Australian Dept of Youth, Sport and Recreation, Perry Lakes Stadium, Wembley, WA 6014. Tel. (09) 387 4400.

Tasmanian Dept of Sport and Recreation, Kirkway House, Kirkway Place, Battery Point, Hobart, Tas. 7000. Tel. (002) 30 8011.

Northern Territory of Youth, Sport, Recreation and Ethnic Affairs, Development House, The Esplanade, Darwin, NT 5790. Tel. (089) 82 1311.

Australian Capital Territory Dept of Sport, Recreation and Tourism, Silverton Centre, Moore Street (Cnr Rudd Street), Canberra City, ACT 2601. Tel. (062) 68 9411.

Australian wines

Australia is becoming internationally recognised for its fine wines. Two of the most famous areas where you can sample Australian wines in the vineyards are the **Barossa Valley**, South Australia and the **Hunter Valley**, **New South Wales**. Visitors are welcome to visit "wineries" throughout both areas where they can taste a large selection of available Australian wines. This is an ideal way to taste a huge variety of wines otherwise not available. Day trips can be booked from Adelaide for the Barossa Valley wineries and from Sydney you can easily join an organised weekend visit or rent a car for the weekend and make your own choice of which wineries to visit.

Vineyards

West Australia—Swan Valley and Margaret River area. Names to look out for: (Houghtons and Sandalfords wines, Leeuwin Estate).

South Australia—Barossa Valley and The Southern Vales. Names to look out for: (Yalumba, Lindemans, Hardy's, Reynella, Orlando).

Victoria—The Murray River Bendigo, Geelong, Glenrowan, Great Western Yarra. Names to look out for: (Ovens Valley Shiraz, Seppelt, Balgownie).

New South Wales—Hunter Valley, Mudgee. Names to look out for: (Tyrrell's, Rothbury Estate, McWilliams, Lindermans, Evans family).

Embassies and high commissions

Arab Republic of Egypt, 125 Monaro Crescent, Red Hill, ACT 2603. Tel. (062) 95 0394.

Argentina, 58 Mugga Way, Red Hill, ACT 2603. Tel. (062) 95 1570.

Austrian Embassy, 12 Talbot Steet, Forrest, ACT 2603. Tel. (0620 95 1533.

Bangladesh High Commission, 11 Molineaux Place, Farrer, ACT 2607. Tel. (062) 86 1200.

Belgium, 19 Arkana Street, Yarralumla, ACT 2600. Tel. (062) 73 2501.

Brazil, 6 Monaro Crescent, Red Hill, ACT 2603. Tel. (062) 73 1202.

British High Commission, Commonwealth Avenue, Yarralumla, ACT 2600. Tel. (062) 70 6666.

Canada High Commission, Commonwealth Avenue, Yarralumla, ACT 2600. Tel. (062) 73 3844.

Chile Embassy of Chancery, 10 Culgoa Circuit, O'Maley, ACT 2600. Tel. (062) 86 2430.

Danish Embassy, 15 Hunter Street, Yarralumla, ACT 2600. Tel. (062) 73 2195.

Embassy of Finland, 10 Darwin Avenue, Yarralumla, ACT 2600. Tel. (062) 73 3800.

Embassy of Greece, Turrana Street, Yarralumla, ACT 2600. Tel. (062) 73 3011.

Embassy of Ireland, Arkana Street, Yarralumla, ACT 2600. Tel. ()062) 73 3022.

Embassy of Lebanon, 27 Endeavour Street, Red Hill, ACT 2603. Tel. (062) 95 7378.

Embassy of Mexico, Cnr Perth Avenue & Empire Circuit, Yarralumla, ACT 2600. Tel. (062) 73 3905.

Embassy of Pakistan, 59 Franklin Street, Forrest, ACT. Tel. (062) 95 0021.

Embassy of Peru, London Circuit, Canberra City, ACT 2601. Tel. (062) 57 2953.

Embassy of Portugal, 8 Astrolabe Street, Red Hill, ACT 2603. Tel. (062) 95 9992.

Embassy of the Republic of Iraq, 48 Culgoa Circuit, O'Malley, ACT. Tel. (062) 86 1333.

Embassy of Spain, 92 Mugga Way, Red Hill, ACT 2603. Tel. (062) 95 3872.

Embassy of Switzerland, 7 Melbourne Avenue, Forrest, ACT 2603. Tel. (062) 73 3977.

Embassy of Thailand, 111 Empire Circuit, Yarralumla, ACT 2600. Tel. (062) 73 1149.

Embassy of the Federal Republic of Germany, 119 Empire Circuit, Yarralumla, ACT 2600. Tel. (062) 70 1911.

Embassy of the German Democratic Republic, 8 Dalman Crescent, O'Malley, ACT. Tel. (062) 86 2300.

Embassy of the Islamic Republic of Iran, 14 Torres Street, Red Hill, ACT 2603. Tel. (062) 95 2544.

Embassy of the Netherlands, 120 Empire Circuit, Yarralumla, ACT 2600. Tel. (062) 73 3111.

Embassy of the Peoples Republic of China, 247 Federal Highway, Watson, ACT 2602. Tel. (062) 41 2446.

Embassy of the Philippines, 1 Moonah Place, Yarralumla, ACT 2600. Tel. (062) 73 2535.

Embassy of the Polish Peoples Republic, 7 Turrana Street, Yarralumla, ACT 2600. Tel. (062) 73 1208.

Embassy of the Republic of Indonesia, 8 Darwin Avenue, Yaralumla, ACT 2600. Tel. (062) 73 3222.

Embassy of the Republic of Korea, 113 Empire Circuit, Yaralumla, ACT 2600. Tel. (062) 73 3044.

Embassy of Yugoslavia, 11 Nuyts Street, Red Hill, ACT 2600. Tel. (062) 95 1458.

Embassy of USA, Moonah Place, Yarralumla, ACT 2600. Tel. (062) 70 5000.

French Embassy, 6 Perth Avenue, Yarralumla, ACT 2600. Tel. (062) 70 5111.

High Commission of Cyprus, 37 Endeavour Street, Red Hill, ACT 2603. Tel. (062) 95 2120.

High Commission of India, 3 Moonal Place, Yarralumla, ACT 2600. Tel. (062) 73 3999.

High Commission of Papua New Guinea, Forster Crs., Yarralumla, ACT 2600. Tel. (062) 73 3322.

Israel, 6 Turrana Street, Yarralumla, ACT 2600. Tel. (062) 73 1309.

Italian Embassy, 12 Grey Street, Deakin, ACT 2600. Tel. (062) 73 3333.

Japanese, 112 Empire Circuit, Yarralumla, ACT 2600. Tel. (062) 73 3244.

The Tall ships at the Bicentennial celebrations (1788—1988), Darling Harbour, Sydney.

Kenya High Commission, 33 Ainslie Avenue, Canberra City, ACT 2601. Tel. (062) 47 4688.

Malayasian High Commission, 7 Perth Avenue, Yarralumla, ACT 2600. Tel. (062) 73 1543.

Malta High Commission, 261 La Perouse Street, Red Hill, ACT 2603. Tel. (062) 95 1586.

Mauritius High Commission, 43 Hampton Circuit, Yarralumla, ACT 2600. Tel. (062) 81 1203.

Nigerian High Commission, 7 Terrigal Circuit, O'Malley, ACT. Tel. (062) 86 1322.

Royal Norwegian Embassy, 17 Hunter Street, Yarralumla, ACT 2600. Tel. (062) 73 3444.

Singapore High Commission, Forster Street, Yarralumla, ACT 2600. Tel. (062) 73 3944.

South Africa, State Close, Yarralumla, ACT 2600. Tel. (062) 73 2424.

Swedish, Turrana Street, Yarralumla, ACT 2600. Tel. (062) 73 3033.

Turkish, 60 Mugga Way, Red Hill, ACT 2603. Tel. (062) 95 0227.

Union of Soviet Socialist Republics, 78 Canberra Avenue, Griffith, ACT 2603. Tel. (062) 95 9033.

Zambia High Commission, 33 Ainslie Avenue, Canberra City, ACT 2601. Tel. (062) 47 2088.

Hospitals

Sydney

Sydney Hospital, Macquarie Street, Sydney, NSW 2000. Tel. (02) 228 2111.

Royal North Shore Hospital, Pacific Highway, St Leonards, NSW 2065. Tel. (02) 438 7111.

Royal Prince Alfred Hospital, Missenden Road, Camperdown, NSW 2050. Tel. (02) 516 6111.

Melbourne

Royal Melbourne Hospital, Grattan Street, Parkdale, Vic. 3194. Tel. (03) 347 7111.

Queen Victoria Medical Centre, 172 Tonsdale Street, Melbourne, Vic. 3000. Tel. (03) 66 6046.

St Vincent's Hospital, Victoria Parade, Fitzroy, Vic. 3065. Tel. (03) 41 0221.

Brisbane

Prince Charles Hospital, Rhode Road, Chermside, Qld 4032. Tel. (07) 350 8111.

Prince Alexandra Hospital, Ipswich Road, Woolloongabba, Qld 4102. Tel. (07) 240 2111.

Hobart

Queen Alexandra Hospital, 31 Argyle Street, Hobart, Tas. 7000. Tel. (002) 38 8308.

Royal Hobart Hospital, 48 Liverpool Street, Hobart, Tas. 7000. Tel. (002) 38 8308.

Darwin

Darwin Hospital, Darwin, NT 5790. Tel. (089) 20 7211.

Alice Springs Hospital, Alice Springs, NT 5750. Tel. (002) 50 2211.

Canberra

Calvary Hospital, Cnr Belconnen Way & Hayden Drive, Bruce, ACT 2617. Tel. (062) 52 9111.

Royal Canberra Hospital, Edinburgh Avenue, Acton, ACT 2601. Tel. (062) 43 2111.

Woden Valley Hospital, Yamba Drive, Garran, ACT 2605. Tel. (062) 84 2222.

Adelaide

Royal Adelaide Hospital, North Adelaide, SA 5006. Tel. (08) 223 0230.

Queen Elizabeth Hospital, Woodville Road, Woodville, SA 5011. Tel. (08) 45 0222.

Perth

Royal Perth Hospital, Wellington Street, Perth, SA 6000. Tel. (09) 325 0101.

Fremantle Hospital, Alma Street, Fremantle, WA 6160. Tel. (09) 335 0111.

Roslyn Kean—the author (Heather Waddell)

Roslyn Kean was born in Sydney in 1953. She was brought up in the countryside on the outskirts of Sydney later moving into Sydney to complete studies in the Fine Arts at the National Art School followed by design at the Shillito Design School. In 1976 she was offered a place at the Slade School of Fine Art in London where she completed a Higher Diploma in Fine Art, specialising in printmaking in 1978. She later taught students at the Slade on the same course as well as being a visiting tutor at the Byam Shaw Art School in London.

In 1981 she returned to Sydney after two successful exhibitions at the Graffiti gallery and at the New South Wales House gallery in London. In 1983 she exhibited her prints at the Hogarth gallery in Sydney and also in Tokyo, Japan. Between 1985 and 1987 she was awarded a Japanese government scholarship specialising in traditional Japanese woodblock printing at Tokyo's National University of Fine Arts and Music. She now runs specialised Japanese woodblock printing workshops. Currently Roslyn is a lecturer in printmaking at Canberra School of Art.